THE THEORY OF HEAT RADIATION

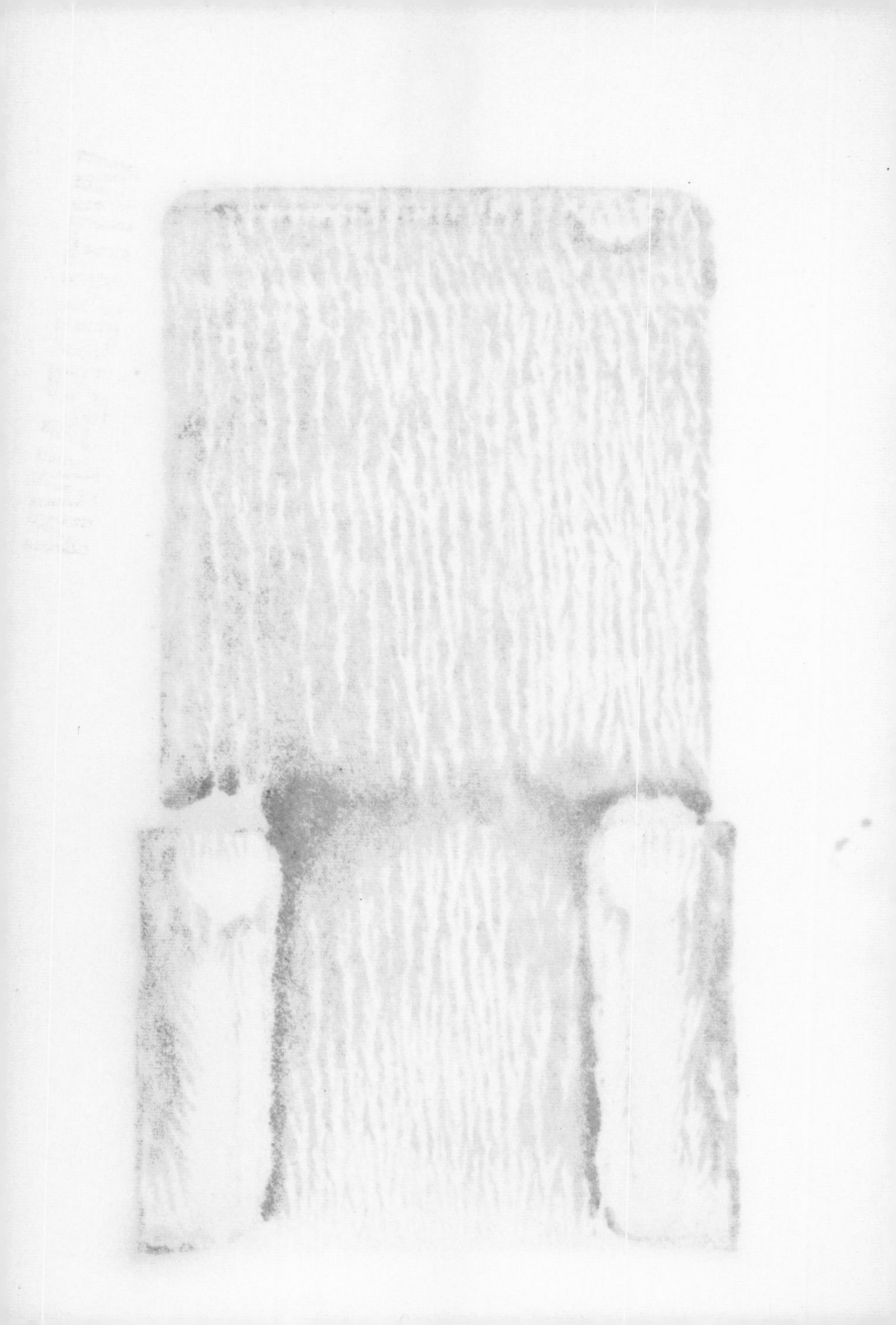

THE THEORY
OF
HEAT RADIATION

BY

MAX PLANCK

AUTHORISED TRANSLATION

BY

MORTON MASIUS

DOVER PUBLICATIONS, INC.

NEW YORK

This new Dover edition first published in 1959 is an unabridged and unaltered republication of the English translation of the Second Edition.

Library of Congress Catalog Card Number: 59-14225

Manufactured in the United States of America.

Dover Publications, Inc.
180 Varick Street
New York 14, N. Y.

TRANSLATOR'S PREFACE

The present volume is a translation of the second edition of Professor *Planck's* WAERMESTRAHLUNG (1913). The profoundly original ideas introduced by *Planck* in the endeavor to reconcile the electromagnetic theory of radiation with experimental facts have proven to be of the greatest importance in many parts of physics. Probably no single book since the appearance of *Clerk Maxwell's* ELECTRICITY AND MAGNETISM has had a deeper influence on the development of physical theories. The great majority of English-speaking physicists are, of course, able to read the work in the language in which it was written, but I believe that many will welcome the opportunity offered by a translation to study the ideas set forth by *Planck* without the difficulties that frequently arise in attempting to follow a new and somewhat difficult line of reasoning in a foreign language.

Recent developments of physical theories have placed the quantum of action in the foreground of interest. Questions regarding the bearing of the quantum theory on the law of equipartition of energy, its application to the theory of specific heats and to photoelectric effects, attempts to form some concrete idea of the physical significance of the quantum, that is, to devise a "model" for it, have created within the last few years a large and ever increasing literature. Professor *Planck* has, however, in this book confined himself exclusively to radiation phenomena and it has seemed to me probable that a brief résumé of this literature might prove useful to the reader who wishes to pursue the subject further. I have, therefore, with Professor *Planck's* permission, given in an appendix a list of the most important papers on the subjects treated of in this book and others closely related to them. I have also added a short note on one or two derivations of formulæ where the treatment in the book seemed too brief or to present some difficulties.

In preparing the translation I have been under obligation for advice and helpful suggestions to several friends and colleagues and especially to Professor A. W. Duff who has read the manuscript and the galley proof.

MORTON MASIUS.

WORCESTER, MASS.,
February, 1914.

PREFACE TO SECOND EDITION

Recent advances in physical research have, on the whole, been favorable to the special theory outlined in this book, in particular to the hypothesis of an elementary quantity of action. My radiation formula especially has so far stood all tests satisfactorily, including even the refined systematic measurements which have been carried out in the Physikalisch-technische Reichsanstalt at Charlottenburg during the last year. Probably the most direct support for the fundamental idea of the hypothesis of quanta is supplied by the values of the elementary quanta of matter and electricity derived from it. When, twelve years ago, I made my first calculation of the value of the elementary electric charge and found it to be $4.69 \cdot 10^{-10}$ electrostatic units, the value of this quantity deduced by *J. J. Thomson* from his ingenious experiments on the condensation of water vapor on gas ions, namely $6.5 \cdot 10^{-10}$ was quite generally regarded as the most reliable value. This value exceeds the one given by me by 38 per cent. Meanwhile the experimental methods, improved in an admirable way by the labors of *E. Rutherford*, *E. Regener*, *J. Perrin*, *R. A. Millikan*, *The Svedberg* and others, have without exception decided in favor of the value deduced from the theory of radiation which lies between the values of *Perrin* and *Millikan*.

To the two mutually independent confirmations mentioned, there has been added, as a further strong support of the hypothesis of quanta, the heat theorem which has been in the meantime announced by *W. Nernst*, and which seems to point unmistakably to the fact that, not only the processes of radiation, but also the molecular processes take place in accordance with certain elementary quanta of a definite finite magnitude. For the hypothesis of quanta as well as the heat theorem of *Nernst* may be reduced to the simple proposition that the thermodynamic probability (Sec. 120) of a physical state is a definite integral number, or, what amounts to the same thing, that the entropy of a state has a quite definite, positive value, which, as a minimum, becomes zero, while in contrast therewith the entropy may, according to the classical thermodynamics, decrease without limit to minus infinity. For the present, I would consider this proposition as the very quintessence of the hypothesis of quanta.

In spite of the satisfactory agreement of the results mentioned with one another as well as with experiment, the ideas from which they originated have met with wide interest but, so far as I am able to judge, with little general acceptance, the reason probably being that the hypothesis of quanta has not as yet been satisfactorily completed. While many physicists, through conservatism, reject the ideas developed by me, or, at any rate, maintain an expectant attitude, a few authors have attacked them for the opposite reason, namely, as being inadequate, and have felt compelled to supplement them by assumptions of a still more radical nature, for example, by the assumption that any radiant energy whatever, even though it travel freely in a vacuum, consists of indivisible quanta or cells. Since nothing probably is a greater drawback to the successful development of a new hypothesis than overstepping its boundaries, I have always stood for making as close a connection between the hypothesis of quanta and the classical dynamics as possible, and for not stepping outside of the boundaries of the latter until the experimental facts leave no other course open. I have attempted to keep to this standpoint in the revision of this treatise necessary for a new edition.

The main fault of the original treatment was that it began with the classical electrodynamical laws of emission and absorption, whereas later on it became evident that, in order to meet the demand of experimental measurements, the assumption of finite energy elements must be introduced, an assumption which is in direct contradiction to the fundamental ideas of classical electrodynamics. It is true that this inconsistency is greatly reduced by the fact that, in reality, only mean values of energy are taken from classical electrodynamics, while, for the statistical calculation, the real values are used; nevertheless the treatment must, on the whole, have left the reader with the unsatisfactory feeling that it was not clearly to be seen, which of the assumptions made in the beginning could, and which could not, be finally retained.

In contrast thereto I have now attempted to treat the subject from the very outset in such a way that none of the laws stated need, later on, be restricted or modified. This presents the advantage that the theory, so far as it is treated here, shows no contradiction in itself, though certainly I do not mean that it does not seem to call for improvements in many respects, as regards both its internal structure and its external form. To treat of the numerous applications, many of them very important, which the hypothesis of quanta has already found in other parts of physics, I have not regarded as part of my task, still less to discuss all differing opinions.

Thus, while the new edition of this book may not claim to bring the theory of heat radiation to a conclusion that is satisfactory in all respects, this deficiency will not be of decisive importance in judging the theory. For any one who would make his attitude concerning the hypothesis of quanta depend on whether the significance of the quantum of action for the elementary physical processes is made clear in every respect or may be demonstrated by some simple dynamical model, misunderstands, I believe, the character and the meaning of the hypothesis of quanta. It is impossible to express a really new principle in terms of a model following old laws. And, as regards the final formulation of the hypothesis, we should not forget that, from the classical point of view, the physics of the atom really has always remained a very obscure, inaccessible region, into which the introduction of the elementary quantum of action promises to throw some light.

Hence it follows from the nature of the case that it will require painstaking experimental and theoretical work for many years to come to make gradual advances in the new field. Any one who, at present, devotes his efforts to the hypothesis of quanta, must, for the time being, be content with the knowledge that the fruits of the labor spent will probably be gathered by a future generation.

THE AUTHOR.

BERLIN,
November, 1912.

PREFACE TO FIRST EDITION

In this book the main contents of the lectures which I gave at the University of Berlin during the winter semester 1906–07 are presented. My original intention was merely to put together in a connected account the results of my own investigations, begun ten years ago, on the theory of heat radiation; it soon became evident, however, that it was desirable to include also the foundation of this theory in the treatment, starting with Kirchhoff's Law on emitting and absorbing power; and so I attempted to write a treatise which should also be capable of serving as an introduction to the study of the entire theory of radiant heat on a consistent thermodynamic basis. Accordingly the treatment starts from the simple known experimental laws of optics and advances, by gradual extension and by the addition of the results of electrodynamics and thermodynamics, to the problems of the spectral distribution of energy and of irreversibility. In doing this I have deviated frequently from the customary methods of treatment, wherever the matter presented or considerations regarding the form of presentation seemed to call for it, especially in deriving Kirchhoff's laws, in calculating Maxwell's radiation pressure, in deriving Wien's displacement law, and in generalizing it for radiations of any spectral distribution of energy whatever.

I have at the proper place introduced the results of my own investigations into the treatment. A list of these has been added at the end of the book to facilitate comparison and examination as regards special details.

I wish, however, to emphasize here what has been stated more fully in the last paragraph of this book, namely, that the theory thus developed does not by any means claim to be perfect or complete, although I believe that it points out a possible way of accounting for the processes of radiant energy from the same point of view as for the processes of molecular motion.

TABLE OF CONTENTS

PART I

FUNDAMENTAL FACTS AND DEFINITIONS

PART II

DEDUCTIONS FROM ELECTRODYNAMICS AND THERMODYNAMICS

PART III

ENTROPY AND PROBABILITY

PART IV

A SYSTEM OF OSCILLATORS IN A STATIONARY FIELD OF RADIATION

PART V

IRREVERSIBLE RADIATION PROCESSES

ERRATA

Page 77. The last sentence of Sec. 77 should be replaced by: The corresponding additional terms may, however, be omitted here without appreciable error, since the correction caused by them would consist merely of the addition to the energy change here calculated of a comparatively infinitesimal energy change of the same kind with an external work that is infinitesimal of the second order.

Page 83. Insert at the end of Sec. 84 a:
These laws hold for any original distribution of energy whatever; hence, *e. g.*, an originally monochromatic radiation remains monochromatic during the process described, its color changing in the way stated.

PART I

FUNDAMENTAL FACTS AND DEFINITIONS

RADIATION OF HEAT

CHAPTER I

GENERAL INTRODUCTION

1. Heat may be propagated in a stationary medium in two entirely different ways, namely, by conduction and by radiation. Conduction of heat depends on the temperature of the medium in which it takes place, or more strictly speaking, on the non-uniform distribution of the temperature in space, as measured by the temperature gradient. In a region where the temperature of the medium is the same at all points there is no trace of heat conduction.

Radiation of heat, however, is in itself entirely independent of the temperature of the medium through which it passes. It is possible, for example, to concentrate the solar rays at a focus by passing them through a converging lens of ice, the latter remaining at a constant temperature of 0°, and so to ignite an inflammable body. Generally speaking, radiation is a far more complicated phenomenon than conduction of heat. The reason for this is that the state of the radiation at a given instant and at a given point of the medium cannot be represented, as can the flow of heat by conduction, by a single vector (that is, a single directed quantity). All heat rays which at a given instant pass through the same point of the medium are perfectly independent of one another, and in order to specify completely the state of the radiation the intensity of radiation must be known in all the directions, infinite in number, which pass through the point in question; for this purpose two opposite directions must be considered as distinct, because the radiation in one of them is quite independent of the radiation in the other.

2. Putting aside for the present any special theory of heat radiation, we shall state for our further use a law supported by a large number of experimental facts. This law is that, so far as their physical properties are concerned, heat rays are identical with light rays of the same wave length. The term "heat radiation," then, will be applied to all physical phenomena of the same nature as light rays. Every light ray is simultaneously a heat ray. We shall also, for the sake of brevity, occasionally speak of the "color" of a heat ray in order to denote its wave length or period. As a further consequence of this law we shall apply to the radiation of heat all the well-known laws of experimental optics, especially those of reflection and refraction, as well as those relating to the propagation of light. Only the phenomena of diffraction, so far at least as they take place in space of considerable dimensions, we shall exclude on account of their rather complicated nature. We are therefore obliged to introduce right at the start a certain restriction with respect to the size of the parts of space to be considered. Throughout the following discussion it will be assumed that the linear dimensions of all parts of space considered, as well as the radii of curvature of all surfaces under consideration, are large compared with the wave lengths of the rays considered. With this assumption we may, without appreciable error, entirely neglect the influence of diffraction caused by the bounding surfaces, and everywhere apply the ordinary laws of reflection and refraction of light. To sum up: We distinguish once for all between two kinds of lengths of entirely different orders of magnitude—dimensions of bodies and wave lengths. Moreover, even the differentials of the former, *i.e.*, elements of length, area and volume, will be regarded as large compared with the corresponding powers of wave lengths. The greater, therefore, the wave length of the rays we wish to consider, the larger must be the parts of space considered. But, inasmuch as there is no other restriction on our choice of size of the parts of space to be considered, this assumption will not give rise to any particular difficulty.

3. Even more essential for the whole theory of heat radiation than the distinction between large and small lengths, is the distinction between long and short intervals of time. For the definition of intensity of a heat ray, as being the energy transmitted by the ray per unit time, implies the assumption that the unit of time chosen is large compared with the period of vibration corresponding to the color of the ray. If this were not so, obviously the value of the intensity of the radiation would, in general, depend upon the particular phase of vibration at which the measurement of the energy of the ray was begun, and the intensity of a ray of constant period and amplitude would not be independent of the initial phase, unless by chance the unit of time were an integral multiple of the period. To avoid this difficulty, we are obliged to postulate quite generally that the unit of time, or rather that element of time used in defining the intensity, even if it appear in the form of a differential, must be large compared with the period of all colors contained in the ray in question.

The last statement leads to an important conclusion as to radiation of variable intensity. If, using an acoustic analogy, we speak of "beats" in the case of intensities undergoing periodic changes, the "unit" of time required for a definition of the instantaneous intensity of radiation must necessarily be small compared with the period of the beats. Now, since from the previous statement our unit must be large compared with a period of vibration, it follows that the period of the beats must be large compared with that of a vibration. Without this restriction it would be impossible to distinguish properly between "beats" and simple "vibrations." Similarly, in the general case of an arbitrarily variable intensity of radiation, the vibrations must take place very rapidly as compared with the relatively slower changes in intensity. These statements imply, of course, a certain far-reaching restriction as to the generality of the radiation phenomena to be considered.

It might be added that a very similar and equally essential restriction is made in the kinetic theory of gases by dividing the motions of a chemically simple gas into two classes: visible, coarse, or molar, and invisible, fine, or molecular. For, since the velocity of a single molecule is a perfectly unambiguous quantity, this distinction cannot be drawn unless the assumption be made that the velocity-components of the molecules contained in sufficiently small volumes have certain mean values, independent of the size of the volumes. This in general need not by any means be the case. If such a mean value, including the value zero, does not exist, the distinction between motion of the gas as a whole and random undirected heat motion cannot be made.

Turning now to the investigation of the laws in accordance with which the phenomena of radiation take place in a medium supposed to be at rest, the problem may be approached in two ways: We must either select a certain point in space and investigate the different rays passing through this one point as time goes on, or we must select one distinct ray and inquire into its history, that is, into the way in which it was created, propagated, and finally destroyed. For the following discussion, it will be advisable to start with the second method of treatment and to consider first the three processes just mentioned.

4. Emission.—The creation of a heat ray is generally denoted by the word emission. According to the principle of the conservation of energy, emission always takes place at the expense of other forms of energy (heat,[1] chemical or electric energy, etc.) and hence it follows that only material particles, not geometrical volumes or surfaces, can emit heat rays. It is true that for the sake of brevity we frequently speak of the surface of a body as radiating heat to the surroundings, but this form of expression does not imply that the surface actually emits heat rays. Strictly speaking, the surface of a body never emits rays, but rather it allows part of the rays coming from the interior to pass through. The other part is reflected inward and according as the fraction transmitted is larger or smaller the surface seems to emit more or less intense radiations.

We shall now consider the interior of an emitting substance assumed to be physically homogeneous, and in it we shall select any volume-element $d\tau$ of not too small size. Then the energy which is emitted by radiation in unit time by all particles in this volume-element will be proportional to $d\tau$. Should we attempt a closer analysis of the process of emission and resolve it into its elements, we should undoubtedly meet very complicated conditions, for then it would be necessary to consider elements of space of such small size that it would no longer be admissible to think of the substance as homogeneous, and we would have to allow for the atomic constitution. Hence the finite quantity

[1] Here as in the following the German "Körperwärme" will be rendered simply as "heat." (Tr.)

obtained by dividing the radiation emitted by a volume-element $d\tau$ by this element $d\tau$ is to be considered only as a certain mean value. Nevertheless, we shall as a rule be able to treat the phenomenon of emission as if all points of the volume-element $d\tau$ took part in the emission in a uniform manner, thereby greatly simplifying our calculation. Every point of $d\tau$ will then be the vertex of a pencil of rays diverging in all directions. Such a pencil coming from one single point of course does not represent a finite amount of energy, because a finite amount is emitted only by a finite though possibly small volume, not by a single point.

We shall next assume our substance to be isotropic. Hence the radiation of the volume-element $d\tau$ is emitted uniformly in all directions of space. Draw a cone in an arbitrary direction, having any point of the radiating element as vertex, and describe around the vertex as center a sphere of unit radius. This sphere intersects the cone in what is known as the solid angle of the cone, and from the isotropy of the medium it follows that the radiation in any such conical element will be proportional to its solid angle. This holds for cones of any size. If we take the solid angle as infinitely small and of size $d\Omega$ we may speak of the radiation emitted in a certain direction, but always in the sense that for the emission of a finite amount of energy an infinite number of directions are necessary and these form a finite solid angle.

5. The distribution of energy in the radiation is in general quite arbitrary; that is, the different colors of a certain radiation may have quite different intensities. The color of a ray in experimental physics is usually denoted by its wave length, because this quantity is measured directly. For the theoretical treatment, however, it is usually preferable to use the frequency ν instead, since the characteristic of color is not so much the wave length, which changes from one medium to another, as the frequency, which remains unchanged in a light or heat ray passing through stationary media. We shall, therefore, hereafter denote a certain color by the corresponding value of ν, and a certain interval of color by the limits of the interval ν and ν', where $\nu' > \nu$. The radiation lying in a certain interval of color divided by the magnitude $\nu' - \nu$ of the interval, we shall call the mean radiation in the interval ν to ν'. We shall then assume that if, keeping ν constant, we take the interval $\nu'-\nu$ sufficiently small and denote it by $d\nu$ the value of the mean radiation approaches a definite limiting value, independent of the size of $d\nu$, and this we shall briefly call the "radiation of frequency ν." To produce a finite intensity of radiation, the frequency interval, though perhaps small, must also be finite.

We have finally to allow for the polarization of the emitted radiation. Since the medium was assumed to be isotropic the emitted rays are unpolarized. Hence every ray has just twice the intensity of one of its plane polarized components, which could, *e.g.*, be obtained by passing the ray through a *Nicol's* prism.

6. Summing up everything said so far, we may equate the total energy in a range of frequency from ν to $\nu+d\nu$ emitted in the time dt in the direction of the conical element $d\Omega$ by a volume element $d\tau$ to

$$dt \cdot d\tau \cdot d\Omega \cdot d\nu \cdot 2\epsilon_\nu. \qquad (1)$$

The finite quantity ϵ_ν is called the coefficient of emission of the medium for the frequency ν. It is a positive function of ν and refers to a plane polarized ray of definite color and direction. The total emission of the volume-element $d\tau$ may be obtained from this by integrating over all directions and all frequencies. Since ϵ_ν is independent of the direction, and since the integral over all conical elements $d\Omega$ is 4π, we get:

$$dt \cdot d\tau . 8\pi \int_o^\infty \epsilon_\nu d\nu. \qquad (2)$$

7. The coefficient of emission ϵ depends, not only on the frequency ν, but also on the condition of the emitting substance contained in the volume-element $d\tau$, and, generally speaking, in a very complicated way, according to the physical and chemical processes which take place in the elements of time and volume in question. But the empirical law that the emission of any volume-element depends entirely on what takes place inside of this element holds true in all cases (*Prevost's* principle). A body A at 100° C. emits toward a body B at 0° C. exactly the same amount of radiation as toward an equally large and similarly situated body B' at 1000° C. The fact that the body A is cooled by B and heated by B' is due entirely to the fact that B is a weaker, B' a stronger emitter than A.

We shall now introduce the further simplifying assumption that the physical and chemical condition of the emitting substance depends on but a single variable, namely, on its absolute temperature T. A necessary consequence of this is that the coefficient of emission ϵ depends, apart from the frequency ν and the nature of the medium, only on the temperature T. The last statement excludes from our consideration a number of radiation phenomena, such as fluorescence, phosphorescence, electrical and chemical luminosity, to which *E. Wiedemann* has given the common name "phenomena of luminescence." We shall deal with pure "temperature radiation" exclusively.

A special case of temperature radiation is the case of the chemical nature of the emitting substance being invariable. In this case the emission takes place entirely at the expense of the heat of the body. Nevertheless, it is possible, according to what has been said, to have temperature radiation while chemical changes are taking place, provided the chemical condition is completely determined by the temperature.

8. Propagation.—The propagation of the radiation in a medium assumed to be homogeneous, isotropic, and at rest takes place in straight lines and with the same velocity in all directions, diffraction phenomena being entirely excluded. Yet, in general, each ray suffers during its propagation a certain weakening, because a certain fraction of its energy is continuously deviated from its original direction and scattered in all directions. This phenomenon of "scattering," which means neither a creation nor a destruction of radiant energy but simply a change in distribution, takes place, generally speaking, in all media differing from an absolute vacuum, even in substances which are perfectly pure chemically.[1] The cause of this is that no substance is homogeneous in the absolute sense of the word. The smallest elements of space always exhibit some discontinuities on account of their atomic structure. Small impurities, as, for instance, particles of dust, increase the influence of scattering without, however, appreciably affecting its general character. Hence, so-called "turbid"

[1] See, *e.g.*, *Lobry de Bruyn* and *L. K. Wolff*, Rec. des Trav. Chim. des Pays-Bas **23**, p. 155, 1904.

media, *i.e.*, such as contain foreign particles, may be quite properly regarded as optically homogeneous,[1] provided only that the linear dimensions of the foreign particles as well as the distances of neighboring particles are sufficiently small compared with the wave lengths of the rays considered. As regards optical phenomena, then, there is no fundamental distinction between chemically pure substances and the turbid media just described. No space is optically void in the absolute sense except a vacuum. Hence a chemically pure substance may be spoken of as a vacuum made turbid by the presence of molecules.

A typical example of scattering is offered by the behavior of sunlight in the atmosphere. When, with a clear sky, the sun stands in the zenith, only about two-thirds of the direct radiation of the sun reaches the surface of the earth. The remainder is intercepted by the atmosphere, being partly absorbed and changed into heat of the air, partly, however, scattered and changed into diffuse skylight. This phenomenon is produced probably not so much by the particles suspended in the atmosphere as by the air molecules themselves.

Whether the scattering depends on reflection, on diffraction, or on a resonance effect on the molecules or particles is a point that we may leave entirely aside. We only take account of the fact that every ray on its path through any medium loses a certain fraction of its intensity. For a very small distance, s, this fraction is proportional to s, say

$$\beta_\nu s \tag{3}$$

where the positive quantity β_ν is independent of the intensity of radiation and is called the "coefficient of scattering" of the medium. Inasmuch as the medium is assumed to be isotropic, β_ν is also independent of the direction of propagation and polarization of the ray. It depends, however, as indicated by the subscript ν, not only on the physical and chemical constitution of the body but also to a very marked degree on the frequency. For certain values of ν, β_ν may be so large that the straight-line propagation of the rays is virtually destroyed. For other values of ν, however, β_ν may become so small that the scattering can

[1] To restrict the word homogeneous to its absolute sense would mean that it could not be applied to any material substance.

be entirely neglected. For generality we shall assume a mean value of β_ν. In the cases of most importance β_ν increases quite appreciably as ν increases, *i.e.*, the scattering is noticeably larger for rays of shorter wave length;[1] hence the blue color of diffuse skylight.

The scattered radiation energy is propagated from the place where the scattering occurs in a way similar to that in which the emitted energy is propagated from the place of emission, since it travels in all directions in space. It does not, however, have the same intensity in all directions, and moreover is polarized in some special directions, depending to a large extent on the direction of the original ray. We need not, however, enter into any further discussion of these questions.

9. While the phenomenon of scattering means a continuous modification in the interior of the medium, a discontinuous change in both the direction and the intensity of a ray occurs when it reaches the boundary of a medium and meets the surface of a second medium. The latter, like the former, will be assumed to be homogeneous and isotropic. In this case, the ray is in general partly reflected and partly transmitted. The reflection and refraction may be "regular," there being a single reflected ray according to the simple law of reflection and a single transmitted ray, according to *Snell's* law of refraction, or, they may be "diffuse," which means that from the point of incidence on the surface the radiation spreads out into the two media with intensities that are different in different directions. We accordingly describe the surface of the second medium as "smooth" or "rough" respectively. Diffuse reflection occurring at a rough surface should be carefully distinguished from reflection at a smooth surface of a turbid medium. In both cases part of the incident ray goes back to the first medium as diffuse radiation. But in the first case the scattering occurs on the surface, in the second in more or less thick layers entirely inside of the second medium.

10. When a smooth surface completely reflects all incident rays, as is approximately the case with many metallic surfaces, it is termed "reflecting." When a rough surface reflects all incident rays completely and uniformly in all directions, it is

[1] *Lord Rayleigh*, Phil. Mag., **47**, p. 379, 1899.

called "white." The other extreme, namely, complete transmission of all incident rays through the surface never occurs with smooth surfaces, at least if the two contiguous media are at all optically different. A rough surface having the property of completely transmitting the incident radiation is described as "black."

In addition to "black surfaces" the term "black body" is also used. According to *G. Kirchhoff*[1] it denotes a body which has the property of allowing all incident rays to enter without surface reflection and not allowing them to leave again. Hence it is seen that a black body must satisfy three independent conditions. First, the body must have a black surface in order to allow the incident rays to enter without reflection. Since, in general, the properties of a surface depend on both of the bodies which are in contact, this condition shows that the property of blackness as applied to a body depends not only on the nature of the body but also on that of the contiguous medium. A body which is black relatively to air need not be so relatively to glass, and *vice versa.* Second, the black body must have a certain minimum thickness depending on its absorbing power, in order to insure that the rays after passing into the body shall not be able to leave it again at a different point of the surface. The more absorbing a body is, the smaller the value of this minimum thickness, while in the case of bodies with vanishingly small absorbing power only a layer of infinite thickness may be regarded as black. Third, the black body must have a vanishingly small coefficient of scattering (Sec. 8). Otherwise the rays received by it would be partly scattered in the interior and might leave again through the surface.[2]

11. All the distinctions and definitions mentioned in the two preceding paragraphs refer to rays of one definite color only. It might very well happen that, *e.g.*, a surface which is rough for a certain kind of rays must be regarded as smooth for a different kind of rays. It is readily seen that, in general, a surface shows

[1] *G. Kirchhoff*, Pogg. Ann., **109**, p. 275, 1860. Gesammelte Abhandlungen, J. A. Barth, Leipzig, 1882, p. 573. In defining a black body *Kirchhoff* also assumes that the absorption of incident rays takes place in a layer "infinitely thin." We do not include this in our definition.

[2] For this point see especially *A. Schuster*, Astrophysical Journal, **21**, p. 1, 1905, who has pointed out that an infinite layer of gas with a black surface need by no means be a black body.

decreasing degrees of roughness for increasing wave lengths Now, since smooth non-reflecting surfaces do not exist (Sec. 10), it follows that all approximately black surfaces which may be realized in practice (lamp black, platinum black) show appreciable reflection for rays of sufficiently long wave lengths.

12. Absorption.—Heat rays are destroyed by "absorption." According to the principle of the conservation of energy the energy of heat radiation is thereby changed into other forms of energy (heat, chemical energy). Thus only material particles can absorb heat rays, not elements of surfaces, although sometimes for the sake of brevity the expression absorbing surfaces is used.

Whenever absorption takes place, the heat ray passing through the medium under consideration is weakened by a certain fraction of its intensity for every element of path traversed. For a sufficiently small distance s this fraction is proportional to s, and may be written

$$\alpha_\nu s \tag{4}$$

Here α_ν is known as the "coefficient of absorption" of the medium for a ray of frequency ν. We assume this coefficient to be independent of the intensity; it will, however, depend in general in non-homogeneous and anisotropic media on the position of s and on the direction of propagation and polarization of the ray (example: tourmaline). We shall, however, consider only homogeneous isotropic substances, and shall therefore suppose that α_ν has the same value at all points and in all directions in the medium, and depends on nothing but the frequency ν, the temperature T, and the nature of the medium.

Whenever α_ν does not differ from zero except for a limited range of the spectrum, the medium shows "selective" absorption. For those colors for which $\alpha_\nu = 0$ and also the coefficient of scattering $\beta_\nu = 0$ the medium is described as perfectly "transparent" or "diathermanous." But the properties of selective absorption and of diathermancy may for a given medium vary widely with the temperature. In general we shall assume a mean value for α_ν. This implies that the absorption in a distance equal to a single wave length is very small, because the distance s, while small, contains many wave lengths (Sec. 2).

13. The foregoing considerations regarding the emission, the propagation, and the absorption of heat rays suffice for a mathematical treatment of the radiation phenomena. The calculation requires a knowledge of the value of the constants and the initial and boundary conditions, and yields a full account of the changes the radiation undergoes in a given time in one or more contiguous media of the kind stated, including the temperature changes caused by it. The actual calculation is usually very complicated. We shall, however, before entering upon the treatment of special cases discuss the general radiation phenomena from a different point of view, namely by fixing our attention not on a definite ray, but on a definite position in space.

14. Let $d\sigma$ be an arbitrarily chosen, infinitely small element of area in the interior of a medium through which radiation passes. At a given instant rays are passing through this element in many different directions. The energy radiated through it in an element of time dt in a definite direction is proportional to the area $d\sigma$, the length of time dt and to the cosine of the angle θ made by the normal of $d\sigma$ with the direction of the radiation. If we make $d\sigma$ sufficiently small, then, although this is only an approximation to the actual state of affairs, we can think of all points in $d\sigma$ as being affected by the radiation in the same way. Then the energy radiated through $d\sigma$ in a definite direction must be proportional to the solid angle in which $d\sigma$ intercepts that radiation and this solid angle is measured by $d\sigma \cos \theta$. It is readily seen that, when the direction of the element is varied relatively to the direction of the radiation, the energy radiated through it vanishes when

$$\theta=\frac{\pi}{2}.$$

Now in general a pencil of rays is propagated from every point of the element $d\sigma$ in all directions, but with different intensities in different directions, and any two pencils emanating from two points of the element are identical save for differences of higher order. A single one of these pencils coming from a single point does not represent a finite quantity of energy, because a finite amount of energy is radiated only through a finite area. This holds also for the passage of rays through a so-called focus. For example, when sunlight passes through a converging lens and is concentrated in the focal plane of the lens, the solar rays do not converge to a single point, but each pencil of parallel rays forms a separate focus and all these foci together constitute a surface representing a small but finite image of the sun. A finite amount of energy does not pass through less than a finite portion of this surface.

15. Let us now consider quite generally the pencil, which is propagated from a point of the element $d\sigma$ as vertex in all directions of space and on both sides of $d\sigma$. A certain direction may be specified by the angle θ (between 0 and π), as already used, and by an azimuth ϕ (between 0 and 2π). The intensity in this direction is the energy propagated in an infinitely thin cone limited by θ and $\theta+d\theta$ and ϕ and $\phi+d\phi$. The solid angle of this cone is

$$d\Omega = \sin\theta \cdot d\theta \cdot d\phi. \tag{5}$$

Thus the energy radiated in time dt through the element of area $d\sigma$ in the direction of the cone $d\Omega$ is:

$$dt\, d\sigma \cos\theta\, d\Omega\, K = K \sin\theta \cos\theta\, d\theta\, d\phi\, d\sigma\, dt. \tag{6}$$

The finite quantity K we shall term the "specific intensity" or the "brightness," $d\Omega$ the "solid angle" of the pencil emanating from a point of the element $d\sigma$ in the direction (θ, ϕ). K is a positive function of position, time, and the angles θ and ϕ. In general the specific intensities of radiation in different directions are entirely independent of one another. For example, on substituting $\pi-\theta$ for θ and $\pi+\phi$ for ϕ in the function K, we obtain the specific intensity of radiation in the diametrically opposite direction, a quantity which in general is quite different from the preceding one.

For the total radiation through the element of area $d\sigma$ toward one side, say the one on which θ is an acute angle, we get, by integrating with respect to ϕ from 0 to 2π and with respect to θ from 0 to $\frac{\pi}{2}$

$$\int_0^{2\pi} d\phi \int_0^{\frac{\pi}{2}} d\theta K \sin\theta \cos\theta\, d\sigma\, dt.$$

Should the radiation be uniform in all directions and hence K be a constant, the total radiation on one side will be

$$\pi K\, d\sigma\, dt. \tag{7}$$

16. In speaking of the radiation in a definite direction (θ, ϕ) one should always keep in mind that the energy radiated in a cone is not finite unless the angle of the cone is finite. No finite radiation of light or heat takes place in one definite direction only, or expressing it differently, in nature there is no such thing as absolutely parallel light or an absolutely plane wave front. From a pencil of rays called "parallel" a finite amount of energy of radiation can only be obtained if the rays or wave normals of the pencil diverge so as to form a finite though perhaps exceedingly narrow cone.

17. The specific intensity K of the whole energy radiated in a certain direction may be further divided into the intensities of the separate rays belonging to the different regions of the spectrum which travel independently of one another. Hence we consider the intensity of radiation within a certain range of frequencies, say from ν to ν'. If the interval $\nu'-\nu$ be taken sufficiently small and be denoted by $d\nu$, the intensity of radiation within the interval is proportional to $d\nu$. Such radiation is called homogeneous or monochromatic.

A last characteristic property of a ray of definite direction, intensity, and color is its state of polarization. If we break up a ray, which is in any state of polarization whatsoever and which travels in a definite direction and has a definite frequency ν, into two plane polarized components, the sum of the intensities of the components will be just equal to the intensity of the ray as a whole, independently of the direction of the two planes, provided the two planes of polarization, which otherwise may be taken at random, are at right angles to each other. If their position be denoted by the azimuth ψ of one of the planes of vibration (plane of the electric vector), then the two components of the intensity may be written in the form

$$\mathsf{K}_\nu \cos^2\psi + \mathsf{K}_\nu' \sin^2\psi$$

and

$$\mathsf{K}_\nu \sin^2\psi + \mathsf{K}_\nu' \cos^2\psi \tag{8}$$

Herein K is independent of ψ. These expressions we shall call the "components of the specific intensity of radiation of frequency ν." The sum is independent of ψ and is always equal to the intensity of the whole ray $\mathsf{K}_\nu + \mathsf{K}_\nu'$. At the same time K_ν and K_ν' represent respectively the largest and smallest values which either of the components may have, namely, when $\psi = 0$ and $\psi = \frac{\pi}{2}$. Hence we call these values the "principal values of the intensities," or the "principal intensities," and the corresponding planes of vibration we call the "principal planes of vibration" of the ray. Of course both, in general, vary with the time. Thus we may write generally

$$K = \int_c^\infty d\nu\ (\mathsf{K}_\nu + \mathsf{K}_\nu') \tag{9}$$

where the positive quantities K_ν and K_ν', the two principal values of the specific intensity of the radiation (brightness) of frequency ν, depend not only on ν but also on their position, the time, and on the angles θ and ϕ. By substitution in (6) the energy radiated in the time dt through the element of area $d\sigma$ in the direction of the conical element $d\Omega$ assumes the value

$$dt\ d\sigma\ \cos\theta\ d\Omega \int_o^\infty d\nu\ (\mathsf{K}_\nu + \mathsf{K}_\nu') \tag{10}$$

and for monochromatic plane polarized radiation of brightness K_ν:

$$dt\ d\sigma\ \cos\theta\ d\Omega\ \mathsf{K}_\nu\ d\nu = dt\ d\sigma\ \sin\theta\ \cos\theta\ d\theta\ d\phi\ \mathsf{K}_\nu\ d\nu. \tag{11}$$

For unpolarized rays $\mathsf{K}_\nu = \mathsf{K}_\nu'$, and hence

$$K = 2\int_o^\infty d\nu\ \mathsf{K}_\nu, \tag{12}$$

and the energy of a monochromatic ray of frequency ν will be:

$$2dt\ d\sigma\ \cos\theta\ d\Omega\ \mathsf{K}_\nu\ d\nu = 2dt\ d\sigma\ \sin\theta\ \cos\theta\ d\theta\ d\phi\ \mathsf{K}_\nu\ d\nu. \tag{13}$$

When, moreover, the radiation is uniformly distributed in all directions, the total radiation through $d\sigma$ toward one side may be found from (7) and (12); it is

$$2\pi\ d\sigma\ dt \int_o^\infty \mathsf{K}_\nu d\nu. \tag{14}$$

18. Since in nature K_ν can never be infinitely large, K will not have a finite value unless K_ν differs from zero over a finite range of frequencies. Hence there exists in nature no absolutely homogeneous or monochromatic radiation of light or heat. A finite amount of radiation contains always a finite although possibly very narrow range of the spectrum. This implies a fundamental difference from the corresponding phenomena of acoustics, where a finite intensity of sound may correspond to a single definite frequency. This difference is, among other things, the cause of the fact that the second law of thermodynamics has an important bearing on light and heat rays, but not on sound waves. This will be further discussed later on.

19. From equation (9) it is seen that the quantity K_ν, the intensity of radiation of frequency ν, and the quantity K, the intensity of radiation of the whole spectrum, are of different dimensions. Further it is to be noticed that, on subdividing the spectrum according to wave lengths λ, instead of frequencies ν, the intensity of radiation E_λ of the wave lengths λ corresponding to the frequency ν is not obtained simply by replacing ν in the expression for K_ν by the corresponding value of λ deduced from

$$\nu = \frac{q}{\lambda} \tag{15}$$

where q is the velocity of propagation. For if $d\lambda$ and $d\nu$ refer to the same interval of the spectrum, we have, not $E_\lambda = \mathsf{K}_\nu$, but $E_\lambda\, d\lambda = \mathsf{K}_\nu\, d\nu$. By differentiating (15) and paying attention to the signs of corresponding values of $d\lambda$ and $d\nu$ the equation

$$d\nu = \frac{q d\lambda}{\lambda^2}$$

is obtained. Hence we get by substitution:

$$E_\lambda = \frac{q\mathsf{K}_\nu}{\lambda^2}. \tag{16}$$

This relation shows among other things that in a certain spectrum the maxima of E_λ and K_ν lie at different points of the spectrum.

20. When the principal intensities K_ν and K_ν' of all monochromatic rays are given at all points of the medium and for all directions, the state of radiation is known in all respects and all questions regarding it may be answered. We shall show this by one or two applications to special cases. Let us first find the amount of energy which is radiated through any element of area $d\sigma$ toward any other element $d\sigma'$. The distance r between the two elements may be thought of as large compared with the linear dimensions of the elements $d\sigma$ and $d\sigma'$ but still so small that no appreciable amount of radiation is absorbed or scattered along it. This condition is, of course, superfluous for diathermanous media.

From any definite point of $d\sigma$ rays pass to all points of $d\sigma'$. These rays form a cone whose vertex lies in $d\sigma$ and whose solid angle is

$$d\Omega = \frac{d\sigma' \cos (\nu', r)}{r^2}$$

where ν' denotes the normal of $d\sigma'$ and the angle (ν', r) is to be taken as an acute angle. This value of $d\Omega$ is, neglecting small quantities of higher order, independent of the particular position of the vertex of the cone on $d\sigma$.

If we further denote the normal to $d\sigma$ by ν the angle θ of (14) will be the angle (ν, r) and hence from expression (6) the energy of radiation required is found to be:

$$K \cdot \frac{d\sigma\, d\sigma' \cos(\nu, r) \cdot \cos(\nu', r)}{r^2}\, dt. \tag{17}$$

For monochromatic plane polarized radiation of frequency ν the energy will be, according to equation (11),

$$\mathsf{K}_\nu\, d\nu \cdot \frac{d\sigma\, d\sigma' \cos(\nu, r) \cos(\nu', r)}{r^2} \cdot dt. \tag{18}$$

The relative size of the two elements $d\sigma$ and $d\sigma'$ may have any value whatever. They may be assumed to be of the same or of a different order of magnitude, provided the condition remains satisfied that r is large compared with the linear dimensions of each of them. If we choose $d\sigma$ small compared with $d\sigma'$, the rays diverge from $d\sigma$ to $d\sigma'$, whereas they converge from $d\sigma$ to $d\sigma'$, if we choose $d\sigma$ large compared with $d\sigma'$.

21. Since every point of $d\sigma$ is the vertex of a cone spreading out toward $d\sigma'$, the whole pencil of rays here considered, which is defined by $d\sigma$ and $d\sigma'$, consists of a double infinity of point pencils or of a fourfold infinity of rays which must all be considered equally for the energy radiation. Similarly the pencil of rays may be thought of as consisting of the cones which, emanating from all points of $d\sigma$, converge in one point of $d\sigma'$ respectively as a vertex. If we now imagine the whole pencil of rays to be cut by a plane at any arbitrary distance from the elements $d\sigma$ and $d\sigma'$ and lying either between them or outside, then the cross-sections of any two point pencils on this plane will not be identical, not even approximately. In general they will partly overlap and partly lie outside of each other, the amount of overlapping being different for different intersecting planes. Hence it follows that there is no definite cross-section of the pencil of rays so far as the uniformity of radiation is concerned. If, however, the intersecting plane coincides with either $d\sigma$ or $d\sigma'$, then the pencil has a definite cross-section. Thus these two planes show an exceptional property. We shall call them the two "focal planes" of the pencil.

In the special case already mentioned above, namely, when one of the two focal planes is infinitely small compared with the other, the whole pencil of rays shows the character of a point pencil inasmuch as its form is approximately that of a cone having its vertex in that focal plane which is small compared with the other. In that case the "cross-section" of the whole pencil at a definite point has a definite meaning. Such a pencil of rays, which is similar to a cone, we shall call an elementary pencil, and the small focal plane we shall call the first focal plane of the elementary pencil. The radiation may be either converging toward the first focal plane or diverging from the first focal plane. All the pencils of rays passing through a medium may be considered as consisting of such elementary pencils, and hence we may base our future considerations on elementary pencils only, which is a great convenience, owing to their simple nature.

As quantities necessary to define an elementary pencil with a given first focal plane $d\sigma$, we may choose not the second focal plane $d\sigma'$ but the magnitude of that solid angle $d\Omega$ under which $d\sigma'$ is seen from $d\sigma$. On the other hand, in the case of an arbitrary pencil, that is, when the two focal planes are of the same order of magnitude, the second focal plane in general cannot be replaced by the solid angle $d\Omega$ without the pencil changing markedly in character. For if, instead of $d\sigma'$ being given, the magnitude and direction of $d\Omega$, to be taken as constant for all points of $d\sigma$, is given, then the rays emanating from $d\sigma$ do not any longer form the original pencil, but rather an elementary pencil whose first focal plane is $d\sigma$ and whose second focal plane lies at an infinite distance.

22. Since the energy radiation is propagated in the medium with a finite velocity q, there must be in a finite space a finite amount of energy. We shall therefore speak of the "space density of radiation," meaning thereby the ratio of the total quantity of energy of radiation contained in a volume-element to the magnitude of the latter. Let us now calculate the space density of radiation u at any arbitrary point of the medium. When we consider an infinitely small element of volume v at the point in question, having any shape whatsoever, we must allow for all rays passing through the volume-element v. For this purpose we shall construct about any point O of v as center a sphere of radius r, r being large compared with the linear dimensions of v but still so small that no appreciable absorption or scattering of the radiation takes place in the distance r (Fig. 1). Every ray which reaches v must then come from some point on the surface of the sphere. If, then, we at first consider only all the rays that come from the points of an infinitely small element of area $d\sigma$ on the surface of the sphere, and reach v, and then sum up for all elements of the spherical surface, we shall have accounted for all rays and not taken any one more than once.

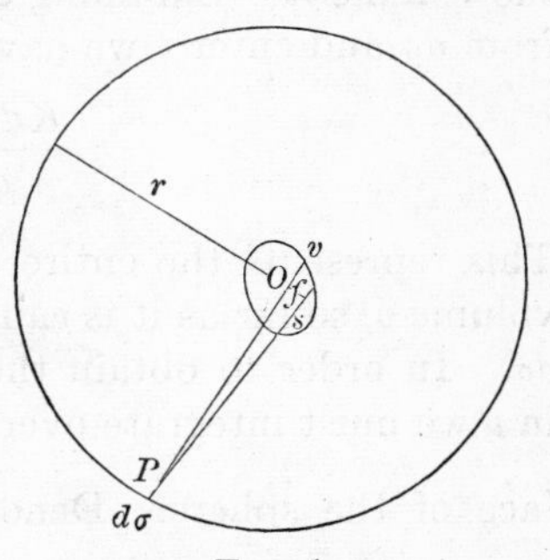

FIG. 1.

Let us then calculate first the amount of energy which is contributed to the energy contained in v by the radiation sent from such an element $d\sigma$ to v. We choose $d\sigma$ so that its linear dimensions are small compared with those of v and consider the cone of rays which, starting at a point of $d\sigma$, meets the volume v. This cone consists of an infinite number of conical elements with the common vertex at P, a point of $d\sigma$, each cutting out of the volume v a certain element of length, say s. The solid angle of such a conical element is $\frac{f}{r^2}$ where f denotes the area of cross-section normal to the axis of the cone at a distance r from the vertex. The time required for the radiation to pass through the distance s is:

$$\tau = \frac{s}{q}$$

From expression (6) we may find the energy radiated through a certain element of area. In the present case $d\Omega = \frac{f}{r^2}$ and $\theta = 0$; hence the energy is:

$$\tau d\sigma \frac{f}{r^2} K = \frac{fs}{r^2 q} \cdot K \, d\sigma. \tag{19}$$

This energy enters the conical element in v and spreads out into the volume fs. Summing up over all conical elements that start from $d\sigma$ and enter v we have

$$\frac{K d\sigma}{r^2 q} \Sigma \, fs = \frac{K d\sigma}{r^2 q} \, v.$$

This represents the entire energy of radiation contained in the volume v, so far as it is caused by radiation through the element $d\sigma$. In order to obtain the total energy of radiation contained in v we must integrate over all elements $d\sigma$ contained in the surface of the sphere. Denoting by $d\Omega$ the solid angle $\frac{d\sigma}{r^2}$ of a cone which has its center in O and intersects in $d\sigma$ the surface of the sphere, we get for the whole energy:

$$\frac{v}{q} \int K \, d\Omega.$$

The volume density of radiation required is found from this by dividing by v. It is

$$u = \frac{1}{q} \int K \, d\Omega. \tag{20}$$

Since in this expression r has disappeared, we can think of K as the intensity of radiation at the point O itself. In integrating, it is to be noted that K in general depends on the direction (θ, ϕ). For radiation that is uniform in all directions K is a constant and on integration we get:

$$u = \frac{4\pi K}{q} \tag{21}$$

23. A meaning similar to that of the volume density of the total radiation u is attached to the volume density of radiation of a definite frequency u_ν. Summing up for all parts of the spectrum we get:

$$u = \int_o^\infty \mathsf{u}_\nu d\nu. \tag{22}$$

Further by combining equations (9) and (20) we have:

$$\mathsf{u}_\nu = \frac{1}{q} \int (\mathsf{K}_\nu + \mathsf{K}_\nu') \, d\Omega, \tag{23}$$

and finally for unpolarized radiation uniformly distributed in all directions:

$$\mathsf{u}_\nu = \frac{8\pi \ \mathsf{K}_\nu}{q} \tag{24}$$

CHAPTER II

RADIATION AT THERMODYNAMIC EQUILIBRIUM. KIRCHHOFF'S LAW. BLACK RADIATION

24. We shall now apply the laws enunciated in the last chapter to the special case of thermodynamic equilibrium, and hence we begin our consideration by stating a certain consequence of the second principle of thermodynamics: A system of bodies of arbitrary nature, shape, and position which is at rest and is surrounded by a rigid cover impermeable to heat will, no matter what its initial state may be, pass in the course of time into a permanent state, in which the temperature of all bodies of the system is the same. This is the state of thermodynamic equilibrium, in which the entropy of the system has the maximum value compatible with the total energy of the system as fixed by the initial conditions. This state being reached, no further increase in entropy is possible.

In certain cases it may happen that, under the given conditions, the entropy can assume not only one but several maxima, of which one is the absolute one, the others having only a relative significance.[1] In these cases every state corresponding to a maximum value of the entropy represents a state of thermodynamic equilibrium of the system. But only one of them, the one corresponding to the absolute maximum of entropy, represents the absolutely stable equilibrium. All the others are in a certain sense unstable, inasmuch as a suitable, however small, disturbance may produce in the system a permanent change in the equilibrium in the direction of the absolutely stable equilibrium. An example of this is offered by supersaturated steam enclosed in a rigid vessel or by any explosive substance. We shall also meet such unstable equilibria in the case of radiation phenomena (Sec. 52).

[1] See, *e.g.*, *M. Planck*, Vorlesungen über Thermodynamik, Leipzig, Veit and Comp., 1911 (or English Translation, Longmans Green & Co.), Secs. 165 and 189, *et seq.*

25. We shall now, as in the previous chapter, assume that we are dealing with homogeneous isotropic media whose condition depends only on the temperature, and we shall inquire what laws the radiation phenomena in them must obey in order to be consistent with the deduction from the second principle mentioned in the preceding section. The means of answering this inquiry is supplied by the investigation of the state of thermodynamic equilibrium of one or more of such media, this investigation to be conducted by applying the conceptions and laws established in the last chapter.

We shall begin with the simplest case, that of a single medium extending very far in all directions of space, and, like all systems we shall here consider, being surrounded by a rigid cover impermeable to heat. For the present we shall assume that the medium has finite coefficients of absorption, emission, and scattering.

Let us consider, first, points of the medium that are far away from the surface. At such points the influence of the surface is, of course, vanishingly small and from the homogeneity and the isotropy of the medium it will follow that in a state of thermodynamic equilibrium the radiation of heat has everywhere and in all directions the same properties. Then K_ν, the specific intensity of radiation of a plane polarized ray of frequency ν (Sec. 17), must be independent of the azimuth of the plane of polarization as well as of position and direction of the ray. Hence to each pencil of rays starting at an element of area $d\sigma$ and diverging within a conical element $d\Omega$ corresponds an exactly equal pencil of opposite direction converging within the same conical element toward the element of area.

Now the condition of thermodynamic equilibrium requires that the temperature shall be everywhere the same and shall not vary in time. Therefore in any given arbitrary time just as much radiant heat must be absorbed as is emitted in each volume-element of the medium. For the heat of the body depends only on the heat radiation, since, on account of the uniformity in temperature, no conduction of heat takes place. This condition is not influenced by the phenomenon of scattering, because scattering refers only to a change in direction of the energy radiated, not to a creation or destruction of it. We shall, therefore, calculate the energy emitted and absorbed in the time dt by a volume-element v.

According to equation (2) the energy emitted has the value

$$dt\, v \cdot 8\pi \int_0^\infty \epsilon_\nu \, d\nu$$

where ϵ_ν, the coefficient of emission of the medium, depends only on the frequency ν and on the temperature in addition to the chemical nature of the medium.

26. For the calculation of the energy absorbed we shall employ the same reasoning as was illustrated by Fig. 1 (Sec. 22) and shall retain the notation there used. The radiant energy absorbed by the volume-element v in the time dt is found by considering the intensities of all the rays passing through the element v and taking that fraction of each of these rays which is absorbed in v. Now, according to (19), the conical element that starts from $d\sigma$ and cuts out of the volume v a part equal to fs has the intensity (energy radiated per unit time)

$$d\sigma \cdot \frac{f}{r^2} \cdot K$$

or, according to (12), by considering the different parts of the spectrum separately:

$$2\, d\sigma \frac{f}{r^2} \int_0^\infty \mathsf{K}_\nu \, d\nu.$$

Hence the intensity of a monochromatic ray is:

$$2\, d\sigma \frac{f}{r^2} \mathsf{K}_\nu \, d\nu.$$

The amount of energy of this ray absorbed in the distance s in the time dt is, according to (4),

$$dt\, \alpha_\nu s\, 2\, d\sigma \frac{f}{r^2} \mathsf{K}_\nu \, d\nu.$$

Hence the absorbed part of the energy of this small cone of rays, as found by integrating over all frequencies, is:

$$dt\, 2\, d\sigma \frac{fs}{r^2} \int_0^\infty \alpha_\nu \mathsf{K}_\nu \, d\nu.$$

When this expression is summed up over all the different cross-sections f of the conical elements starting at $d\sigma$ and passing through v, it is evident that $\Sigma fs = v$, and when we sum up over all elements $d\sigma$ of the spherical surface of radius r we have

$$\int \frac{d\sigma}{r^2} = 4\pi.$$

Thus for the total radiant energy absorbed in the time dt by the volume-element v the following expression is found:

$$dt\ v\ 8\pi \int_o^\infty \alpha_\nu\ \mathsf{K}_\nu\ d\nu. \tag{25}$$

By equating the emitted and absorbed energy we obtain:

$$\int_o^\infty \epsilon_\nu\ d\nu = \int_o^\infty \alpha_\nu\ \mathsf{K}_\nu\ d\nu.$$

A similar relation may be obtained for the separate parts of the spectrum. For the energy emitted and the energy absorbed in the state of thermodynamic equilibrium are equal, not only for the entire radiation of the whole spectrum, but also for each monochromatic radiation. This is readily seen from the following. The magnitudes of ϵ_ν, α_ν, and K_ν are independent of position. Hence, if for any single color the absorbed were not equal to the emitted energy, there would be everywhere in the whole medium a continuous increase or decrease of the energy radiation of that particular color at the expense of the other colors. This would be contradictory to the condition that K_ν for each separate frequency does not change with the time. We have therefore for each frequency the relation:

$$\epsilon_\nu = \alpha_\nu\ \mathsf{K}_\nu, \text{ or} \tag{26}$$

$$\mathsf{K}_\nu = \frac{\epsilon_\nu}{\alpha_\nu}, \tag{27}$$

i.e.: *in the interior of a medium in a state of thermodynamic equilibrium the specific intensity of radiation of a certain frequency is equal to the coefficient of emission divided by the coefficient of absorption of the medium for this frequency.*

27. Since ϵ_ν and α_ν depend only on the nature of the medium, the temperature, and the frequency ν, the intensity of radiation of a definite color in the state of thermodynamic equilibrium is completely defined by the nature of the medium and the temperature. An exceptional case is when $\alpha_\nu=0$, that is, when the medium does not at all absorb the color in question. Since K_ν cannot become infinitely large, a first consequence of this is that in that case $\epsilon_\nu=0$ also, that is, a medium does not emit any color which it does not absorb. A second consequence is that if ϵ_ν and α_ν both vanish, equation (26) is satisfied by every value of K_ν. *In a medium which is diathermanous for a certain color thermodynamic equilibrium can exist for any intensity of radiation whatever of that color.*

This supplies an immediate illustration of the cases spoken of before (Sec. 24), where, for a given value of the total energy of a system enclosed by a rigid cover impermeable to heat, several states of equilibrium can exist, corresponding to several relative maxima of the entropy. That is to say, since the intensity of radiation of the particular color in the state of thermodynamic equilibrium is quite independent of the temperature of a medium which is diathermanous for this color, the given total energy may be arbitrarily distributed between radiation of that color and the heat of the body, without making thermodynamic equilibrium impossible. Among all these distributions there is one particular one, corresponding to the absolute maximum of entropy, which represents absolutely stable equilibrium. This one, unlike all the others, which are in a certain sense unstable, has the property of not being appreciably affected by a small disturbance. Indeed we shall see later (Sec. 48) that among the infinite number of values, which the quotient $\frac{\epsilon_\nu}{\alpha_\nu}$ can have, if numerator and denominator both vanish, there exists one particular one which depends in a definite way on the nature of the medium, the frequency ν, and the temperature. This distinct value of the fraction is accordingly called the stable intensity of radiation K_ν in the medium, which at the temperature in question is diathermanous for rays of the frequency ν.

Everything that has just been said of a medium which is diathermanous for a certain kind of rays holds true for an absolute vacuum, which is a medium diathermanous for rays of all kinds, the only difference being that one cannot speak of the heat and the temperature of an absolute vacuum in any definite sense.

For the present we again shall put the special case of diathermancy aside and assume that all the media considered have a finite coefficient of absorption.

28. Let us now consider briefly the phenomenon of scattering at thermodynamic equilibrium. Every ray meeting the volume-element v suffers there, apart from absorption, a certain weakening of its intensity because a certain fraction of its energy is diverted in different directions. The value of the total energy of scattered radiation received and diverted, in the time dt by the volume-element v in all directions, may be calculated from expression (3) in exactly the same way as the value of the absorbed energy was calculated in Sec. 26. Hence we get an expression similar to (25), namely,

$$dt\ v\ 8\pi \int_0^\infty \beta_\nu\ \mathsf{K}_\nu\ d\nu. \tag{28}$$

The question as to what becomes of this energy is readily answered. On account of the isotropy of the medium, the energy scattered in v and given by (28) is radiated uniformly in all directions just as in the case of the energy entering v. Hence that part of the scattered energy received in v which is radiated out in a cone of solid angle $d\Omega$ is obtained by multiplying the last expression by $\frac{d\Omega}{4\pi}$. This gives

$$2\ dt\ v\ d\Omega \int_0^\infty \beta_\nu\ \mathsf{K}_\nu\ d\nu,$$

and, for monochromatic plane polarized radiation,

$$dt\ v\ d\Omega\ \beta_\nu\ \mathsf{K}_\nu\ d\nu. \tag{29}$$

Here it must be carefully kept in mind that this uniformity of radiation in all directions holds only for all rays striking the element v taken together; a single ray, even in an isotropic medium, is scattered in different directions with different intensities and different directions of polarization. (See end of Sec. 8.)

It is thus found that, when thermodynamic equilibrium of radiation exists inside of the medium, the process of scattering produces, on the whole, no effect. The radiation falling on a volume-element from all sides and scattered from it in all directions behaves exactly as if it had passed directly through the volume-element without the least modification. Every ray loses by scattering just as much energy as it regains by the scattering of other rays.

29. We shall now consider from a different point of view the radiation phenomena in the interior of a very extended homogeneous isotropic medium which is in thermodynamic equilibrium. That is to say, we shall confine our attention, not to a definite volume-element, but to a definite pencil, and in fact to an elementary pencil (Sec. 21). Let this pencil be specified by the infinitely small focal plane $d\sigma$ at the point O (Fig. 2), perpendicular to the axis of the pencil, and by the solid angle $d\Omega$, and let the radiation take place toward the focal plane in the direction of the arrow. We shall consider exclusively rays which belong to this pencil.

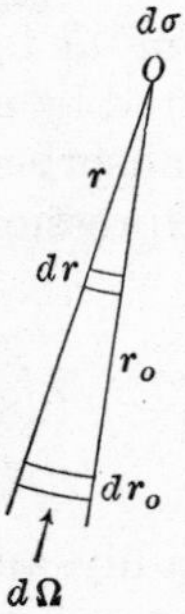

$d\sigma$ O r dr r_o dr_o $d\Omega$

FIG. 2.

The energy of monochromatic plane polarized radiation of the pencil considered passing in unit time through $d\sigma$ is represented, according to (11), since in this case $dt=1$, $\theta=0$, by

$$d\sigma\, d\Omega\, \mathsf{K}_\nu\, d\nu. \tag{30}$$

The same value holds for any other cross-section of the pencil. For first, $\mathsf{K}_\nu\, d\nu$ has everywhere the same magnitude (Sec. 25), and second, the product of any right section of the pencil and the solid angle at which the focal plane $d\sigma$ is seen from this section has the constant value $d\sigma\, d\Omega$, since the magnitude of the cross-section increases with the distance from the vertex O of the pencil in the proportion in which the solid angle decreases. Hence the radiation inside of the pencil takes place just as if the medium were perfectly diathermanous.

On the other hand, the radiation is continuously modified along its path by the effect of emission, absorption, and scattering. We shall consider the magnitude of these effects separately.

30. Let a certain volume-element of the pencil be bounded by two cross-sections at distances equal to r_o (of arbitrary length) and r_o+dr_o respectively from the vertex O. The volume will be represented by $dr_o \cdot r_o^2\, d\Omega$. It emits in unit time toward the focal plane $d\sigma$ at O a certain quantity E of energy of monochromatic plane polarized radiation. E may be obtained from (1) by putting

$$dt=1,\ d\tau=dr_o\ r_o^2\ d\Omega,\ d\Omega=\frac{d\sigma}{r_o^2}$$

and omitting the numerical factor 2. We thus get

$$E=dr_o \cdot d\Omega\ d\sigma\ \epsilon_\nu\ d\nu. \tag{31}$$

Of the energy E, however, only a fraction E_o reaches O, since in every infinitesimal element of distance s which it traverses before reaching O the fraction $(\alpha_\nu+\beta_\nu)s$ is lost by absorption and scattering. Let E_r represent that part of E which reaches a cross-section at a distance $r(<r_o)$ from O. Then for a small distance $s=dr$ we have

$$E_{r+dr}-E_r=E_r(\alpha_\nu+\beta_\nu)dr,$$

or,

$$\frac{dE_r}{dr}=E_r(\alpha_\nu+\beta_\nu),$$

and, by integration,

$$E_r=Ee^{(\alpha_\nu+\beta_\nu)(r-r_o)}$$

since, for $r=r_o$, $E_r=E$ is given by equation (31). From this, by putting $r=0$, the energy emitted by the volume-element at r_o which reaches O is found to be

$$E_o=Ee^{-(\alpha_\nu+\beta_\nu)r_o}=dr_o\ d\Omega\ d\sigma\ \epsilon_\nu\ e^{-(\alpha_\nu+\beta_\nu)r_o}\,d\nu. \tag{32}$$

All volume-elements of the pencils combined produce by their emission an amount of energy reaching $d\sigma$ equal to

$$d\Omega\ d\sigma\ d\nu\ \epsilon_\nu \int_o^\infty dr_o\, e^{-(\alpha_\nu+\beta_\nu)r_o}=d\Omega\, d\sigma \frac{\epsilon_\nu}{\alpha_\nu+\beta_\nu}\,d\nu. \tag{33}$$

31. If the scattering did not affect the radiation, the total energy reaching $d\sigma$ would necessarily consist of the quantities of energy emitted by the different volume-elements of the pencil, allowance being made, however, for the losses due to absorption on the way. For $\beta_\nu = 0$ expressions (33) and (30) are identical, as may be seen by comparison with (27). Generally, however, (30) is larger than (33) because the energy reaching $d\sigma$ contains also some rays which were not at all emitted from elements inside of the pencil, but somewhere else, and have entered later on by scattering. In fact, the volume-elements of the pencil do not merely scatter outward the radiation which is being transmitted inside the pencil, but they also collect into the pencil rays coming from without. The radiation E' thus collected by the volume-element at r_o is found, by putting in (29),

$$dt = 1,\ v = dr_o\, d\Omega\, r_o^2,\ d\Omega = \frac{d\sigma}{r_o^2},$$

to be

$$E' = dr_o\, d\Omega\, d\sigma\, \beta_\nu\, \mathsf{K}_\nu\, d\nu.$$

This energy is to be added to the energy E emitted by the volume-element, which we have calculated in (31). Thus for the total energy contributed to the pencil in the volume-element at r_o we find:

$$E + E' = dr_o\, d\Omega\, d\sigma\, (\epsilon_\nu + \beta_\nu\, \mathsf{K}_\nu)\, d\nu.$$

The part of this reaching O is, similar to (32):

$$dr_o\, d\Omega\, d\sigma\, (\epsilon_\nu + \beta_\nu\, \mathsf{K}_\nu)\, d\nu\, e^{-r_o(\alpha_\nu + \beta_\nu)}$$

Making due allowance for emission and collection of scattered rays entering on the way, as well as for losses by absorption and scattering, all volume-elements of the pencil combined give for the energy ultimately reaching $d\sigma$

$$d\Omega\, d\sigma\, (\epsilon_\nu + \beta_\nu\, \mathsf{K}_\nu)\, d\nu \int_o^\infty dr_o\, e^{-r_o(\alpha_\nu + \beta_\nu)} = d\Omega\, d\sigma \frac{\epsilon_\nu + \beta_\nu\, \mathsf{K}_\nu}{\alpha_\nu + \beta_\nu} d\nu,$$

and this expression is really exactly equal to that given by (30), as may be seen by comparison with (26).

32. The laws just derived for the state of radiation of a homogeneous isotropic medium when it is in thermodynamic equilibrium hold, so far as we have seen, only for parts of the medium which lie very far away from the surface, because for such parts only may the radiation be considered, by symmetry, as independent of position and direction. A simple consideration, however, shows that the value of K_ν, which was already calculated and given by (27), and which depends only on the temperature and the nature of the medium, gives the correct value of the intensity of radiation of the frequency considered for all directions up to points directly below the surface of the medium. For in the state of thermodynamic equilibrium every ray must have just the same intensity as the one travelling in an exactly opposite direction, since otherwise the radiation would cause a unidirectional transport of energy. Consider then any ray coming from the surface of the medium and directed inward; it must have the same intensity as the opposite ray, coming from the interior. A further immediate consequence of this is *that the total state of radiation of the medium is the same on the surface as in the interior.*

33. While the radiation that starts from a surface element and is directed toward the interior of the medium is in every respect equal to that emanating from an equally large parallel element of area in the interior, it nevertheless has a different history. That is to say, since the surface of the medium was assumed to be impermeable to heat, it is produced only by reflection at the surface of radiation coming from the interior. So far as special details are concerned, this can happen in very different ways, depending on whether the surface is assumed to be smooth, *i.e.*, in this case reflecting, or rough, *e.g.*, white (Sec. 10). In the first case there corresponds to each pencil which strikes the surface another perfectly definite pencil, symmetrically situated and having the same intensity, while in the second case every incident pencil is broken up into an infinite number of reflected pencils, each having a different direction, intensity, and polarization. While this is the case, nevertheless the rays that strike a surface-element from all different directions with the same intensity K_ν also produce, all taken together, a uniform radiation of the same intensity K_ν, directed toward the interior of the medium.

34. Hereafter there will not be the slightest difficulty in dispensing with the assumption made in Sec. 25 that the medium in question extends very far in all directions. For after thermodynamic equilibrium has been everywhere established in our medium, the equilibrium is, according to the results of the last paragraph, in no way disturbed, if we assume any number of rigid surfaces impermeable to heat and rough or smooth to be inserted in the medium. By means of these the whole system is divided into an arbitrary number of perfectly closed separate systems, each of which may be chosen as small as the general restrictions stated in Sec. 2 permit. It follows from this that the value of the specific intensity of radiation K_ν given in (27) remains valid for the thermodynamic equilibrium of a substance enclosed in a space as small as we please and of any shape whatever.

35. From the consideration of a system consisting of a single homogeneous isotropic substance we now pass on to the treatment of a system consisting of two different homogeneous isotropic substances contiguous to each other, the system being, as before, enclosed by a rigid cover impermeable to heat. We consider the state of radiation when thermodynamic equilibrium exists, at first, as before, with the assumption that the media are of considerable extent. Since the equilibrium is nowise disturbed, if we think of the surface separating the two media as being replaced for an instant by an area entirely impermeable to heat radiation, the laws of the last paragraphs must hold for each of the two substances separately. Let the specific intensity of radiation of frequency ν polarized in an arbitrary plane be K_ν in the first substance (the upper one in Fig. 3), and K_ν' in the second, and, in general, let all quantities referring to the second substance be indicated by the addition of an accent. Both of the quantities K_ν and K_ν' depend, according to equation (27), only on the temperature, the frequency ν, and the nature of the two substances, and these values of the intensities of radiation hold up to very small distances from the bounding surface of the substances, and hence are entirely independent of the properties of this surface.

36. We shall now suppose, to begin with, that the bounding surface of the media is smooth (Sec. 9). Then every ray coming from the first medium and falling on the bounding surface is divided into two rays, the reflected and the transmitted ray. The directions of these two rays vary with the angle of incidence and the color of the incident ray; the intensity also varies with its polarization. Let us denote by ρ (coefficient of reflection) the fraction of the energy reflected, then the fraction transmitted is $(1-\rho)$, ρ depending on the angle of incidence, the frequency, and the polarization of the incident ray. Similar remarks apply to

ρ' the coefficient of reflection of a ray coming from the second medium and falling on the bounding surface.

Now according to (11) we have for the monochromatic plane polarized radiation of frequency ν, emitted in time dt toward the first medium (in the direction of the feathered arrow upper left

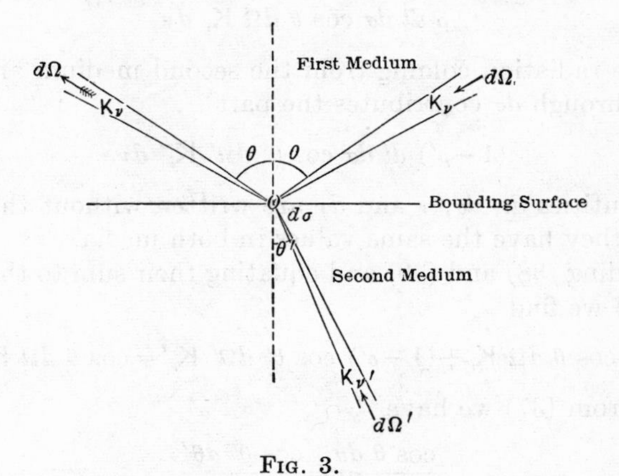

FIG. 3.

hand in Fig. 3), from an element $d\sigma$ of the bounding surface and contained in the conical element $d\Omega$,

$$dt\ d\sigma\ \cos\theta\ d\Omega\ \mathsf{K}_\nu\ d\nu, \tag{34}$$

where

$$d\Omega = \sin\theta\ d\theta\ d\phi. \tag{35}$$

This energy is supplied by the two rays which come from the first and the second medium and are respectively reflected from or transmitted by the element $d\sigma$ in the corresponding direction (the unfeathered arrows). (Of the element $d\sigma$ only the one point O is indicated.) The first ray, according to the law of reflection, continues in the symmetrically situated conical element $d\Omega$, the second in the conical element

$$d\Omega' = \sin\theta'\ d\theta'\ d\phi' \tag{36}$$

where, according to the law of refraction,

$$\phi' = \phi \text{ and } \frac{\sin\theta}{\sin\theta'} = \frac{q}{q'} \tag{37}$$

If we now assume the radiation (34) to be polarized either in the plane of incidence or at right angles thereto, the same will be true for the two radiations of which it consists, and the radiation coming from the first medium and reflected from $d\sigma$ contributes the part

$$\rho\, dt\, d\sigma \cos\theta\, d\Omega\, \mathsf{K}_\nu\, d\nu \tag{38}$$

while the radiation coming from the second medium and transmitted through $d\sigma$ contributes the part

$$(1-\rho')\, dt\, d\sigma \cos\theta'\, d\Omega'\, \mathsf{K}_\nu'\, d\nu. \tag{39}$$

The quantities dt, $d\sigma$, ν and $d\nu$ are written without the accent, because they have the same values in both media.

By adding (38) and (39) and equating their sum to the expression (34) we find

$$\rho \cos\theta\, d\Omega\, \mathsf{K}_\nu + (1-\rho') \cos\theta'\, d\Omega'\, \mathsf{K}_\nu' = \cos\theta\, d\Omega\, \mathsf{K}_\nu.$$

Now from (37) we have

$$\frac{\cos\theta\, d\theta}{q} = \frac{\cos\theta'\, d\theta'}{q'}$$

and further by (35) and (36)

$$d\Omega' \cos\theta' = \frac{d\Omega \cos\theta\, q'^2}{q^2}.$$

Therefore we find

$$\rho\, \mathsf{K}_\nu + (1-\rho')\frac{q'^2}{q^2}\, \mathsf{K}_\nu' = \mathsf{K}$$

or

$$\frac{\mathsf{K}_\nu}{\mathsf{K}_\nu'} \cdot \frac{q^2}{q'^2} = \frac{1-\rho'}{1-\rho}.$$

37. In the last equation the quantity on the left side is independent of the angle of incidence θ and of the particular kind of polarization; hence the same must be true for the right side. Hence, whenever the value of this quantity is known for a single angle of incidence and any definite kind of polarization, this value will remain valid for all angles of incidence and all kinds of polarization. Now in the special case when the rays are polarized at right angles to the plane of incidence and strike the bounding surface at the angle of polarization, $\rho=0$, and $\rho'=0$. The expression on the right side of the last equation then becomes 1; hence it must always be 1 and we have the general relations:

$$\rho=\rho' \tag{40}$$

and

$$q^2\ \mathsf{K}_\nu = q'^2\ \mathsf{K}_\nu' \tag{41}$$

38. The first of these two relations, which states that the coefficient of reflection of the bounding surface is the same on both sides, is a special case of a general law of reciprocity first stated by *Helmholtz.*[1] According to this law the loss of intensity which a ray of definite color and polarization suffers on its way through any media by reflection, refraction, absorption, and scattering is exactly equal to the loss suffered by a ray of the same intensity, color, and polarization pursuing an exactly opposite path. An immediate consequence of this law is that the radiation striking the bounding surface of any two media is always transmitted as well as reflected equally on both sides, for every color, direction, and polarization.

39. The second formula (41) establishes a relation between the intensities of radiation in the two media, for it states that, when thermodynamic equilibrium exists, *the specific intensities of radiation of a certain frequency in the two media are in the inverse ratio of the squares of the velocities of propagation or in the direct ratio of the squares of the indices of refraction.*[2]

By substituting for K_ν its value from (27) we obtain the following theorem: *The quantity*

$$q^2\ \mathsf{K}_\nu = q^2\ \frac{\epsilon_\nu}{\alpha_\nu} \tag{42}$$

does not depend on the nature of the substance, and is, therefore, a universal function of the temperature T and the frequency ν alone.

The great importance of this law lies evidently in the fact that it states a property of radiation which is the same for all bodies

[1] *H. v. Helmholtz,* Handbuch d. physiologischen Optik 1. Lieferung, Leipzig, Leop. Voss, 1856, p. 169. See also *Helmholtz,* Vorlesungen über die Theorie der Wärme herausgegeben von *F. Richarz,* Leipzig, J. A. Barth, 1903, p. 161. The restrictions of the law of reciprocity made there do not bear on our problems, since we are concerned with temperature radiation only (Sec. 7).

[2] *G. Kirchhoff,* Gesammelte Abhandlungen, Leipzig, J. A. Barth, 1882, p. 594. *R. Clausius,* Pogg. Ann. **121**, p. 1, 1864.

in nature, and which need be known only for a single arbitrarily chosen body, in order to be stated quite generally for all bodies. We shall later on take advantage of the opportunity offered by this statement in order actually to calculate this universal function (Sec. 165).

40. We now consider the other case, that in which the bounding surface of the two media is rough. This case is much more general than the one previously treated, inasmuch as the energy of a pencil directed from an element of the bounding surface into the first medium is no longer supplied by two definite pencils, but by an arbitrary number, which come from both media and strike the surface. Here the actual conditions may be very complicated according to the peculiarities of the bounding surface, which moreover may vary in any way from one element to another. However, according to Sec. 35, the values of the specific intensities of radiation K_ν and K_ν' remain always the same in all directions in both media, just as in the case of a smooth bounding surface. That this condition, necessary for thermodynamic equilibrium, is satisfied is readily seen from *Helmholtz's* law of reciprocity, according to which, in the case of stationary radiation, for each ray striking the bounding surface and diffusely reflected from it on both sides, there is a corresponding ray at the same point, of the same intensity and opposite direction, produced by the inverse process at the same point on the bounding surface, namely by the gathering of diffusely incident rays into a definite direction, just as is the case in the interior of each of the two media.

41. We shall now further generalize the laws obtained. First, just as in Sec. 34, the assumption made above, namely, that the two media extend to a great distance, may be abandoned since we may introduce an arbitrary number of bounding surfaces without disturbing the thermodynamic equilibrium. Thereby we are placed in a position enabling us to pass at once to the case of any number of substances of any size and shape. For when a system consisting of an arbitrary number of contiguous substances is in the state of thermodynamic equilibrium, the equilibrium is in no way disturbed, if we assume one or more of the surfaces of contact to be wholly or partly impermeable to heat. Thereby we can always reduce the case of any number of substances to that of two substances in an enclosure impermeable to heat, and, therefore, the law may be stated quite generally, that, when any arbitrary system is in the state of thermodynamic equilibrium, the specific intensity of radiation K_ν is determined in each separate substance by the universal function (42).

42. We shall now consider a system in a state of thermodynamic equilibrium, contained within an enclosure impermeable to heat and consisting of n emitting and absorbing adjacent bodies of any size and shape whatever. As in Sec. 36, we again confine our attention to a monochromatic plane polarized pencil which proceeds from an element $d\sigma$ of the bounding surface of the two media in the direction toward the first medium (Fig. 3, feathered arrow) within the conical element $d\Omega$. Then, as in (34), the energy supplied by the pencil in unit time is

$$d\sigma \cos \theta \, d\Omega \, \mathsf{K}_\nu \, d\nu = I. \tag{43}$$

This energy of radiation I consists of a part coming from the first medium by regular or diffuse reflection at the bounding surface and of a second part coming through the bounding surface from the second medium. We shall, however, not stop at this mode of division, but shall further subdivide I according to that one of the n media from which the separate parts of the radiation I have been emitted. This point of view is distinctly different from the preceding, since, *e.g.*, the rays transmitted from the second medium through the bounding surface into the pencil considered have not necessarily been emitted in the second medium, but may, according to circumstances, have traversed a long and very complicated path through different media and may have undergone therein the effect of refraction, reflection, scattering, and partial absorption any number of times. Similarly the rays of the pencil, which coming from the first medium are reflected at $d\sigma$, were not necessarily all emitted in the first medium. It may even happen that a ray emitted from a certain medium, after passing on its way through other media, returns to the original one and is there either absorbed or emerges from this medium a second time.

We shall now, considering all these possibilities, denote that part of I which has been emitted by volume-elements of the first medium by I_1 no matter what paths the different constituents have pursued, that which has been emitted by volume-elements of the second medium by I_2, etc. Then since every part of I must have been emitted by an element of some body, the following equation must hold,

$$I = I_1+I_2+I_3+ \; . \; . \; . \; . \; . \; I_n. \tag{44}$$

43. The most adequate method of acquiring more detailed information as to the origin and the paths of the different rays of which the radiations I_1, I_2, I_3, ... I_n consist, is to pursue the opposite course and to inquire into the future fate of that pencil, which travels exactly in the opposite direction to the pencil I and which therefore comes from the first medium in the cone $d\Omega$ and falls on the surface element $d\sigma$ of the second medium. For since every optical path may also be traversed in the opposite direction, we may obtain by this consideration all paths along which rays can pass into the pencil I, however complicated they may otherwise be. Let J represent the intensity of this inverse pencil, which is directed toward the bounding surface and is in the same state of polarization. Then, according to Sec. 40,

$$J = I. \tag{45}$$

At the bounding surface $d\sigma$ the rays of the pencil J are partly reflected and partly transmitted regularly or diffusely, and thereafter, travelling in both media, are partly absorbed, partly scattered, partly again reflected or transmitted to different media, etc., according to the configuration of the system. But finally the whole pencil J after splitting into many separate rays will be completely absorbed in the n media. Let us denote that part of J which is finally absorbed in the first medium by J_1, that which is finally absorbed in the second medium by J_2, etc., then we shall have

$$J = J_1+J_2+J_3+ \; . \; . \; . \; . \; . \; +J_n.$$

Now the volume-elements of the n media, in which the absorption of the rays of the pencil J takes place, are precisely the same as those in which takes place the emission of the rays constituting the pencil I, the first one considered above. For, according to *Helmholtz's* law of reciprocity, no appreciable radiation of the pencil J can enter a volume-element which contributes no appreciable radiation to the pencil I and *vice versa*.

Let us further keep in mind that the absorption of each volume-element is, according to (42), proportional to its emission and that, according to *Helmholtz's* law of reciprocity, the decrease which the energy of a ray suffers on any path is always equal to the decrease suffered by the energy of a ray pursuing the opposite path. It will then be clear that the volume-elements considered absorb the rays of the pencil J in just the same ratio as they contribute by their emission to the energy of the opposite pencil I. Since, moreover, the sum I of the energies given off by emission by all volume-elements is equal to the sum J of the energies absorbed by all elements, the quantity of energy absorbed by each separate volume-element from the pencil J must be equal to the quantity of energy emitted by the same element into the pencil I. In other words: *the part of a pencil I which has been emitted from a certain volume of any medium is equal to the part of the pencil $J(=I)$ oppositely directed, which is absorbed in the same volume.*

Hence not only are the sums I and J equal, but their constituents are also separately equal or

$$J_1=I_1,\ J_2=I_2,\ \ldots\ldots\ J_n=I_n. \tag{46}$$

44. Following *G. Kirchhoff*[1] we call the quantity I_2, *i.e.*, the intensity of the pencil emitted from the second medium into the first, the *emissive power* E of the second medium, while we call the ratio of J_2 to J, *i.e.*, that fraction of a pencil incident on the second medium which is absorbed in this medium, the *absorbing power* A of the second medium. Therefore

$$E=I_2(\leqq I), \quad A=\frac{J_2}{J}(\leqq 1). \tag{47}$$

The quantities E and A depend (a) on the nature of the two media, (b) on the temperature, the frequency ν, and the direction and the polarization of the radiation considered, (c) on the nature of the bounding surface and on the magnitude of the surface element $d\sigma$ and that of the solid angle $d\Omega$, (d) on the geometrical extent and the shape of the total surface of the two media, (e) on the nature and form of all other bodies of the system. For a ray may pass from the first into the second medium, be partly transmitted by the latter, and then, after reflection somewhere else,

[1] *G. Kirchhoff*, Gesammelte Abhandlungen, 1882, p. 574.

may return to the second medium and may be there entirely absorbed.

With these assumptions, according to equations (46), (45), and (43), *Kirchhoff's* law holds,

$$\frac{E}{A} = I = d\sigma \cos\theta \, d\Omega \, \mathsf{K}_\nu \, d\nu, \tag{48}$$

i.e., the ratio of the emissive power to the absorbing power of any body is independent of the nature of the body. For this ratio is equal to the intensity of the pencil passing through the *first* medium, which, according to equation (27), does not depend on the second medium at all. The value of this ratio does, however, depend on the nature of the first medium, inasmuch as, according to (42), it is not the quantity K_ν but the quantity $q^2\mathsf{K}_\nu$, which is a universal function of the temperature and frequency. The proof of this law given by *G. Kirchhoff l.c.* was later greatly simplified by *E. Pringsheim.*[1]

45. When in particular the second medium is a black body (Sec. 10) it absorbs all the incident radiation. Hence in that case $J_2 = J$, $A = 1$, and $E = A$, *i.e., the emissive power of a black body is independent of its nature. Its emissive power is larger than that of any other body at the same temperature and, in fact, is just equal to the intensity of radiation in the contiguous medium.*

46. We shall now add, without further proof, another general law of reciprocity, which is closely connected with that stated at the end of Sec. 43 and which may be stated thus: *When any emitting and absorbing bodies are in the state of thermodynamic equilibrium, the part of the energy of definite color emitted by a body A, which is absorbed by another body B, is equal to the part of the energy of the same color emitted by B which is absorbed by A.* Since a quantity of energy emitted causes a decrease of the heat of the body, and a quantity of energy absorbed an increase of the heat of the body, it is evident that, when thermodynamic equilibrium exists, any two bodies or elements of bodies selected at random exchange by radiation equal amounts of heat with each other. Here, of course, care must be taken to distinguish between the radiation emitted and the total radiation which reaches one body from the other.

[1] *E. Pringsheim,* Verhandlungen der Deutschen Physikalischen Gesellschaft, **3**, p. 81, 1901.

47. The law holding for the quantity (42) can be expressed in a different form, by introducing, by means of (24), the volume density $\mathfrak{u}_\nu$ of monochromatic radiation instead of the intensity of radiation $\mathfrak{K}_\nu$. We then obtain the law that, for radiation in a state of thermodynamic equilibrium, the quantity

$$\mathfrak{u}_\nu \, q^3 \tag{49}$$

is a function of the temperature T and the frequency ν, and is the same for all substances.[1] This law becomes clearer if we consider that the quantity

$$\mathfrak{u}_\nu \, d\nu \frac{q^3}{\nu^3} \tag{50}$$

also is a universal function of T, ν, and $\nu + d\nu$, and that the product $\mathfrak{u}_\nu \, d\nu$ is, according to (22), the volume density of the radiation whose frequency lies between ν and $\nu + d\nu$, while the quotient $\frac{q}{\nu}$ represents the wave length of a ray of frequency ν in the medium in question. The law then takes the following simple form: *When any bodies whatever are in thermodynamic equilibrium, the energy of monochromatic radiation of a definite frequency, contained in a cubical element of side equal to the wave length, is the same for all bodies.*

48. We shall finally take up the case of diathermanous (Sec. 12) media, which has so far not been considered. In Sec. 27 we saw that, in a medium which is diathermanous for a given color and is surrounded by an enclosure impermeable to heat, there can be thermodynamic equilibrium for any intensity of radiation of this color. There must, however, among all possible intensities of radiation be a definite one, corresponding to the absolute maximum of the total entropy of the system, which designates the absolutely stable equilibrium of radiation. In fact, in equation (27) the intensity of radiation $\mathfrak{K}_\nu$ for $\alpha_\nu = 0$ and $\epsilon_\nu = 0$ assumes the value $\frac{0}{0}$, and hence cannot be calculated from this equation. But we see also that this indeterminateness is removed by equation (41), which states that in the case of thermodynamic

[1] In this law it is assumed that the quantity q in (24) is the same as in (37). This does not hold for strongly dispersing or absorbing substances. For the generalization applying to such cases see *M. Laue*, Annalen d. Physik, **32**, p. 1085, 1910.

equilibrium the product $q^2 \mathsf{K}_\nu$ has the same value for all substances. From this we find immediately a definite value of K_ν which is thereby distinguished from all other values. Furthermore the physical significance of this value is immediately seen by considering the way in which that equation was obtained. It is that intensity of radiation which exists in a diathermanous medium, if it is in thermodynamic equilibrium when in contact with an arbitrary absorbing and emitting medium. The volume and the form of the second medium do not matter in the least, in particular the volume may be taken as small as we please. Hence we can formulate the following law: *Although generally speaking thermodynamic equilibrium can exist in a diathermanous medium for any intensity of radiation whatever, nevertheless there exists in every diathermanous medium for a definite frequency at a definite temperature an intensity of radiation defined by the universal function* (42). *This may be called the stable intensity, inasmuch as it will always be established, when the medium is exchanging stationary radiation with an arbitrary emitting and absorbing substance.*

49. According to the law stated in Sec. 45, the intensity of a pencil, when a state of stable heat radiation exists in a diathermanous medium, is equal to the emissive power E of a black body in contact with the medium. On this fact is based the possibility of measuring the emissive power of a black body, although absolutely black bodies do not exist in nature.[1] A diathermanous cavity is enclosed by strongly emitting walls[2] and the walls kept at a certain constant temperature T. Then the radiation in the cavity, when thermodynamic equilibrium is established for every frequency ν, assumes the intensity corresponding to the velocity of propagation q in the diathermanous medium, according to the universal function (42). Then any element of area of the walls radiates into the cavity just as if the wall were a black body of temperature T. The amount lacking in the intensity of the rays actually emitted by the walls as compared with the emission of a black body is supplied by rays

[1] *W. Wien* and *O. Lummer*, Wied. Annalen, **56**, p. 451, 1895.

[2] The strength of the emission influences only the time required to establish stationary radiation, but not its character. It is essential, however, that the walls transmit no radiation to the exterior.

which fall on the wall and are reflected there. Similarly every element of area of a wall receives the same radiation.

In fact, the radiation I starting from an element of area of a wall consists of the radiation E emitted by the element of area and of the radiation reflected from the element of area from the incident radiation I, *i.e.*, the radiation which is not absorbed $(1-A)I$. We have, therefore, in agreement with *Kirchhoff's* law (48),

$$I=E+(1-A)I.$$

If we now make a hole in one of the walls of a size $d\sigma$, so small that the intensity of the radiation directed toward the hole is not changed thereby, then radiation passes through the hole to the exterior where we shall suppose there is the same diathermanous medium as within. This radiation has exactly the same properties as if $d\sigma$ were the surface of a black body, and this radiation may be measured for every color together with the temperature T.

50. Thus far all the laws derived in the preceding sections for diathermanous media hold for a definite frequency, and it is to be kept in mind that a substance may be diathermanous for one color and adiathermanous for another. Hence the radiation of a medium completely enclosed by absolutely reflecting walls is, when thermodynamic equilibrium has been established for all colors for which the medium has a finite coefficient of absorption, always the stable radiation corresponding to the temperature of the medium such as is represented by the emission of a black body. Hence this is briefly called "black" radiation.[1] On the other hand, the intensity of colors for which the medium is diathermanous is not necessarily the stable black radiation, unless the medium is in a state of stationary exchange of radiation with an absorbing substance.

There is but one medium that is diathermanous for all kinds of rays, namely, the absolute vacuum, which to be sure cannot be produced in nature except approximately. However, most gases, *e.g.*, the air of the atmosphere, have, at least if they are not too dense, to a sufficient approximation the optical properties of a vacuum with respect to waves of not too short length. So far as

[1] *M. Thiesen*, Verhandlungen d. Deutschen Physikal. Gesellschaft, **2**, p. 65, 1900.

this is the case the velocity of propagation q may be taken as the same for all frequencies, namely,

$$c = 3 \times 10^{10} \frac{\text{cm}}{\text{sec}} \tag{51}$$

51. Hence in a vacuum bounded by totally reflecting walls any state of radiation may persist. But as soon as an arbitrarily small quantity of matter is introduced into the vacuum, a stationary state of radiation is gradually established. In this the radiation of every color which is appreciably absorbed by the substance has the intensity K_ν corresponding to the temperature of the substance and determined by the universal function (42) for $q = c$, the intensity of radiation of the other colors remaining indeterminate. If the substance introduced is not diathermanous for any color, *e.g.*, a piece of carbon however small, there exists at the stationary state of radiation in the whole vacuum for all colors the intensity K_ν of black radiation corresponding to the temperature of the substance. The magnitude of K_ν regarded as a function of ν gives the spectral distribution of black radiation in a vacuum, or the so-called *normal energy spectrum,* which depends on nothing but the temperature. In the normal spectrum, since it is the spectrum of emission of a black body, the intensity of radiation of every color is the largest which a body can emit at that temperature at all.

52. It is therefore possible to change a perfectly arbitrary radiation, which exists at the start in the evacuated cavity with perfectly reflecting walls under consideration, into black radiation by the introduction of a minute particle of carbon. The characteristic feature of this process is that the heat of the carbon particle may be just as small as we please, compared with the energy of radiation contained in the cavity of arbitrary magnitude. Hence, according to the principle of the conservation of energy, the total energy of radiation remains essentially constant during the change that takes place, because the changes in the heat of the carbon particle may be entirely neglected, even if its changes in temperature should be finite. Herein the carbon particle exerts only a releasing (auslösend) action. Thereafter the intensities of the pencils of different frequencies originally present and having different frequencies, directions, and different states of polarization change at the expense of one another, corresponding to the passage of the system from a less to a more stable state of radiation or from a state of smaller to a state of larger entropy. From a thermodynamic point of view this process is perfectly analogous, since the time necessary for the process is not essential, to the change produced by a minute spark in a quantity of oxy-hydrogen gas or by a small drop of liquid in a quantity of super-saturated vapor. In all these cases the magnitude of the disturbance is exceedingly small and cannot be compared with the magnitude of the energies undergoing the resultant changes, so that in applying the two principles of thermodynamics the cause of the disturbance of equilibrium, *viz.*, the carbon particle, the spark, or the drop, need not be considered. It is always a case of a system passing from a more or less unstable into a more stable state, wherein, according to the first principle of thermodynamics, the energy of the system remains constant, and, according to the second principle, the entropy of the system increases.

PART II

DEDUCTIONS FROM ELECTRODYNAMICS AND THERMODYNAMICS

CHAPTER I

MAXWELL'S RADIATION PRESSURE

53. While in the preceding part the phenomena of radiation have been presented with the assumption of only well known elementary laws of optics summarized in Sec. 2, which are common to all optical theories, we shall hereafter make use of the electromagnetic theory of light and shall begin by deducing a consequence characteristic of that theory. We shall, namely, calculate the magnitude of the mechanical force, which is exerted by a light or heat ray passing through a vacuum on striking a reflecting (Sec. 10) surface assumed to be at rest.

For this purpose we begin by stating Maxwell's general equations for an electromagnetic process in a vacuum. Let the vector E denote the electric field-strength (intensity of the electric field) in electric units and the vector H the magnetic field-strength in magnetic units. Then the equations are, in the abbreviated notation of the vector calculus,

$$\begin{aligned} \dot{\mathsf{E}} &= c \text{ curl } \mathsf{H} \qquad & \dot{\mathsf{H}} &= -c \text{ curl } \mathsf{E} \\ \text{div. } \mathsf{E} &= 0 \qquad & \text{div. } \mathsf{H} &= 0 \end{aligned} \tag{52}$$

Should the reader be unfamiliar with the symbols of this notation, he may readily deduce their meaning by working backward from the subsequent equations (53).

54. In order to pass to the case of a plane wave in any direction we assume that all the quantities that fix the state depend only on the time t and on one of the coordinates x', y', z', of an orthogonal right-handed system of coordinates, say on x'. Then the equations (52) reduce to

$$\frac{\partial \mathsf{E}_{x'}}{\partial t} = 0 \qquad\qquad \frac{\partial \mathsf{H}_{x'}}{\partial t} = 0$$

$$\frac{\partial \mathsf{E}_{y'}}{\partial t} = -c\, \frac{\partial \mathsf{H}_{z'}}{\partial x'} \qquad\qquad \frac{\partial \mathsf{H}_{y'}}{\partial t} = c\, \frac{\partial \mathsf{E}_{z'}}{\partial x'}$$

$$\frac{\partial \mathsf{E}_{z'}}{\partial t} = c\frac{\partial \mathsf{H}_{y'}}{\partial x'} \qquad \frac{\partial \mathsf{H}_{z'}}{\partial t} = -c\frac{\partial \mathsf{E}_{y'}}{\partial x'} \tag{53}$$

$$\frac{\partial \mathsf{E}_{x'}}{\partial x'} = 0 \qquad \frac{\partial \mathsf{H}_{x'}}{\partial x'} = 0$$

Hence the most general expression for a plane wave passing through a vacuum in the direction of the positive x'-axis is

$$\begin{aligned} \mathsf{E}_{x'} &= 0 & \mathsf{H}_{x'} &= 0 \\ \mathsf{E}_{y'} &= f\left(t-\frac{x'}{c}\right) & \mathsf{H}_{y'} &= -g\left(t-\frac{x'}{c}\right) \\ \mathsf{E}_{z'} &= g\left(t-\frac{x'}{c}\right) & \mathsf{H}_{z'} &= f\left(t-\frac{x'}{c}\right) \end{aligned} \tag{54}$$

where f and g represent two arbitrary functions of the same argument.

55. Suppose now that this wave strikes a reflecting surface, *e.g.*, the surface of an absolute conductor (metal) of infinitely large conductivity. In such a conductor even an infinitely small electric field-strength produces a finite conduction current; hence the electric field-strength E in it must be always and everywhere infinitely small. For simplicity we also suppose the conductor to be non-magnetizable, *i.e.*, we assume the magnetic induction B in it to be equal to the magnetic field-strength H, just as is the case in a vacuum.

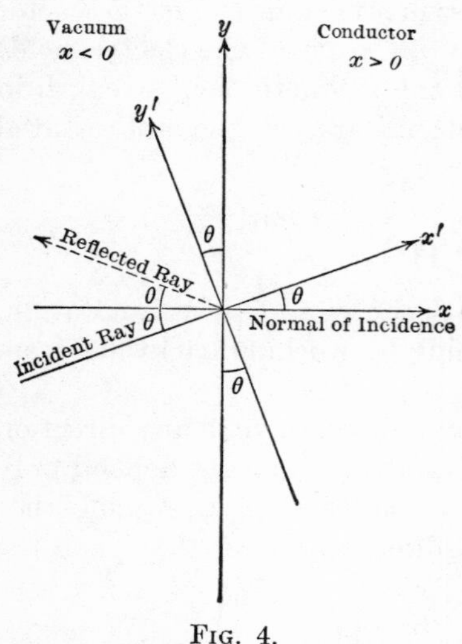

FIG. 4.

If we place the x-axis of a right-handed coordinate system (xyz) along the normal of the surface directed toward the interior of the conductor, the x-axis is the normal of incidence. We place the $(x'y')$ plane in the plane of incidence and take this as the plane of the figure (Fig. 4). Moreover, we can also, without any restriction of generality, place the y-axis in the plane of the figure, so that the z-axis coincides with the z'-axis (directed from the figure toward the observer). Let the common origin O of the two coordinate systems lie in the surface. If finally θ represents the angle of incidence, the coordinates with and without accent are related to each other by the following equations:

$$x = x' \cos \theta - y' \sin \theta \qquad x' = x \cos \theta + y \sin \theta$$
$$y = x' \sin \theta + y' \cos \theta \qquad y' = -x \sin \theta + y \cos \theta$$
$$z = z' \qquad z' = z$$

By the same transformation we may pass from the components of the electric or magnetic field-strength in the first coordinate system to their components in the second system. Performing this transformation the following values are obtained from (54) for the components of the electric and magnetic field-strengths of the incident wave in the coordinate system without accent,

$$\begin{aligned} \mathsf{E}_x &= -\sin\theta \cdot f & \mathsf{H}_x &= \sin\theta \cdot g \\ \mathsf{E}_y &= \cos\theta \cdot f & \mathsf{H}_y &= -\cos\theta \cdot g \\ \mathsf{E}_z &= g & \mathsf{H}_z &= f \end{aligned} \qquad (55)$$

Herein the argument of the functions f and g is

$$t - \frac{x'}{c} = t - \frac{x \cos \theta + y \sin \theta}{c} \qquad (56)$$

56. In the surface of separation of the two media $x=0$. According to the general electromagnetic boundary conditions the components of the field-strengths in the surface of separation, *i.e.*, the four quantities E_y, E_z, H_y, H_z must be equal to each other on the two sides of the surface of separation for this value of x. In the conductor the electric field-strength E is infinitely small in accordance with the assumption made above. Hence E_y and E_z must vanish also in the vacuum for $x=0$. This condition cannot be satisfied unless we assume in the vacuum, besides the incident, also a reflected wave superposed on the former in such a way that the components of the electric field of the two waves in the y and z direction just cancel at every instant and at every point in the surface of separation. By this assumption and the condition that the reflected wave is a plane wave returning into the interior of the vacuum, the other four components of the reflected wave are also completely determined. They are all functions of the single argument

$$t-\frac{-x\cos\theta+y\sin\theta}{c}. \tag{57}$$

The actual calculation yields as components of the total electromagnetic field produced in the vacuum by the superposition of the two waves, the following expressions valid for points of the surface of separation $x=0$,

$$\begin{aligned}
\mathsf{E}_x &= -\sin\theta\cdot f - \sin\theta\cdot f = -2\sin\theta\cdot f \\
\mathsf{E}_y &= \cos\theta\cdot f - \cos\theta\cdot f = 0 \\
\mathsf{E}_z &= g - g = 0 \\
\mathsf{H}_x &= \sin\theta\cdot g - \sin\theta\cdot g = 0 \\
\mathsf{H}_y &= -\cos\theta\cdot g - \cos\theta\cdot g = -2\cos\theta\cdot g \\
\mathsf{H}_z &= f + f = 2f.
\end{aligned} \tag{58}$$

In these equations the argument of the functions f and g is, according to (56) and (57),

$$t-\frac{y\sin\theta}{c}$$

From these values the electric and magnetic field-strength within the conductor in the immediate neighborhood of the separating surface $x=0$ is obtained:

$$\begin{aligned}
\mathsf{E}_x &= 0 \qquad & \mathsf{H}_x &= 0 \\
\mathsf{E}_y &= 0 \qquad & \mathsf{H}_y &= -2\cos\theta\cdot g \\
\mathsf{E}_z &= 0 \qquad & \mathsf{H}_z &= 2f
\end{aligned} \tag{59}$$

where again the argument $t-\frac{y\sin\theta}{c}$ is to be substituted in the functions f and g. For the components of E all vanish in an absolute conductor and the components H_x, H_y, H_z are all continuous at the separating surface, the two latter since they are tangential components of the field-strength, the former since it is the normal component of the magnetic induction B (Sec. 55), which likewise remains continuous on passing through any surface of separation.

On the other hand, the normal component of the electric field-strength E_x is seen to be discontinuous; the discontinuity shows the existence of an electric charge on the surface, the surface density of which is given in magnitude and sign as follows:

$$\frac{1}{4\pi}\,2\,\sin\theta\cdot f=\frac{1}{2\pi}\,\sin\theta\cdot f. \tag{60}$$

In the interior of the conductor at a finite distance from the bounding surface, *i.e.*, for $x>0$, all six field components are infinitely small. Hence, on increasing x, the values of H_y and H_z, which are finite for $x=0$, approach the value 0 at an infinitely rapid rate.

57. A certain mechanical force is exerted on the substance of the conductor by the electromagnetic field considered. We shall calculate the component of this force normal to the surface. It is partly of electric, partly of magnetic, origin. Let us first consider the former, F_e. Since the electric charge existing on the surface of the conductor is in an electric field, a mechanical force equal to the product of the charge and the field-strength is exerted on it. Since, however, the field-strength is discontinuous, having the value $-2\sin\theta f$ on the side of the vacuum and 0 on the side of the conductor, from a well-known law of electrostatics the magnitude of the mechanical force F_e acting on an element of surface $d\sigma$ of the conductor is obtained by multiplying the electric charge of the element of area calculated in (60) by the arithmetic mean of the electric field-strength on the two sides. Hence

$$\mathsf{F}_e=\frac{\sin\theta}{2\pi}\,f\,d\sigma(-\sin\theta f)=-\frac{\sin^2\theta}{2\pi}\,f^2\,d\sigma$$

This force acts in the direction toward the vacuum and therefore exerts a tension.

58. We shall now calculate the mechanical force of magnetic origin F_m. In the interior of the conducting substance there are certain conduction currents, whose intensity and direction are determined by the vector I of the current density

$$\mathsf{I}=\frac{c}{4\pi}\,\mathrm{curl}\,\mathsf{H}. \tag{61}$$

A mechanical force acts on every element of space $d\tau$ of the conductor through which a conduction current flows, and is given by the vector product

$$\frac{d\tau}{c}\,[\mathsf{IH}] \tag{62}$$

Hence the component of this force normal to the surface of the conductor $x=0$ is equal to

$$\frac{d\tau}{c}(\mathsf{I}_y\mathsf{H}_z-\mathsf{I}_z\mathsf{H}_y).$$

On substituting the values of I_y and I_z from (61) we obtain

$$\frac{d\tau}{4\pi}\left[\mathsf{H}_z\left(\frac{\partial \mathsf{H}_x}{\partial z}-\frac{\partial \mathsf{H}_z}{\partial x}\right)-\mathsf{H}_y\left(\frac{\partial \mathsf{H}_y}{\partial x}-\frac{\partial \mathsf{H}_x}{\partial y}\right)\right].$$

In this expression the differential coefficients with respect to y and z are negligibly small in comparison to those with respect to x, according to the remark at the end of Sec. 56; hence the expression reduces to

$$-\frac{d\tau}{4\pi}\left(\mathsf{H}_y\frac{\partial \mathsf{H}_y}{\partial x}+\mathsf{H}_z\frac{\partial \mathsf{H}_z}{\partial x}\right).$$

Let us now consider a cylinder cut out of the conductor perpendicular to the surface with the cross-section $d\sigma$, and extending from $x=0$ to $x=\infty$. The entire mechanical force of magnetic origin acting on this cylinder in the direction of the x-axis, since $d\tau=d\sigma\ x$, is given by

$$\mathsf{F}_m=-\frac{d\sigma}{4\pi}\int_o^\infty dx\left(H_y\frac{\partial \mathsf{H}_y}{\partial x}+\mathsf{H}_z\frac{\partial \mathsf{H}_z}{\partial x}\right).$$

On integration, since H vanishes for $x=\infty$, we obtain

$$\mathsf{F}_m=\frac{d\sigma}{8\pi}(\mathsf{H}^2{}_y+\mathsf{H}^2{}_z)_{x=0}$$

or by equation (59)

$$\mathsf{F}_m=\frac{d\sigma}{2\pi}\,(\cos^2\theta\cdot g^2+f^2).$$

By adding F_e and F_m the total mechanical force acting on the cylinder in question in the direction of the x-axis is found to be

$$\mathsf{F}=\frac{d\sigma}{2\pi}\cos^2\theta\ (f^2+g^2). \tag{63}$$

This force exerts on the surface of the conductor a pressure, which acts in a direction normal to the surface toward the interior and is called "*Maxwell's* radiation pressure." The existence and the magnitude of the radiation pressure as predicted by the theory was first found by delicate measurements with the radiometer by *P. Lebedew.*[1]

59. We shall now establish a relation between the radiation pressure and the energy of radiation Idt falling on the surface element $d\sigma$ of the conductor in a time element dt. The latter from *Poynting's* law of energy flow is

$$Idt = \frac{c}{4\pi}(\mathsf{E}_y\mathsf{H}_z - \mathsf{E}_z\mathsf{H}_y)\, d\sigma\, dt,$$

hence from (55)

$$Idt = \frac{c}{4\pi} \cos\theta\, (f^2+g^2)\, d\sigma\, dt.$$

By comparison with (63) we obtain

$$\mathsf{F} = \frac{2\cos\theta}{c} I. \tag{64}$$

From this we finally calculate the total pressure p, *i.e.*, that mechanical force, which an arbitrary radiation proceeding from the vacuum and totally reflected upon incidence on the conductor exerts in a normal direction on a unit surface of the conductor. The energy radiated in the conical element

$$d\Omega = \sin\theta\, d\theta\, d\phi$$

in the time dt on the element of area $d\sigma$ is, according to (6),

$$Idt = K\cos\theta\, d\Omega\, d\sigma\, dt,$$

where K represents the specific intensity of the radiation in the direction $d\Omega$ toward the reflector. On substituting this in (64) and integrating over $d\Omega$ we obtain for the total pressure of all pencils which fall on the surface and are reflected by it

$$p = \frac{2}{c}\int K\cos^2\theta\, d\Omega, \tag{65}$$

the integration with respect to ϕ extending from 0 to 2π and with respect to θ from 0 to $\frac{\pi}{2}$.

[1] *P. Lebedew*, Annalen d. Phys., **6**, p. 433, 1901. See also *E. F. Nichols* and *G. F. Hull*, Annalen d. Phys., **12**, p. 225, 1903.

In case K is independent of direction as in the case of black radiation, we obtain for the radiation pressure

$$p = \frac{2K}{c}\int_0^{2\pi} d\phi \int_0^{\frac{\pi}{2}} d\theta \cos^2\theta \sin\theta = \frac{4\pi K}{3c}$$

or, if we introduce instead of K the volume density of radiation u from (21)

$$p = \frac{u}{3}. \qquad (66)$$

This value of the radiation pressure holds only when the reflection of the radiation occurs at the surface of an absolute non-magnetizable conductor. Therefore we shall in the thermodynamic deductions of the next chapter make use of it only in such cases. Nevertheless it will be shown later on (Sec. 66) that equation (66) gives the pressure of uniform radiation against any totally reflecting surface, no matter whether it reflects uniformly or diffusely.

60. In view of the extraordinarily simple and close relation between the radiation pressure and the energy of radiation, the question might be raised whether this relation is really a special consequence of the electromagnetic theory, or whether it might not, perhaps, be founded on more general energetic or thermodynamic considerations. To decide this question we shall calculate the radiation pressure that would follow by Newtonian mechanics from *Newton's* (emission) theory of light, a theory which, in itself, is quite consistent with the energy principle. According to it the energy radiated onto a surface by a light ray passing through a vacuum is equal to the kinetic energy of the light particles striking the surface, all moving with the constant velocity c. The decrease in intensity of the energy radiation with the distance is then explained simply by the decrease of the volume density of the light particles.

Let us denote by n the number of the light particles contained in a unit volume and by m the mass of a particle. Then for a beam of parallel light the number of particles impinging in unit time on the element $d\sigma$ of a reflecting surface at the angle of incidence θ is

$$nc \cos\theta \, d\sigma. \qquad (67)$$

Their kinetic energy is given according to Newtonian mechanics by

$$I = nc \cos \theta \, d\sigma \frac{mc^2}{2} = nm \cos \theta \frac{c^3}{2} d\sigma. \qquad (68)$$

Now, in order to determine the normal pressure of these particles on the surface, we may note that the normal component of the velocity $c \cos \theta$ of every particle is changed on reflection into a component of opposite direction. Hence the normal component of the momentum of every particle (impulse-coordinate) is changed through reflection by $-2mc \cos \theta$. Then the change in momentum for all particles considered will be, according to (67),

$$-2nm \cos^2 \theta \, c^2 \, d\sigma. \qquad (69)$$

Should the reflecting body be free to move in the direction of the normal of the reflecting surface and should there be no force acting on it except the impact of the light particles, it would be set into motion by the impacts. According to the law of action and reaction the ensuing motion would be such that the momentum acquired in a certain interval of time would be equal and opposite to the change in momentum of all the light particles reflected from it in the same time interval. But if we allow a separate constant force to act from outside on the reflector, there is to be added to the change in momenta of the light particles the impulse of the external force, *i.e.*, the product of the force and the time interval in question.

Therefore the reflector will remain continuously at rest, whenever the constant external force exerted on it is so chosen that its impulse for any time is just equal to the change in momentum of all the particles reflected from the reflector in the same time. Thus it follows that the force F itself which the particles exert by their impact on the surface element $d\sigma$ is equal and opposite to the change of their momentum in unit time as expressed in (69)

$$\mathsf{F} = 2 \, nm \cos^2 \theta \, c^2 \, d\sigma$$

and by making use of (68),

$$\mathsf{F} = \frac{4 \cos \theta}{c} I.$$

On comparing this relation with equation (64) in which all symbols have the same physical significance, it is seen that

Newton's radiation pressure is twice as large as *Maxwell's* for the same energy radiation. A necessary consequence of this is that the magnitude of *Maxwell's* radiation pressure cannot be deduced from general energetic considerations, but is a special feature of the electromagnetic theory and hence all deductions from *Maxwell's* radiation pressure are to be regarded as consequences of the electromagnetic theory of light and all confirmations of them are confirmations of this special theory.

CHAPTER II

STEFAN-BOLTZMANN LAW OF RADIATION

61. For the following we imagine a perfectly evacuated hollow cylinder with an absolutely tight-fitting piston free to move in a vertical direction with no friction. A part of the walls of the cylinder, say the rigid bottom, should consist of a black body, whose temperature T may be regulated arbitrarily from the outside. The rest of the walls including the inner surface of the piston may be assumed as totally reflecting. Then, if the piston remains stationary and the temperature, T, constant, the radiation in the vacuum will, after a certain time, assume the character of black radiation (Sec. 50) uniform in all directions. The specific intensity, K, and the volume density, u, depend only on the temperature, T, and are independent of the volume, V, of the vacuum and hence of the position of the piston.

If now the piston is moved downward, the radiation is compressed into a smaller space; if it is moved upward the radiation expands into a larger space. At the same time the temperature of the black body forming the bottom may be arbitrarily changed by adding or removing heat from the outside. This always causes certain disturbances of the stationary state. If, however, the arbitrary changes in V and T are made sufficiently slowly, the departure from the conditions of a stationary state may always be kept just as small as we please. Hence the state of radiation in the vacuum may, without appreciable error, be regarded as a state of thermodynamic equilibrium, just as is done in the thermodynamics of ordinary matter in the case of so-called infinitely slow processes, where, at any instant, the divergence from the state of equilibrium may be neglected, compared with the changes which the total system considered undergoes as a result of the entire process.

If, *e.g.*, we keep the temperature T of the black body forming the bottom constant, as can be done by a suitable connection between it and a heat reservoir of large capacity, then, on raising the piston, the black body will emit more than it absorbs, until the newly made space is filled with the same density of radiation as was the original one. *Vice versa,* on lowering the piston the black body will absorb the superfluous radiation until the original radiation corresponding to the temperature T is again established. Similarly, on raising the temperature T of the black body, as can be done by heat conduction from a heat reservoir which is slightly warmer, the density of radiation in the vacuum will be correspondingly increased by a larger emission, etc. To accelerate the establishment of radiation equilibrium the reflecting mantle of the hollow cylinder may be assumed white (Sec. 10), since by diffuse reflection the predominant directions of radiation that may, perhaps, be produced by the direction of the motion of the piston, are more quickly neutralized. The reflecting surface of the piston, however, should be chosen for the present as a perfect metallic reflector, to make sure that the radiation pressure (66) on the piston is *Maxwell's.* Then, in order to produce mechanical equilibrium, the piston must be loaded by a weight equal to the product of the radiation pressure p and the cross-section of the piston. An exceedingly small difference of the loading weight will then produce a correspondingly slow motion of the piston in one or the other direction.

Since the effects produced from the outside on the system in question, the cavity through which the radiation travels, during the processes we are considering, are partly of a mechanical nature (displacement of the loaded piston), partly of a thermal nature (heat conduction away from and toward the reservoir), they show a certain similarity to the processes usually considered in thermodynamics, with the difference that the system here considered is not a material system, *e.g.*, a gas, but a purely energetic one. If, however, the principles of thermodynamics hold quite generally in nature, as indeed we shall assume, then they must also hold for the system under consideration. That is to say, in the case of any change occurring in nature the energy of all systems taking part in the change must remain constant (first principle), and, moreover, the entropy of all systems taking part in the change must increase, or in the limiting case of reversible processes must remain constant (second principle).

62. Let us first establish the equation of the first principle for an infinitesimal change of the system in question. That the cavity enclosing the radiation has a certain energy we have already (Sec. 22) deduced from the fact that the energy radiation is propagated with a finite velocity. We shall denote the energy by U. Then we have

$$U = Vu, \tag{70}$$

where u the volume density of radiation depends only on the temperature of T the black body at the bottom.

The work done by the system, when the volume V of the cavity increases by dV against the external forces of pressure (weight of the loaded piston), is pdV, where p represents *Maxwell's* radiation pressure (66). This amount of mechanical energy is therefore gained by the surroundings of the system, since the weight is raised. The error made by using the radiation pressure on a stationary surface, whereas the reflecting surface moves during the volume change, is evidently negligible, since the motion may be thought of as taking place with an arbitrarily small velocity.

If, moreover, Q denotes the infinitesimal quantity of heat in mechanical units, which, owing to increased emission, passes from the black body at the bottom to the cavity containing the radiation, the bottom or the heat reservoir connected to it loses this heat Q, and its internal energy is decreased by that amount. Hence, according to the first principle of thermodynamics, since the sum of the energy of radiation and the energy of the material bodies remains constant, we have

$$dU + pdV - Q = 0. \tag{71}$$

According to the second principle of thermodynamics the cavity containing the radiation also has a definite entropy. For when the heat Q passes from the heat reservoir into the cavity, the entropy of the reservoir decreases, the change being

$$-\frac{Q}{T}$$

Therefore, since no changes occur in the other bodies—inasmuch as the rigid absolutely reflecting piston with the weight on it does not change its internal condition with the motion—there must somewhere in nature occur a compensation of entropy having at least the value $\frac{Q}{T}$, by which the above diminution is compensated, and this can be nowhere except in the entropy of the cavity containing the radiation. Let the entropy of the latter be denoted by S.

Now, since the processes described consist entirely of states of equilibrium, they are perfectly reversible and hence there is no increase in entropy. Then we have

$$dS-\frac{Q}{T}=0, \tag{72}$$

or from (71)

$$dS=\frac{dU+pdV}{T} \tag{73}$$

In this equation the quantities U, p, V, S represent certain properties of the heat radiation, which are completely defined by the instantaneous state of the radiation. Therefore the quantity T is also a certain property of the state of the radiation, *i.e.*, the black radiation in the cavity has a certain temperature T and this temperature is that of a body which is in heat equilibrium with the radiation.

63. We shall now deduce from the last equation a consequence which is based on the fact that the state of the system considered, and therefore also its entropy, is determined by the values of two independent variables. As the first variable we shall take V, as the second either T, u, or p may be chosen. Of these three quantities any two are determined by the third together with V. We shall take the volume V and the temperature T as independent variables. Then by substituting from (66) and (70) in (73) we have

$$dS=\frac{V}{T}\frac{du}{dT}\,dT+\frac{4u}{3T}\,dV. \tag{74}$$

From this we obtain

$$\left(\frac{\partial S}{\partial T}\right)_V=\frac{V}{T}\frac{du}{dT} \qquad \left(\frac{\partial S}{\partial V}\right)_T=\frac{4u}{3T}$$

On partial differentiation of these equations, the first with respect to V, the second with respect to T, we find

$$\frac{\partial^2 S}{\partial T \partial V} = \frac{1}{T}\frac{du}{dT} = \frac{4}{3T}\frac{du}{dT} - \frac{4u}{3T^2}$$

or

$$\frac{du}{dT} = \frac{4u}{T}$$

and on integration

$$u = aT^4 \qquad (75)$$

and from (21) for the specific intensity of black radiation

$$K = \frac{c}{4\pi} \cdot u = \frac{ac}{4\pi} T^4. \qquad (76)$$

Moreover for the pressure of black radiation

$$p = \frac{a}{3} T^4, \qquad (77)$$

and for the total radiant energy

$$U = aT^4 \cdot V. \qquad (78)$$

This law, which states that the volume density and the specific intensity of black radiation are proportional to the fourth power of the absolute temperature, was first established by *J. Stefan*[1] on a basis of rather rough measurements. It was later deduced by *L. Boltzmann*[2] on a thermodynamic basis from *Maxwell's* radiation pressure and has been more recently confirmed by *O. Lummer* and *E. Pringsheim*[3] by exact measurements between 100° and 1300° C., the temperature being defined by the gas thermometer. In ranges of temperature and for requirements of precision for which the readings of the different gas thermometers no longer agree sufficiently or cannot be obtained at all, the *Stefan-Boltzmann* law of radiation can be used for an absolute definition of temperature independent of all substances.

64. The numerical value of the constant a is obtained from measurements made by *F. Kurlbaum*.[4] According to them, if

[1] *J. Stefan*, Wien. Berichte, **79**, p. 391, 1879.

[2] *L. Boltzmann*, Wied. Annalen, **22**, p. 291, 1884.

[3] *O. Lummer* und *E. Pringsheim*, Wied. Annalen, **63**, p. 395, 1897. Annalen d. Physik, **3**, p. 159, 1900.

[4] *F. Kurlbaum*, Wied. Annalen, **65**, p. 759, 1898.

we denote by S_t the total energy radiated in one second into air by a square centimeter of a black body at a temperature of $t°$ C., the following equation holds

$$S_{100}-S_o=0.0731\ \frac{\text{watt}}{\text{cm}^2}=7.31\times10^5\frac{\text{erg}}{\text{cm}^2\ \text{sec}}$$

Now, since the radiation in air is approximately identical with the radiation into a vacuum, we may according to (7) and (76) put

$$S_t=\pi K=\frac{ac}{4}\ (273+t)^4$$

and from this

$$S_{100}-S_o=\frac{ac}{4}\ (373^4-273^4),$$

therefore

$$a=\frac{4\times7.31\times10^5}{3\times10^{10}\times(373^4-273^4)}=7.061\times10^{-15}\frac{\text{erg}}{\text{cm}^3\ \text{degree}^4}$$

Recently *Kurlbaum* has increased the value measured by him by 2.5 per cent.,[1] on account of the bolometer used being not perfectly black, whence it follows that $a=7.24\cdot10^{-15}$.

Meanwhile the radiation constant has been made the object of as accurate measurements as possible in various places. Thus it was measured by *Féry*, *Bauer* and *Moulin*, *Valentiner*, *Féry* and *Drecq*, *Shakespear*, *Gerlach*, with in some cases very divergent results, so that a mean value may hardly be formed.

For later computations we shall use the most recent determination made in the physical laboratory of the University of Berlin[2]

$$\frac{ac}{4}=\sigma=5.46\cdot10^{-12}\frac{\text{watt}}{\text{cm}^2\ \text{degree}^4}$$

From this a is found to be

$$a=\frac{4\cdot5.46\cdot10^{-12}\cdot10^7}{3\cdot10^{10}}=7.28\cdot10^{-15}\frac{\text{erg}}{\text{cm}^3\ \text{degree}^4}$$

which agrees rather closely with *Kurlbaum's* corrected value.

[1] *F. Kurlbaum*, Verhandlungen d. Deutsch. physikal. Gesellschaft, **14,** p. 580, 1912.

[2] According to private information kindly furnished by my colleague *H. Rubens* (July, 1912). (These results have since been published. See *W. H. Westphal*, Verhandlungen d. Deutsch. physikal. Gesellschaft, **14,** p. 987, 1912, Tr.)

65. The magnitude of the entropy S of black radiation found by integration of the differential equation (73) is

$$S=\frac{4}{3}aT^3V. \tag{80}$$

In this equation the additive constant is determined by a choice that readily suggests itself, so that at the zero of the absolute scale of temperature, that is to say, when u vanishes, S shall become zero. From this the entropy of unit volume or the volume density of the entropy of black radiation is obtained,

$$\frac{S}{V}=s=\frac{4}{3}aT^3. \tag{81}$$

66. We shall now remove a restricting assumption made in order to enable us to apply the value of *Maxwell's* radiation pressure, calculated in the preceding chapter. Up to now we have assumed the cylinder to be fixed and only the piston to be free to move. We shall now think of the whole of the vessel, consisting of the cylinder, the black bottom, and the piston, the latter attached to the walls in a definite height above the bottom, as being free to move in space. Then, according to the principle of action and reaction, the vessel as a whole must remain constantly at rest, since no external force acts on it. This is the conclusion to which we must necessarily come, even without, in this case, admitting *a priori* the validity of the principle of action and reaction. For if the vessel should begin to move, the kinetic energy of this motion could originate only at the expense of the heat of the body forming the bottom or the energy of radiation, as there exists in the system enclosed in a rigid cover no other available energy; and together with the decrease of energy the entropy of the body or the radiation would also decrease, an event which would contradict the second principle, since no other changes of entropy occur in nature. Hence the vessel as a whole is in a state of mechanical equilibrium. An immediate consequence of this is that the pressure of the radiation on the black bottom is just as large as the oppositely directed pressure of the radiation on the reflecting piston. Hence the pressure of black radiation is the same on a black as on a reflecting body of the same temperature and the same may be readily proven for any completely reflecting surface whatsoever, which we may assume to be at the bottom of the cylinder without in the least disturbing the stationary state of radiation. Hence we may also in all the foregoing considerations replace the reflecting metal by any completely reflecting or black body whatsoever, at the same temperature as the body forming the bottom, and it may be stated as a quite general law that the radiation pressure depends only on the properties of the radiation passing to and fro, not on the properties of the enclosing substance.

67. If, on raising the piston, the temperature of the black body forming the bottom is kept constant by a corresponding addition of heat from the heat reservoir, the process takes place isothermally. Then, along with the temperature T of the black body, the energy density u, the radiation pressure p, and the density of the entropy s also remain constant; hence the total energy of radiation increases from $U=uV$ to $U'=uV'$, the entropy from $S=sV$ to $S'=sV'$ and the heat supplied from the heat reservoir is obtained by integrating (72) at constant T,

$$Q=T(S'-S)=Ts(V'-V)$$

or, according to (81) and (75),

$$Q=\frac{4}{3}aT^4(V'-V)=\frac{4}{3}(U'-U).$$

Thus it is seen that the heat furnished from the outside exceeds the increase in energy of radiation $(U'-U)$ by $\frac{1}{3}(U'-U)$. This excess in the added heat is necessary to do the external work accompanying the increase in the volume of radiation.

68. Let us also consider a reversible adiabatic process. For this it is necessary not merely that the piston and the mantle but also that the bottom of the cylinder be assumed as completely reflecting, *e.g.*, as white. Then the heat furnished on compression or expansion of the volume of radiation is $Q=0$ and the energy of radiation changes only by the value pdV of the external work. To insure, however, that in a finite adiabatic process the radiation shall be perfectly stable at every instant, *i.e.*, shall have the character of black radiation, we may assume that inside the evacuated cavity there is a carbon particle of minute size. This particle, which may be assumed to possess an absorbing power differing from zero for all kinds of rays, serves merely to produce stable equilibrium of the radiation in the cavity (Sec. 51 *et seq.*) and thereby to insure the reversibility of the process, while its heat contents may be taken as so small compared with the energy of radiation, U, that the addition of heat required for an appreciable temperature change of the particle is perfectly negligible. Then at every instant in the process there exists absolutely stable equilibrium of radiation and the radiation has the temperature of the particle in the cavity. The volume, energy, and entropy of the particle may be entirely neglected.

On a reversible adiabatic change, according to (72), the entropy S of the system remains constant. Hence from (80) we have as a condition for such a process

$$T^3 V = \text{const.},$$

or, according to (77),

$$p V^{\frac{4}{3}} = \text{const.},$$

i.e., on an adiabatic compression the temperature and the pressure of the radiation increase in a manner that may be definitely stated. The energy of the radiation, U, in such a case varies according to the law

$$\frac{U}{T} = \frac{3}{4} S = \text{const.},$$

i.e., it increases in proportion to the absolute temperature, although the volume becomes smaller.

69. Let us finally, as a further example, consider a simple case of an irreversible process. Let the cavity of volume V, which is everywhere enclosed by absolutely reflecting walls, be uniformly filled with black radiation. Now let us make a small hole through any part of the walls, *e.g.*, by opening a stopcock, so that the radiation may escape into another completely evacuated space, which may also be surrounded by rigid, absolutely reflecting walls. The radiation will at first be of a very irregular character; after some time, however, it will assume a stationary condition and will fill both communicating spaces uniformly, its total volume being, say, V'. The presence of a carbon particle will cause all conditions of black radiation to be satisfied in the new state. Then, since there is neither external work nor addition of heat from the outside, the energy of the new state is, according to the first principle, equal to that of the original one, or $U' = U$ and hence from (78)

$$T'^4 V' = T^4 V$$

$$\frac{T'}{T} = \sqrt[4]{\frac{V}{V'}}$$

which defines completely the new state of equilibrium. Since $V' > V$ the temperature of the radiation has been lowered by the process.

According to the second principle of thermodynamics the entropy of the system must have increased, since no external changes have occurred; in fact we have from (80)

$$\frac{S'}{S} = \frac{T'^3 V'}{T^3\ V} = \sqrt[4]{\frac{V'}{V}} > 1. \tag{82}$$

70. If the process of irreversible adiabatic expansion of the radiation from the volume V to the volume V' takes place as just described with the single difference that there is no carbon particle present in the vacuum, after the stationary state of radiation is established, as will be the case after a certain time on account of the diffuse reflection from the walls of the cavity, the radiation in the new volume V' will not any longer have the character of black radiation, and hence no definite temperature. Nevertheless the radiation, like every system in a definite physical state, has a definite entropy, which, according to the second principle, is larger than the original S, but not as large as the S' given in (82). The calculation cannot be performed without the use of laws to be taken up later (see Sec. 103). If a carbon particle is afterward introduced into the vacuum, absolutely stable equilibrium is established by a second irreversible process, and, the total energy as well as the total volume remaining constant, the radiation assumes the normal energy distribution of black radiation and the entropy increases to the maximum value S' given by (82).

CHAPTER III

WIEN'S DISPLACEMENT LAW

71. Though the manner in which the volume density u and the specific intensity K of black radiation depend on the temperature is determined by the *Stefan-Boltzmann* law, this law is of comparatively little use in finding the volume density $\mathfrak{u}_\nu$ corresponding to a definite frequency ν, and the specific intensity of radiation $\mathfrak{K}_\nu$ of monochromatic radiation, which are related to each other by equation (24) and to u and K by equations (22) and (12). There remains as one of the principal problems of the theory of heat radiation the problem of determining the quantities $\mathfrak{u}_\nu$ and $\mathfrak{K}_\nu$ for black radiation in a vacuum and hence, according to (42), in any medium whatever, as functions of ν and T, or, in other words, to find the distribution of energy in the normal spectrum for any arbitrary temperature. An essential step in the solution of this problem is contained in the so-called "displacement law" stated by *W. Wien*,[1] the importance of which lies in the fact that it reduces the functions $\mathfrak{u}_\nu$ and $\mathfrak{K}_\nu$ of the two arguments ν and T to a function of a single argument.

The starting point of *Wien's* displacement law is the following theorem. If the black radiation contained in a perfectly evacuated cavity with absolutely reflecting walls is compressed or expanded adiabatically and infinitely slowly, as described above in Sec. 68, *the radiation always retains the character of black radiation, even without the presence of a carbon particle.* Hence the process takes place in an absolute vacuum just as was calculated in Sec. 68 and the introduction, as a precaution, of a carbon particle is shown to be superfluous. But this is true only in this special case, not at all in the case described in Sec. 70.

The truth of the proposition stated may be shown as follows:

[1] *W. Wien*, Sitzungsberichte d. Akad. d. Wissensch. Berlin, Febr. 9, 1893, p. 55. Wiedemann's Annal., **52**, p. 132, 1894. See also among others *M. Thiesen*, Verhandl. d. Deutsch. phys. Gesellsch, **2**, p. 65, 1900. *H. A. Lorentz*, Akad. d. Wissensch. Amsterdam, May 18, 1901, p. 607. *M. Abraham*, Annal. d. Physik. **14**, p. 236, 1904.

Let the completely evacuated hollow cylinder, which is at the start filled with black radiation, be compressed adiabatically and infinitely slowly to a finite fraction of the original volume. If, now, the compression being completed, the radiation were no longer black, there would be no stable thermodynamic equilibrium of the radiation (Sec. 51). It would then be possible to produce a finite change at constant volume and constant total energy of radiation, namely, the change to the absolutely stable state of radiation, which would cause a finite increase of entropy. This change could be brought about by the introduction of a carbon particle, containing a negligible amount of heat as compared with the energy of radiation. This change, of course, refers only to the spectral density of radiation u_ν, whereas the total density of energy u remains constant. After this has been accomplished, we could, leaving the carbon particle in the space, allow the hollow cylinder to return adiabatically and infinitely slowly to its original volume and then remove the carbon particle. The system will then have passed through a cycle without any external changes remaining. For heat has been neither added nor removed, and the mechanical work done on compression has been regained on expansion, because the latter, like the radiation pressure, depends only on the total density u of the energy of radiation, not on its spectral distribution. Therefore, according to the first principle of thermodynamics, the total energy of radiation is at the end just the same as at the beginning, and hence also the temperature of the black radiation is again the same. The carbon particle and its changes do not enter into the calculation, for its energy and entropy are vanishingly small compared with the corresponding quantities of the system. The process has therefore been reversed in all details; it may be repeated any number of times without any permanent change occurring in nature. This contradicts the assumption, made above, that a finite increase in entropy occurs; for such a finite increase, once having taken place, cannot in any way be completely reversed. Therefore no finite increase in entropy can have been produced by the introduction of the carbon particle in the space of radiation, but the radiation was, before the introduction and always, in the state of stable equilibrium.

72. In order to bring out more clearly the essential part of this important proof, let us point out an analogous and more or less obvious consideration. Let a cavity containing originally a vapor in a state of saturation be compressed adiabatically and infinitely slowly.

"Then on an arbitrary adiabatic compression the vapor remains always just in the state of saturation. For let us suppose that it becomes supersaturated on compression. After the compression to an appreciable fraction of the original volume has taken place, condensation of a finite amount of vapor and thereby a change into a more stable state, and hence a finite increase of entropy of the system, would be produced at constant volume and constant total energy by the introduction of a minute drop of liquid, which has no appreciable mass or heat capacity. After this has been done, the volume could again be increased adiabatically and infinitely slowly until again all liquid is evaporated and thereby the process completely reversed, which contradicts the assumed increase of entropy."

Such a method of proof would be erroneous, because, by the process described, the change that originally took place is not at all completely reversed. For since the mechanical work expended on the compression of the supersaturated steam is not equal to the amount gained on expanding the saturated steam, there corresponds to a definite volume of the system when it is being compressed an amount of energy different from the one during expansion and therefore the volume at which all liquid is just vaporized cannot be equal to the original volume. The supposed analogy therefore breaks down and the statement made above in quotation marks is incorrect.

73. We shall now again suppose the reversible adiabatic process described in Sec. 68 to be carried out with the black radiation contained in the evacuated cavity with white walls and white bottom, by allowing the piston, which consists of absolutely reflecting metal, to move downward infinitely slowly, with the single difference that now there shall be no carbon particle in the cylinder. The process will, as we now know, take place exactly as there described, and, since no absorption or emission of radiation takes place, we can now give an account of the changes of color and intensity which the separate pencils of the system undergo. Such changes will of course occur only on reflection from the moving metallic reflector, not on reflection from the stationary walls and the stationary bottom of the cylinder.

If the reflecting piston moves down with the constant, infinitely small, velocity v, the monochromatic pencils striking it during the motion will suffer on reflection a change of color, intensity, and direction. Let us consider these different influences in order.[1]

74. To begin with, we consider the *change of color* which a monochromatic ray suffers by reflection from the reflector, which is moving with an infinitely small velocity. For this purpose we consider first the case of a ray which falls normally from below on the reflector and hence is reflected normally downward. Let the plane A (Fig. 5) represent the position of the reflector at the time t, the plane A' the position at the time $t+\delta t$, where the distance AA' equals $v\delta t$, v denoting the velocity of the reflector.

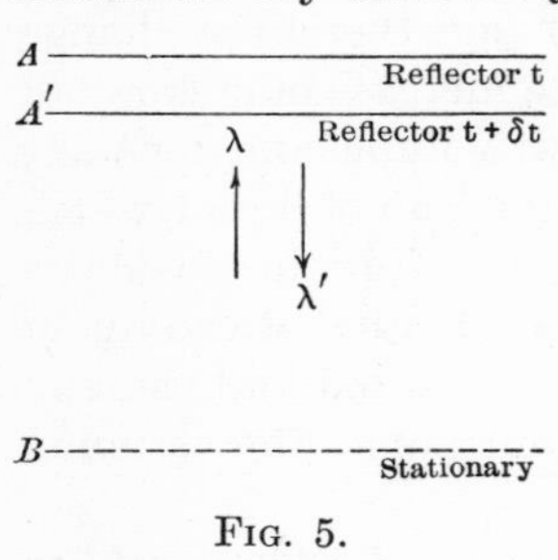

Fig. 5.

Let us now suppose a stationary plane B to be placed parallel to A at a suitable distance and let us denote by λ the wave length of the ray incident on the reflector and by λ' the wave length of the ray reflected from it. Then at a time t there are in the interval AB in the vacuum containing the radiation $\frac{AB}{\lambda}$ waves of the incident and $\frac{AB}{\lambda'}$ waves of the reflected ray, as can be seen, *e.g.*, by thinking of the electric field-strength as being drawn at the different points of each of the two rays at the time t in the form of a sine curve. Reckoning both incident and reflected ray there are at the time t

$$AB\left(\frac{1}{\lambda}+\frac{1}{\lambda'}\right)$$

waves in the interval between A and B. Since this is a large number, it is immaterial whether the number is an integer or not.

[1] The complete solution of the problem of reflection of a pencil from a moving absolutely reflecting surface including the case of an arbitrarily large velocity of the surface may be found in the paper by *M. Abraham* quoted in Sec. 71. See also the text-book by the same author. Electromagnetische Theorie der Strahlung, 1908 (Leipzig, B. G. Teubner).

Similarly at the time $t+\delta t$, when the reflector is at A', there are

$$A'B\left(\frac{1}{\lambda}+\frac{1}{\lambda'}\right)$$

waves in the interval between A' and B all told.

The latter number will be smaller than the former, since in the shorter distance $A'B$ there is room for fewer waves of both kinds than in the longer distance AB. The remaining waves must have been expelled in the time δt from the space between the stationary plane B and the moving reflector, and this must have taken place through the plane B downward; for in no other way could a wave disappear from the space considered.

Now $\nu\delta t$ waves pass in the time δt through the stationary plane B in an upward direction and $\nu'\delta t$ waves in a downward direction; hence we have for the difference

$$(\nu'-\nu)\ \delta t=(AB-A'B)\left(\frac{1}{\lambda}+\frac{1}{\lambda'}\right)$$

or, since

$$AB-A'B=v\delta t,$$

and

$$\lambda=\frac{c}{\nu}\quad \lambda'=\frac{c}{\nu'}$$

$$\nu'=\frac{c+v}{c-v}\nu$$

or, since v is infinitely small compared with c,

$$\nu'=\nu\left(1+\frac{2v}{c}\right)$$

75. When the radiation does not fall on the reflector normally but at an acute angle of incidence θ, it is possible to pursue a very similar line of reasoning, with the difference that then A, the point of intersection of a definite ray BA with the reflector at the time t, has not the same position on the reflector as the point of intersection, A', of the same ray with the reflector at the time $t+\delta t$ (Fig. 6). The number of waves which lie in the interval BA at the time t is $\frac{BA}{\lambda}\cdot$ Similarly, at the time t the number of waves in the interval AC representing the distance of the point

A from a wave plane CC', belonging to the reflected ray and stationary in the vacuum, is $\frac{AC}{\lambda'}$.

Hence there are, all told, at the time t in the interval BAC

$$\frac{BA}{\lambda}+\frac{AC}{\lambda'}$$

waves of the ray under consideration. We may further note that the angle of reflection θ' is not exactly equal to the angle

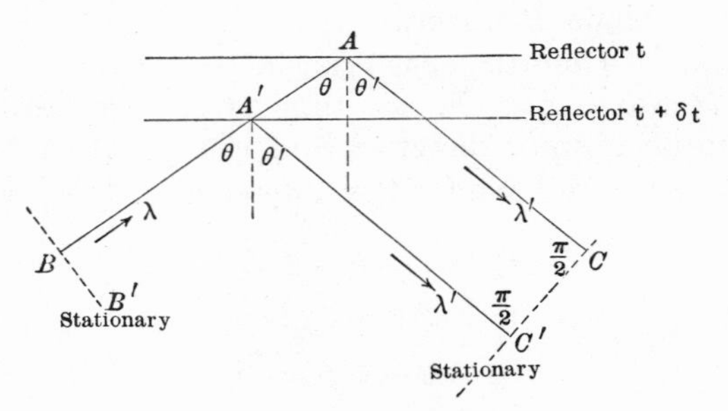

FIG. 6.

of incidence, but is a little smaller as can be shown by a simple geometric consideration based on *Huyghens'* principle. The difference of θ and θ', however, will be shown to be non-essential for our calculation. Moreover there are at the time $t+\delta t$, when the reflector passes through A',

$$\frac{BA'}{\lambda}+\frac{A'C'}{\lambda'}$$

waves in the distance $BA'C'$. The latter number is smaller than the former and the difference must equal the total number of waves which are expelled in the time δt from the space which is bounded by the stationary planes BB' and CC'.

Now $\nu\delta t$ waves enter into the space through the plane BB' in the time δt and $\nu'\delta t$ waves leave the space through the plane CC' Hence we have

$$(\nu'-\nu)\,\delta t=\left(\frac{BA}{\lambda}+\frac{AC}{\lambda'}\right)-\left(\frac{BA'}{\lambda}+\frac{A'C'}{\lambda'}\right)$$

but

$$BA - BA' = AA' = \frac{v\delta t}{\cos\theta}$$

$$AC - A'C' = AA' \cos(\theta + \theta')$$

$$\lambda = \frac{c}{\nu}, \ \lambda' = \frac{c}{\nu'}.$$

Hence

$$\nu' = \frac{c\cos\theta + v}{c\cos\theta - v\cos(\theta+\theta')}\nu.$$

This relation holds for any velocity v of the moving reflector. Now, since in our case v is infinitely small compared with c, we have the simpler expression

$$\nu' = \nu\left(1 + \frac{v}{c\cos\theta}[1 + \cos(\theta + \theta')]\right)$$

The difference between the two angles θ and θ' is in any case of the order of magnitude $\frac{v}{c}$; hence we may without appreciable error replace θ' by θ, thereby obtaining the following expression for the frequency of the reflected ray for oblique incidence

$$\nu' = \nu\left(1 + \frac{2v\cos\theta}{c}\right) \tag{83}$$

76. From the foregoing it is seen that the frequency of all rays which strike the moving reflector are increased on reflection, when the reflector moves toward the radiation, and decreased, when the reflector moves in the direction of the incident rays ($v < 0$). However, the total radiation of a definite frequency ν striking the moving reflector is by no means reflected as monochromatic radiation but the change in color on reflection depends also essentially on the angle of incidence θ. Hence we may not speak of a certain spectral "displacement" of color except in the case of a single pencil of rays of definite direction, whereas in the case of the entire monochromatic radiation we must refer to a spectral "dispersion." The change in color is the largest for normal incidence and vanishes entirely for grazing incidence.

77. Secondly, let us calculate the *change in energy*, which the moving reflector produces in the incident radiation, and let us consider from the outset the general case of oblique incidence. Let a monochromatic, infinitely thin, unpolarized pencil of rays. which falls on a surface element of the reflector at the angle of incidence θ, transmit the energy $I\delta t$ to the reflector in the time δt. Then, ignoring vanishingly small quantities, the mechanical pressure of the pencil of rays normally to the reflector is, according to equation (64),

$$\mathsf{F}=\frac{2\cos\theta}{c}I,$$

and to the same degree of approximation the work done from the outside on the incident radiation in the time δt is

$$\mathsf{F}v\delta t=\frac{2v\cos\theta}{c}I\delta t. \tag{84}$$

According to the principle of the conservation of energy this amount of work must reappear in the energy of the reflected radiation. Hence the reflected pencil has a larger intensity than the incident one. It produces, namely, in the time δt the energy[1]

$$I\delta t+\mathsf{F}v\delta t=I\left(1+\frac{2v\cos\theta}{c}\right)\delta t=I'\delta t. \tag{85}$$

Hence we may summarize as follows: By the reflection of a monochromatic unpolarized pencil, incident at an angle θ on a reflector moving toward the radiation with the infinitely small velocity v, the radiant energy $I\delta t$, whose frequencies extend from ν to $\nu+d\nu$, is in the time δt changed into the radiant energy $I'\delta t$ with the interval of frequency $(\nu', \nu'+d\nu')$, where I' is given by (85), ν' by (83), and accordingly $d\nu'$, the spectral breadth of the reflected pencil, by

$$d\nu'=d\nu\left(1+\frac{2v\cos\theta}{c}\right) \tag{86}$$

A comparison of these values shows that

$$\frac{I'}{I}=\frac{\nu'}{\nu}=\frac{d\nu'}{d\nu} \tag{87}$$

[1] It is clear that the change in intensity of the reflected radiation caused by the motion of the reflector can also be derived from purely electrodynamical considerations, since electrodynamics are consistent with the energy principle. This method is somewhat lengthy, but it affords a deeper insight into the details of the phenomenon of reflection.

The absolute value of the radiant energy which has disappeared in this change is, from equation (13),

$$I\delta t = 2\mathsf{K}_\nu \, d\sigma \cos\theta \, d\Omega \, d\nu \, \delta t, \tag{88}$$

and hence the absolute value of the radiant energy which has been formed is, according to (85),

$$I'\delta t = 2\mathsf{K}_\nu d\sigma \cos\theta \, d\Omega \, d\nu \left(1 + \frac{2v\cos\theta}{c}\right)\delta t. \tag{89}$$

Strictly speaking these last two expressions would require an infinitely small correction, since the quantity I from equation (88) represents the energy radiation on a stationary element of area $d\sigma$, while, in reality, the incident radiation is slightly increased by the motion of $d\sigma$ toward the incident pencil. The additional terms resulting therefrom may, however, be omitted here without appreciable error.

78. As regards finally the *changes in direction*, which are imparted to the incident ray by reflection from the moving reflector, we need not calculate them at all at this stage. For if the motion of the reflector takes place sufficiently slowly, all irregularities in the direction of the radiation are at once equalized by further reflection from the walls of the vessel. We may, indeed, think of the whole process as being accomplished in a very large number of short intervals, in such a way that the piston, after it has moved a very small distance with very small velocity, is kept at rest for a while, namely, until all irregularities produced in the directions of the radiation have disappeared as the result of the reflection from the white walls of the hollow cylinder. If this procedure be carried on sufficiently long, the compression of the radiation may be continued to an arbitrarily small fraction of the original volume, and while this is being done, the radiation may be always regarded as uniform in all directions. This continuous process of equalization refers, of course, only to difference in the direction of the radiation; for changes in the color or intensity of the radiation of however small size, having once occurred, can evidently never be equalized by reflection from totally reflecting stationary walls but continue to exist forever.

79. With the aid of the theorems established we are now in a position to calculate the change of the density of radiation for every frequency for the case of infinitely slow adiabatic compression of the perfectly evacuated hollow cylinder, which is filled with uniform radiation. For this purpose we consider the radiation at the time t in a definite infinitely small interval of frequencies, from ν to $\nu+d\nu$, and inquire into the change which the total energy of radiation contained in this definite constant interval suffers in the time δt.

At the time t this radiant energy is, according to Sec. 23, $V \mathsf{u} d\nu$; at the time $t+\delta t$ it is $(V\mathsf{u}+\delta\,(V\mathsf{u}))d\nu$, hence the change to be calculated is

$$\delta(V\mathsf{u})d\nu. \tag{90}$$

In this the density of monochromatic radiation u is to be regarded as a function of the mutually independent variables ν and t, the differentials of which are distinguished by the symbols d and δ.

The change of the energy of monochromatic radiation is produced only by the reflection from the moving reflector, that is to say, firstly by certain rays, which at the time t belong to the interval $(\nu,d\nu)$, leaving this interval on account of the change in color suffered by reflection, and secondly by certain rays, which at the time t do not belong to the interval $(\nu,d\nu)$, coming into this interval on account of the change in color suffered on reflection. Let us calculate these influences in order. The calculation is greatly simplified by taking the width of this interval $d\nu$ so small that

$$d\nu \text{ is small compared with } \frac{v}{c}\nu, \tag{91}$$

a condition which can always be satisfied, since $d\nu$ and v are mutually independent.

80. The rays which at the time t belong to the interval $(\nu,d\nu)$ and leave this interval in the time δt on account of reflection from the moving reflector, are simply those rays which strike the moving reflector in the time δt. For the change in color which such a ray undergoes is, from (83) and (91), large compared with $d\nu$, the width of the whole interval. Hence we need only calculate the energy, which in the time δt is transmitted to the reflector by the rays in the interval $(\nu,d\nu)$.

For an elementary pencil, which falls on the element $d\sigma$ of the reflecting surface at the angle of incidence θ, this energy is, according to (88) and (5),

$$I\delta t = 2\mathsf{K}_\nu d\sigma \cos\theta \, d\Omega \, d\nu \, \delta t = 2\mathsf{K}_\nu \, d\sigma \sin\theta \cos\theta \, d\theta \, d\phi \, d\nu \, \delta t.$$

Hence we obtain for the total monochromatic radiation, which falls on the whole surface F of the reflector, by integration with respect to ϕ from 0 to 2π, with respect to θ from 0 to $\frac{\pi}{2}$, and with respect to $d\sigma$ from 0 to F,

$$2\pi \, F \, \mathsf{K}_\nu \, d\nu \, \delta t. \tag{92}$$

Thus this radiant energy leaves, in the time δt, the interval of frequencies $(\nu, d\nu)$ considered.

81. In calculating the radiant energy which enters the interval $(\nu, d\nu)$ in the time δt on account of reflection from the moving reflector, the rays falling on the reflector at different angles of incidence must be considered separately. Since in the case of a positive v, the frequency is increased by the reflection, the rays which must be considered have, at the time t, the frequency $\nu_1 < \nu$. If we now consider at the time t a monochromatic pencil of frequency $(\nu_1, d\nu_1)$, falling on the reflector at an angle of incidence θ, a necessary and sufficient condition for its entrance, by reflection, into the interval $(\nu, d\nu)$ is

$$\nu = \nu_1\left(1 + \frac{2v \cos\theta}{c}\right) \text{ and } d\nu = d\nu_1\left(1 + \frac{2v \cos\theta}{c}\right)$$

These relations are obtained by substituting ν_1 and ν respectively in the equations (83) and (86) in place of the frequencies before and after reflection ν and ν'.

The energy which this pencil carries into the interval $(\nu_1, d\nu)$ in the time δt is obtained from (89), likewise by substituting ν_1 for ν. It is

$$2\mathsf{K}_{\nu 1} \, d\sigma \cos\theta \, d\Omega \, d\nu_1\left(1 + \frac{2v \cos\theta}{c}\right)\delta t = 2\mathsf{K}_{\nu 1} \, d\sigma \cos\theta \, d\Omega \, d\nu \, \delta t.$$

Now we have

$$\mathsf{K}_{\nu 1} = \mathsf{K}_\nu + (\nu_1 - \nu)\frac{\partial \mathsf{K}}{\partial \nu} + \; . \; . \; . \; . \; .$$

where we shall assume $\frac{\partial \mathsf{K}}{\partial \nu}$ to be finite.

Hence, neglecting small quantities of higher order,

$$\mathsf{K}_{\nu_1} = \mathsf{K}_\nu - \frac{2\nu v \cos\theta}{c} \frac{\partial \mathsf{K}}{\partial \nu}$$

Thus the energy required becomes

$$2d\sigma\left(\mathsf{K}_\nu - \frac{2\nu v \cos\theta}{c} \frac{\partial \mathsf{K}}{\partial \nu}\right) \sin\theta \cos\theta \, d\theta \, d\phi \, d\nu \, \delta t,$$

and, integrating this expression as above, with respect to $d\sigma$, ϕ, and θ, the total radiant energy which enters into the interval $(\nu, d\nu)$ in the time δt becomes

$$2\pi F\left(\mathsf{K}_\nu - \frac{4}{3} \frac{\nu v}{c} \frac{\partial \mathsf{K}}{\partial \nu}\right) d\nu \, \delta t. \tag{93}$$

82. The difference of the two expressions (93) and (92) is equal to the whole change (90), hence

$$-\frac{8\pi}{3} F \frac{\nu v}{c} \frac{\partial \mathsf{K}}{\partial \nu} \delta t = \delta(V\mathsf{u}),$$

or, according to (24),

$$-\frac{1}{3} F \nu \, v \frac{\partial \mathsf{u}}{\partial \nu} \delta t = \delta(V\mathsf{u}),$$

or, finally, since $Fv\delta t$ is equal to the decrease of the volume V,

$$\frac{1}{3} \nu \frac{\partial \mathsf{u}}{\partial \nu} \delta V = \delta(V\mathsf{u}) = \mathsf{u}\delta V + V\delta\mathsf{u}, \tag{94}$$

whence it follows that

$$\delta\mathsf{u} = \left(\frac{\nu}{3} \frac{\partial \mathsf{u}}{\partial \nu} - \mathsf{u}\right) \frac{\delta V}{V}. \tag{95}$$

This equation gives the change of the energy density of any definite frequency ν, which occurs on an infinitely slow adiabatic compression of the radiation. It holds, moreover, not only for black radiation, but also for *radiation originally of a perfectly arbitrary distribution of energy*, as is shown by the method of derivation.

Since the changes taking place in the state of the radiation in the time δt are proportional to the infinitely small velocity v and are reversed on changing the sign of the latter, this equation holds for any sign of δV; *hence the process is reversible.*

83. Before passing on to the general integration of equation (95) let us examine it in the manner which most easily suggests itself. According to the energy principle, the change in the radiant energy

$$U = Vu = V\int_0^\infty \mathfrak{u}\,d\nu,$$

occurring on adiabatic compression, must be equal to the external work done against the radiation pressure

$$-p\delta V = -\frac{u}{3}\,\delta V = -\frac{\delta V}{3}\int_0^\infty \mathfrak{u}\,d\nu. \qquad (96)$$

Now from (94) the change in the total energy is found to be

$$\delta U = \int_0^\infty d\nu\;\delta\,(V\mathfrak{u}) = \frac{\delta V}{3}\int_0^\infty \nu\frac{\partial \mathfrak{u}}{\partial \nu}\,d\nu,$$

or, by partial integration,

$$\delta U = \frac{\delta V}{3}\left([\nu\mathfrak{u}]_0^\infty - \int_0^\infty \mathfrak{u}\,d\nu\right),$$

and this expression is, in fact, identical with (96), since the product $\nu\mathfrak{u}$ vanishes for $\nu = 0$ as well as for $\nu = \infty$. The latter might at first seem doubtful; but it is easily seen that, if $\nu\mathfrak{u}$ for $\nu = \infty$ had a value different from zero, the integral of $\mathfrak{u}$ with respect to ν taken from 0 to ∞ could not have a finite value, which, however, certainly is the case.

84. We have already emphasized (Sec. 79) that $\mathfrak{u}$ must be regarded as a function of two independent variables, of which we have taken as the first the frequency ν and as the second the time t. Since, now, in equation (95) the time t does not explicitly appear, it is more appropriate to introduce the volume V, which depends only on t, as the second variable instead of t itself. Then equation (95) may be written as a partial differential equation as follows:

$$V\frac{\partial \mathfrak{u}}{\partial V} = \frac{\nu}{3}\,\frac{\partial \mathfrak{u}}{\partial \nu} - \mathfrak{u}. \qquad (97)$$

From this equation, if, for a definite value of V, $\mathfrak{u}$ is known as a function of ν, it may be calculated for all other values of V as a function of ν. The general integral of this differential equation, as may be readily seen by substitution, is

$$\mathsf{u}=\frac{1}{V}\,\phi(\nu^3\,V), \tag{98}$$

where ϕ denotes an arbitrary function of the single argument $\nu^3 V$. Instead of this we may, on substituting $\nu^3 V\phi(\nu^3 V)$ for $\phi(\nu^3 V)$, write

$$\mathsf{u}=\nu^3\phi(\nu^3 V). \tag{99}$$

Either of the last two equations is the general expression of *Wien's* displacement law.

If for a definitely given volume V the spectral distribution of energy is known (*i.e.*, u as a function of ν), it is possible to deduce therefrom the dependence of the function ϕ on its argument, and thence the distribution of energy for any other volume V', into which the radiation filling the hollow cylinder may be brought by a reversible adiabatic process.

84a. The characteristic feature of this new distribution of energy may be stated as follows: If we denote all quantities referring to the new state by the addition of an accent, we have the following equation in addition to (99)

$$\mathsf{u}'=\nu'^3\phi\,(\nu'^3 V').$$

Therefore, if we put

$$\nu'^3 V'=\nu^3 V, \tag{99a}$$

we shall also have

$$\frac{\mathsf{u}'}{\nu'^3}=\frac{\mathsf{u}}{\nu^3}\text{ and }\mathsf{u}'V'=\mathsf{u}V, \tag{99b}$$

i.e., if we coordinate with every frequency ν in the original state that frequency ν' which is to ν in the inverse ratio of the cube roots of the respective volumes, the corresponding energy densities u' and u will be in the inverse ratio of the volumes.

The meaning of these relations will be more clearly seen, if we write

$$\frac{V'}{\lambda'^3}=\frac{V}{\lambda^3}$$

This is the number of the cubes of the wave lengths, which correspond to the frequency ν and are contained in the volume of the radiation. Moreover $\mathsf{u}\,d\nu V=\mathsf{U}\,d\nu$ denotes the radiant energy lying between the frequencies ν and $\nu+d\nu$, which is contained in the volume V. Now since, according to (99a),

$$\sqrt[3]{V'}\;\;d\nu'=\sqrt[3]{V}\;\;d\nu \text{ or } \frac{d\nu'}{\nu'}=\frac{d\nu}{\nu} \tag{99c}$$

we have, taking account of (99b),

$$\mathsf{U}'\,\frac{d\nu'}{\nu'}=\mathsf{U}\,\frac{d\nu}{\nu}$$

These results may be summarized thus: On an infinitely slow reversible adiabatic change in volume of radiation contained in a cavity and uniform in all directions, the frequencies change in such a way that the number of cubes of wave lengths of every frequency contained in the total volume remains unchanged, and the radiant energy of every infinitely small spectral interval changes in proportion to the frequency.

85. Returning now to the discussion of Sec. 73 we introduce the assumption that at first the spectral distribution of energy is the normal one, corresponding to black radiation. Then, according to the law there proven, the radiation retains this property without change during a reversible adiabatic change of volume and the laws derived in Sec. 68 hold for the process. The radiation then possesses in every state a definite temperature T, which depends on the volume V according to the equation derived in that paragraph,

$$T^3V=\text{const.}\;=T'^3V'. \tag{100}$$

Hence we may now write equation (99) as follows:.

$$\mathsf{u}=\nu^3\phi\left(\frac{\nu^3}{T^3}\right)$$

or

$$\mathsf{u}=\nu^3\phi\left(\frac{T}{\nu}\right)$$

Therefore, if for a single temperature the spectral distribution of black radiation, *i.e.*, u as a function of ν, is known, the dependence of the function ϕ on its argument, and hence the spectral distribution for any other temperature, may be deduced therefrom.

If we also take into account the law proved in Sec. 47, that, for the black radiation of a definite temperature, the product $\mathsf{u}q^3$ has for all media the same value, we may also write

$$\mathsf{u}=\frac{\nu^3}{c^3}F\left(\frac{T}{\nu}\right) \tag{101}$$

where now the function F no longer contains the velocity of propagation.

86. For the total radiation density in space of the black radiation in the vacuum we find

$$u=\int_0^\infty \mathsf{u}\,d\nu=\frac{1}{c^3}\int_0^\infty \nu^3 F\left(\frac{T}{\nu}\right)d\nu, \tag{102}$$

or, on introducing $\frac{T}{\nu}=x$ as the variable of integration instead of ν,

$$u=\frac{T^4}{c^3}\int_0^\infty \frac{F(x)}{x^5}dx. \tag{103}$$

If we let the absolute constant

$$\frac{1}{c^3}\int_0^\infty \frac{F(x)}{x^5}dx=a \tag{104}$$

the equation reduces to the form of the *Stefan-Boltzmann* law of radiation expressed in equation (75).

87. If we combine equation (100) with equation (99a) we obtain

$$\frac{\nu'}{T'}=\frac{\nu}{T} \tag{105}$$

Hence the laws derived at the end of Sec. 84a assume the following form: On infinitely slow reversible adiabatic change in volume of black radiation contained in a cavity, the temperature T varies in the inverse ratio of the cube root of the volume V, the frequencies ν vary in proportion to the temperature, and the radiant energy $\mathsf{U}d\nu$ of an infinitely small spectral interval varies in the same ratio. Hence the total radiant energy U as the sum of the energies of all spectral intervals varies also in proportion to the temperature, a statement which agrees with the conclusion arrived at already at the end of Sec. 68, while the space density of radiation, $u=\frac{U}{V}$, varies in proportion to the fourth power of the temperature, in agreement with the *Stefan-Boltzmann* law.

88. *Wien's* displacement law may also in the case of black radiation be stated for the specific intensity of radiation K_ν of a plane polarized monochromatic ray. In this form it reads according to (24)

$$\mathsf{K}_\nu=\frac{\nu^3}{c^3}F\left(\frac{T}{\nu}\right) \tag{106}$$

If, as is usually done in experimental physics, the radiation intensity is referred to wave lengths λ instead of frequencies ν, according to (16), namely

$$\mathsf{E}_\lambda=\frac{c\mathsf{K}_\nu}{\lambda^2}$$

equation (106) takes the following form:

$$E_\lambda=\frac{c^2}{\lambda^5}F\left(\frac{\lambda T}{c}\right). \tag{107}$$

This form of *Wien's* displacement law has usually been the starting-point for an experimental test, the result of which has in all cases been a fairly accurate verification of the law.[1]

89. Since E_λ vanishes for $\lambda=0$ as well as for $\lambda=\infty$, E_λ must have a maximum with respect to λ, which is found from the equation

$$\frac{dE_\lambda}{d\lambda}=0=-\frac{5}{\lambda^6}F\left(\frac{\lambda T}{c}\right)+\frac{1}{\lambda^5}\frac{T}{c}\dot{F}\left(\frac{\lambda T}{c}\right)$$

where $\dot{F}$ denotes the differential coefficient of F with respect to its argument. Or

$$\frac{\lambda T}{c}\dot{F}\left(\frac{\lambda T}{c}\right)-5F\left(\frac{\lambda T}{c}\right)=0. \tag{108}$$

This equation furnishes a definite value for the argument $\frac{\lambda T}{c}$, so

[1] *E.g., F. Paschen*, Sitzungsber. d. Akad. d. Wissensch. Berlin, pp. 405 and 959, 1899. *O. Lummer* und *E. Pringsheim*, Verhandlungen d. Deutschen physikalischen Gesellschaft **1**, pp. 23 and 215, 1899. Annal. d. Physik **6**, p. 192, 1901.

that for the wave length λ_m corresponding to the maximum of the radiation intensity E_λ the relation holds

$$\lambda_m T = b. \tag{109}$$

With increasing temperature the maximum of radiation is therefore displaced in the direction of the shorter wave lengths.

The numerical value of the constant b as determined by *Lummer* and *Pringsheim*[1] is

$$b = 0.294 \text{ cm. degree.} \tag{110}$$

Paschen[2] has found a slightly smaller value, about 0.292.

We may emphasize again at this point that, according to Sec. 19, the maximum of E_λ does not by any means occur at the same point in the spectrum as the maximum of K_ν and that hence the significance of the constant b is essentially dependent on the fact that the intensity of monochromatic radiation is referred to wave lengths, not to frequencies.

90. The value also of the maximum of E_λ is found from (107) by putting $\lambda = \lambda_m$. Allowing for (109) we obtain

$$E_{max} = \text{const. } T^5, \tag{111}$$

i.e., the value of the maximum of radiation in the spectrum of the black radiation is proportional to the fifth power of the absolute temperature.

Should we measure the intensity of monochromatic radiation not by E_λ but by K_ν, we would obtain for the value of the radiation maximum a quite different law, namely,

$$\mathsf{K}_{max} = \text{const. } T^3. \tag{112}$$

[1] *O. Lummer* und *E. Pringsheim*, l. c.
[2] *F. Paschen*, Annal. d. Physik, **6**, p. 657, 1901.

CHAPTER IV

RADIATION OF ANY ARBITRARY SPECTRAL DISTRIBUTION OF ENERGY. ENTROPY AND TEMPERATURE OF MONOCHROMATIC RADIATION

91. We have so far applied *Wien's* displacement law only to the case of black radiation; it has, however, a much more general importance. For equation (95), as has already been stated, gives, for any original spectral distribution of the energy radiation contained in the evacuated cavity and radiated uniformly in all directions, the change of this energy distribution accompanying a reversible adiabatic change of the total volume. Every state of radiation brought about by such a process is perfectly stationary and can continue infinitely long, subject, however, to the condition that no trace of an emitting or absorbing substance exists in the radiation space. For otherwise, according to Sec. 51, the distribution of energy would, in the course of time, change through the releasing action of the substance irreversibly, *i.e.*, with an increase of the total entropy, into the stable distribution correponding to black radiation.

The difference of this general case from the special one dealt with in the preceding chapter is that we can no longer, as in the case of black radiation, speak of a definite temperature of the radiation. Nevertheless, since the second principle of thermodynamics is supposed to hold quite generally, the radiation, like every physical system which is in a definite state, has a definite entropy, $S=Vs$. This entropy consists of the entropies of the monochromatic radiations, and, since the separate kinds of rays are independent of one another, may be obtained by addition. Hence

$$s=\int_{o}^{\infty}\mathfrak{s}\,d\nu, \qquad S=V\int_{o}^{\infty}\mathfrak{s}\,d\nu, \tag{113}$$

where $\mathfrak{s}\,d\nu$ denotes the entropy of the radiation of frequencies between ν and $\nu+d\nu$ contained in unit volume. $\mathfrak{s}$ is a definite

function of the two independent variables ν and u and in the following will always be treated as such.

92. If the analytical expression of the function s were known, the law of energy distribution in the normal spectrum could immediately be deduced from it; for the normal spectral distribution of energy or that of black radiation is distinguished from all others by the fact that it has the maximum of the entropy of radiation S.

Suppose then we take s to be a known function of ν and u. Then as a condition for black radiation we have

$$\delta S=0, \tag{114}$$

for any variations of energy distribution, which are possible with a constant total volume V and constant total energy of radiation U. Let the variation of energy distribution be characterized by making an infinitely small change $\delta\mathsf{u}$ in the energy u of every separate definite frequency ν. Then we have as fixed conditions

$$\delta V=0 \text{ and } \int_0^\infty \delta\mathsf{u}\, d\nu=0. \tag{115}$$

The changes d and δ are of course quite independent of each other.

Now since $\delta V=0$, we have from (114) and (113)

$$\int_0^\infty \delta\mathsf{s}\, d\nu=0,$$

or, since ν remains unvaried

$$\int_0^\infty \frac{\partial\mathsf{s}}{\partial\mathsf{u}}\delta\mathsf{u}\, d\nu=0,$$

and, by allowing for (115), the validity of this equation for all values of $\delta\mathsf{u}$ whatever requires that

$$\frac{\partial\mathsf{s}}{\partial\mathsf{u}}=\text{const.} \tag{116}$$

for all different frequencies. This equation states the law of energy distribution in the case of black radiation.

93. The constant of equation (116) bears a simple relation to the temperature of black radiation. For if the black radiation,

by conduction into it of a certain amount of heat at constant volume V, undergoes an infinitely small change in energy δU, then, according to (73), its change in entropy is

$$\delta S = \frac{\delta U}{T} \cdot$$

However, from (113) and (116),

$$\delta S = V \int_o^\infty \frac{\partial \mathsf{s}}{\partial \mathsf{u}} \, \delta \mathsf{u} \, d\nu = \frac{\partial \mathsf{s}}{\partial \mathsf{u}} V \int_o^\infty \delta \mathsf{u} \, d\nu = \frac{\partial \mathsf{s}}{\partial \mathsf{u}} \delta U$$

hence

$$\frac{\partial \mathsf{s}}{\partial \mathsf{u}} = \frac{1}{T} \tag{117}$$

and the above quantity, which was found to be the same for all frequencies in the case of black radiation, is shown to be the reciprocal of the temperature of black radiation.

Through this law the concept of temperature gains significance also for radiation of a quite arbitrary distribution of energy. For since s depends only on u and ν, *monochromatic radiation, which is uniform in all directions and has a definite energy density* u, *has also a definite temperature given by* (117), *and, among all conceivable distributions of energy, the normal one is characterized by the fact that the radiations of all frequencies have the same temperature.*

Any change in the energy distribution consists of a passage of energy from one monochromatic radiation into another, and, if the temperature of the first radiation is higher, the energy transformation causes an increase of the total entropy and is hence possible in nature without compensation; on the other hand, if the temperature of the second radiation is higher, the total entropy decreases and therefore the change is impossible in nature, unless compensation occurs simultaneously, just as is the case with the transfer of heat between two bodies of different temperatures.

94. Let us now investigate *Wien's* displacement law with regard to the dependence of the quantity s on the variables u and ν.

From equation (101) it follows, on solving for T and substituting the value given in (117), that

$$\frac{1}{T}=\frac{1}{\nu}F\left(\frac{c^3\mathsf{u}}{\nu^3}\right)=\frac{\partial \mathsf{s}}{\partial \mathsf{u}} \tag{118}$$

where again F represents a function of a single argument and the constants do not contain the velocity of propagation c. On integration with respect to the argument we obtain

$$\mathsf{s}=\frac{\nu^2}{c^3}F_1\left(\frac{c^3\mathsf{u}}{\nu^3}\right) \tag{119}$$

the notation remaining the same. In this form *Wien*'s displacement law has a significance for every separate monochromatic radiation and hence also for radiations of any arbitrary energy distribution.

95. According to the second principle of thermodynamics, the total entropy of radiation of quite arbitrary distribution of energy must remain constant on adiabatic reversible compression. We are now able to give a direct proof of this proposition on the basis of equation (119). For such a process, according to equation (113), the relation holds:

$$\delta S=\int_0^\infty d\nu(V\delta\mathsf{s}+\mathsf{s}\delta V)$$

$$=\int_0^\infty d\nu\left(V\frac{\partial \mathsf{s}}{\partial \mathsf{u}}\delta\mathsf{u}+\mathsf{s}\delta V\right)\cdot \tag{120}$$

Here, as everywhere, s should be regarded as a function of u and ν, and $\delta\nu=0$.

Now for a reversible adiabatic change of state the relation (95) holds. Let us take from the latter the value of $\delta\mathsf{u}$ and substitute. Then we have

$$\delta S=\delta V\int_0^\infty d\nu\left\{\frac{\partial \mathsf{s}}{\partial \mathsf{u}}\left(\frac{\nu}{3}\frac{d\mathsf{u}}{d\nu}-\mathsf{u}\right)+\mathsf{s}\right\}.$$

In this equation the differential coefficient of u with respect to ν refers to the spectral distribution of energy originally assigned arbitrarily and is therefore, in contrast to the partial differential coefficients, denoted by the letter d.

Now the complete differential is:

$$\frac{d\mathsf{s}}{d\nu}=\frac{\partial\mathsf{s}}{\partial\mathsf{u}}\frac{d\mathsf{u}}{d\nu}+\frac{\partial\mathsf{s}}{\partial\nu}$$

Hence by substitution:

$$\delta S=\delta V\int_o^\infty d\nu\left\{\frac{\nu}{3}\left(\frac{d\mathsf{s}}{d\nu}-\frac{\partial\mathsf{s}}{\partial\nu}\right)-\mathsf{u}\frac{\partial\mathsf{s}}{\partial\mathsf{u}}+\mathsf{s}\right\}. \tag{121}$$

But from equation (119) we obtain by differentiation

$$\frac{\partial\mathsf{s}}{\partial\mathsf{u}}=\frac{1}{\nu}\dot{F}\left(\frac{c^3\mathsf{u}}{\nu^3}\right) \text{ and } \frac{\partial\mathsf{s}}{\partial\nu}=\frac{2\nu}{c^3}F\left(\frac{c^3\mathsf{u}}{\nu^3}\right)-\frac{3\mathsf{u}}{\nu^2}\dot{F}\left(\frac{c^3\mathsf{u}}{\nu^3}\right) \tag{122}$$

Hence

$$\frac{\nu\partial\mathsf{s}}{\partial\nu}=2\mathsf{s}-3\mathsf{u}\frac{\partial\mathsf{s}}{\partial\mathsf{u}} \tag{123}$$

On substituting this in (121), we obtain

$$\delta S=\delta V\int_o^\infty d\nu\left(\frac{\nu}{3}\frac{d\mathsf{s}}{d\nu}+\frac{1}{3}\mathsf{s}\right) \tag{124}$$

or,

$$\delta S=\frac{\delta V}{3}[\nu\mathsf{s}]_o^\infty=0,$$

as it should be. That the product $\nu\mathsf{s}$ vanishes also for $\nu=\infty$ may be shown just as was done in Sec. 83 for the product $\nu\mathsf{u}$.

96. By means of equations (118) and (119) it is possible to give to the laws of reversible adiabatic compression a form in which their meaning is more clearly seen and which is the generalization of the laws stated in Sec. 87 for black radiation and a supplement to them. It is, namely, possible to derive (105) again from (118) and (99b). Hence the laws deduced in Sec. 87 for the change of frequency and temperature of the monochromatic radiation energy remain valid for a radiation of an originally quite arbitrary distribution of energy. The only difference as compared with the black radiation consists in the fact that now every frequency has its own distinct temperature.

Moreover it follows from (119) and (99b) that

$$\frac{\mathsf{s}'}{\nu'^2}=\frac{\mathsf{s}}{\nu^2} \tag{125}$$

Now $\mathfrak{s}d\nu V = \mathfrak{S}d\nu$ denotes the radiation entropy between the frequencies ν and $\nu + d\nu$ contained in the volume V. Hence on account of (125), (99a), and (99c)

$$\mathfrak{S}'d\nu' = \mathfrak{S}d\nu, \tag{126}$$

i.e., the radiation entropy of an infinitely small spectral interval remains constant. This is another statement of the fact that the total entropy of radiation, taken as the sum of the entropies of all monochromatic radiations contained therein, remains constant.

97. We may go one step further, and, from the entropy $\mathfrak{s}$ and the temperature T of an unpolarized monochromatic radiation which is uniform in all directions, draw a certain conclusion regarding the entropy and temperature of a single, plane polarized, monochromatic pencil. That every separate pencil also has a certain entropy follows by the second principle of thermodynamics from the phenomenon of emission. For since, by the act of emission, heat is changed into radiant heat, the entropy of the emitting body decreases during emission, and, along with this decrease, there must be, according to the principle of increase of the total entropy, an increase in a different form of entropy as a compensation. This can only be due to the energy of the emitted radiation. Hence every separate, plane polarized, monochromatic pencil has its definite entropy, which can depend only on its energy and frequency and which is propagated and spreads into space with it. We thus gain the idea of entropy radiation, which is measured, as in the analogous case of energy radiation, by the amount of entropy which passes in unit time through unit area in a definite direction. Hence statements, exactly similar to those made in Sec. 14 regarding energy radiation, will hold for the radiation of entropy, inasmuch as every pencil possesses and conveys, not only its energy, but also its entropy. Referring the reader to the discussions of Sec. 14, we shall, for the present, merely enumerate the most important laws for future use.

98. In a space filled with any radiation whatever the entropy radiated in the time dt through an element of area $d\sigma$ in the direction of the conical element $d\Omega$ is given by an expression of the form

$$dt\, d\sigma \cos\theta\, d\Omega\, L = L \sin\theta \cos\theta\, d\theta\, d\phi\, d\sigma\, dt. \tag{127}$$

The positive quantity L we shall call the "specific intensity of entropy radiation" at the position of the element of area $d\sigma$ in the direction of the solid angle $d\Omega$. L is, in general, a function of position, time, and direction.

The total radiation of entropy through the element of area $d\sigma$ toward one side, say the one where θ is an acute angle, is obtained by integration with respect to ϕ from 0 to 2π and with respect to θ from 0 to $\frac{\pi}{2}$. It is

$$d\sigma\, dt \int_0^{2\pi} d\phi \int_0^{\frac{\pi}{2}} d\theta\, L \sin\theta \cos\theta.$$

When the radiation is uniform in all directions, and hence L constant, the entropy radiation through $d\sigma$ toward one side is

$$\pi L\, d\sigma\, dt. \tag{128}$$

The specific intensity L of the entropy radiation in every direction consists further of the intensities of the separate rays belonging to the different regions of the spectrum, which are propagated independently of one another. Finally for a ray of definite color and intensity the nature of its polarization is characteristic. When a monochromatic ray of frequency ν consists of two mutually independent[1] components, polarized at right angles to each other, with the principal intensities of energy radiation (Sec. 17) K_ν and K_ν', the specific intensity of entropy radiation is of the form

$$L = \int_0^{\infty} d\nu (\mathsf{L}_\nu + \mathsf{L}'_\nu). \tag{129}$$

The positive quantities L_ν and L'_ν in this expression, the principal intensities of entropy radiation of frequency ν, are determined by the values of K_ν and K_ν'. By substitution in (127), this gives for the entropy which is radiated in the time

[1] "Independent" in the sense of "noncoherent." If, *e.g.*, a ray with the principal intensities K and K' is elliptically polarized, its entropy is not equal to $\mathsf{L} + \mathsf{L}'$, but equal to the entropy of a plane polarized ray of intensity $\mathsf{K} + \mathsf{K}'$. For an elliptically polarized ray may be transformed at once into a plane polarized one, *e.g.*, by total reflection. For the entropy of a ray with coherent components see below Sec. 104, *et seq.*

dt through the element of area $d\sigma$ in the direction of the conical element $d\Omega$ the expression

$$dt\, d\sigma \cos\theta\, d\Omega \int_o^\infty d\nu(\mathsf{L}_\nu + \mathsf{L}'_\nu),$$

and, for monochromatic plane polarized radiation,

$$dt\, d\sigma \cos\theta\, d\Omega\, \mathsf{L}_\nu\, d\nu = \mathsf{L}_\nu\, d\nu \sin\theta \cos\theta\, d\theta\, d\phi\, d\sigma\, dt. \quad (130)$$

For unpolarized rays $\mathsf{L}_\nu = \mathsf{L}'_\nu$ and (129) becomes

$$L = 2\int_o^\infty \mathsf{L}_\nu\, d\nu.$$

For radiation which is uniform in all directions the total entropy radiation toward one side is, according to (128),

$$2\pi\, d\sigma\, dt \int_o^\infty \mathsf{L}_\nu\, d\nu.$$

99. From the intensity of the propagated entropy radiation the expression for the *space density* of the radiant entropy may also be obtained, just as the space density of the radiant energy follows from the intensity of the propagated radiant energy. (Compare Sec. 22.) In fact, in analogy with equation (20), the space density, s, of the entropy of radiation at any point in a vacuum is

$$s = \frac{1}{c}\int L\, d\Omega, \quad (131)$$

where the integration is to be extended over the conical elements which spread out from the point in question in all directions. L is constant for uniform radiation and we obtain

$$s = \frac{4\pi L}{c} \quad (132)$$

By spectral resolution of the quantity L, according to equation (129), we obtain from (131) also the space density of the monochromatic radiation entropy:

$$\mathsf{s} = \frac{1}{c}\int (\mathsf{L} + \mathsf{L}')d\Omega,$$

and for unpolarized radiation, which is uniform in all directions

$$\mathsf{s} = \frac{8\pi \mathsf{L}}{c} \quad (133)$$

100. As to how the entropy radiation L depends on the energy radiation K *Wien's* displacement law in the form of (119) affords immediate information. It follows, namely, from it, considering (133) and (24), that

$$\mathsf{L}=\frac{\nu^2}{c^2}F\left(\frac{c^2\mathsf{K}}{\nu^3}\right) \tag{134}$$

and, moreover, on taking into account (118),

$$\frac{\partial \mathsf{L}}{\partial \mathsf{K}}=\frac{\partial \mathsf{s}}{\partial \mathsf{u}}=\frac{1}{T} \tag{135}$$

Hence also

$$T=\nu F_1\left(\frac{c^2\mathsf{K}}{\nu^3}\right) \tag{136}$$

or

$$\mathsf{K}=\frac{\nu^3}{c^2}F_2\left(\frac{T}{\nu}\right) \tag{137}$$

It is true that these relations, like the equations (118) and (119), were originally derived for radiation which is unpolarized and uniform in all directions. They hold, however, generally in the case of any radiation whatever for each separate monochromatic plane polarized ray. For, since the separate rays behave and are propagated quite independently of one another, the intensity, L, of the entropy radiation of a ray can depend only on the intensity of the energy radiation, K, of the same ray. Hence every separate monochromatic ray has not only its energy but also its entropy defined by (134) and its temperature defined by (136).

101. The extension of the conception of temperature to a single monochromatic ray, just discussed, implies that at the same point in a medium, through which any rays whatever pass, there exist in general an infinite number of temperatures, since every ray passing through the point has its separate temperature, and, moreover, even the rays of different color traveling in the same direction show temperatures that differ according to the spectral distribution of energy. In addition to all these temperatures there is finally the temperature of the medium itself, which at the outset is entirely independent of the temperature of the radiation. This complicated method of consideration lies in the nature of the case and corresponds to the complexity of the physical processes in a medium through which radiation travels in such a way. It is only in the case of stable thermodynamic equilibrium that there is but one temperature, which then is common to the medium itself and to all rays of whatever color crossing it in different directions.

In practical physics also the necessity of separating the conception of radiation temperature from that of body temperature has made itself felt to a continually increasing degree. Thus it has for some time past been found advantageous to speak, not only of the real temperature of the sun, but also of an "apparent" or "effective" temperature of the sun, *i.e.*, that temperature which the sun would need to have in order to send to the earth the heat radiation actually observed, if it radiated like a black body. Now the apparent temperature of the sun is obviously nothing but the actual temperature of the solar rays,[1] depending entirely on the nature of the rays, and hence a property of the rays and not a property of the sun itself. Therefore it would be, not only more convenient, but also more correct, to apply this notation directly, instead of speaking of a fictitious temperature of the sun, which can be made to have a meaning only by the introduction of an assumption that does not hold in reality.

Measurements of the brightness of monochromatic light have recently led *L. Holborn* and *F. Kurlbaum*[2] to the introduction of the concept of "black" temperature of a radiating surface. The black temperature of a radiating surface is measured by the brightness of the rays which it emits. It is in general a separate one for each ray of definite color, direction, and polarization, which the surface emits, and, in fact, merely represents the temperature of such a ray. It is, according to equation (136), determined by its brightness (specific intensity), K, and its frequency, ν, without any reference to its origin and previous states. The definite numerical form of this equation will be given below in Sec. 166. Since a black body has the maximum emissive power, the temperature of an emitted ray can never be higher than that of the emitting body.

[1] On the average, since the solar rays of different color do not have exactly the same temperature.

[2] *L. Holborn* und *F. Kurlbaum*, Annal. d. Physik., **10**, p. 229, 1903.

102. Let us make one more simple application of the laws just found to the special case of black radiation. For this, according to (81), the total space density of entropy is

$$s=\frac{4}{3}\,a^3T. \tag{138}$$

Hence, according to (132), the specific intensity of the total entropy radiation in any direction is

$$L=\frac{c}{3\pi}\,aT^3, \tag{139}$$

and the total entropy radiation through an element of area $d\sigma$ toward one side is, according to (128),

$$\frac{c}{3}\,aT^3\,d\sigma\,dt. \tag{140}$$

As a special example we shall now apply the two principles of thermodynamics to the case in which the surface of a black body of temperature T and of infinitely large heat capacity is struck by black radiation of temperature T' coming from all directions. Then, according to (7) and (76), the black body emits per unit area and unit time the energy

$$\pi K=\frac{ac}{4}\,T^4,$$

and, according to (140), the entropy

$$\frac{ac}{3}\,T^3.$$

On the other hand, it absorbs the energy

$$\frac{ac}{4}T'^4$$

and the entropy

$$\frac{ac}{3}\,T'^3.$$

Hence, according to the first principle, the total heat added to the body, positive or negative according as T' is larger or smaller than T, is

$$Q=\frac{ac}{4}\,T'^4-\frac{ac}{4}\,T^4=\frac{ac}{4}\,(T'^4-T^4),$$

and, according to the second principle, the change of the entire entropy is positive or zero. Now the entropy of the body changes by $\frac{Q}{T}$, the entropy of the radiation in the vacuum by

$$\frac{ac}{3}(T^3 - T'^3).$$

Hence the change per unit time and unit area of the entire entropy of the system considered is

$$\frac{ac}{4}\frac{T'^4 - T^4}{T} + \frac{ac}{3}(T^3 - T'^3) \geqq 0.$$

In fact this relation is satisfied for all values of T and T'. The minimum value of the expression on the left side is zero; this value is reached when $T = T'$. In that case the process is reversible. If, however, T differs from T', we have an appreciable increase of entropy; hence the process is irreversible. In particular we find that if $T = 0$ the increase in entropy is ∞, *i.e.*, the absorption of heat radiation by a black body of vanishingly small temperature is accompanied by an infinite increase in entropy and cannot therefore be reversed by any finite compensation. On the other hand for $T' = 0$, the increase in entropy is only equal to $\frac{ac}{12}T^3$, *i.e.*, the emission of a black body of temperature T without simultaneous absorption of heat radiation is irreversible without compensation, but can be reversed by a compensation of at least the stated finite amount. For example, if we let the rays emitted by the body fall back on it, say by suitable reflection, the body, while again absorbing these rays, will necessarily be at the same time emitting new rays, and this is the compensation required by the second principle.

Generally we may say: Emission without simultaneous absorption is irreversible, while the opposite process, absorption without emission, is impossible in nature.

103. A further example of the application of the two principles of thermodynamics is afforded by the irreversible expansion of originally black radiation of volume V and temperature T to the larger volume V' as considered above in Sec. 70, but in the absence of any absorbing or emitting substance whatever. Then not only the total energy but also the energy of every separate frequency ν remains constant; hence, when on account of diffuse reflection from the walls the radiation has again become uniform in all directions, $\mathsf{u}_\nu V = \mathsf{u}'_\nu V'$; moreover by this relation, according to (118), the temperature T'_ν of the monochromatic radiation of frequency ν in the final state is determined. The actual calculation, however, can be performed only with the help of equation (275) (see below). The total entropy of radiation, *i.e.*, the sum of the entropies of the radiations of all frequencies,

$$V' \int_0^\infty \mathsf{s}'_\nu \, d\nu,$$

must, according to the second principle, be larger in the final state than in the original state. Since T'_ν has different values for the different frequencies ν, the final radiation is no longer black. Hence, on subsequent introduction of a carbon particle into the cavity, a finite change of the distribution of energy is obtained, and simultaneously the entropy increases further to the value S' calculated in (82).

104. In Sec. 98 we have found the intensity of entropy radiation of a definite frequency in a definite direction by adding the entropy radiations of the two independent components K and K', polarized at right angles to each other, or

$$\mathsf{L}(\mathsf{K}) + \mathsf{L}(\mathsf{K}'), \tag{141}$$

where L denotes the function of K given in equation (134). This method of procedure is based on the general law that the entropy of two mutually independent physical systems is equal to the sum of the entropies of the separate systems.

If, however, the two components of a ray, polarized at right angles to each other, are not independent of each other, this method of procedure no longer remains correct. This may be seen, *e.g.*, on resolving the radiation intensity, not with reference to the two principal planes of polarization with the principal intensities K and K', but with reference to any other two planes at right angles to each other, where, according to equation (8), the intensities of the two components assume the following values

$$\begin{aligned} \mathsf{K} \cos^2 \psi + \mathsf{K}' \sin^2 \psi &= \mathsf{K}'' \\ \mathsf{K} \sin^2 \psi + \mathsf{K}' \cos^2 \psi &= \mathsf{K}'''. \end{aligned} \tag{142}$$

In that case, of course, the entropy radiation is not equal to $\mathsf{L}(\mathsf{K}'') + \mathsf{L}(\mathsf{K}''')$.

Thus, while the energy radiation is always obtained by the summation of any two components which are polarized at right angles to each other, no matter according to which azimuth the resolution is performed, since always

$$\mathsf{K}'' + \mathsf{K}''' = \mathsf{K} + \mathsf{K}', \tag{143}$$

a corresponding equation does not hold in general for the entropy radiation. The cause of this is that the two components, the intensities of which we have denoted by K'' and K''', are, unlike K and K', not independent or noncoherent in the optic sense. In such a case

$$\mathsf{L}(\mathsf{K}'') + \mathsf{L}(\mathsf{K}''') > \mathsf{L}(\mathsf{K}) + \mathsf{L}(\mathsf{K}'), \tag{144}$$

as is shown by the following consideration.

Since in the state of thermodynamic equilibrium all rays of the same frequency have the same intensity of radiation, the intensities of radiation of any two plane polarized rays will tend to become equal, *i.e.*, the passage of energy between them will be accompanied by an increase of entropy, when it takes place in the direction from the ray of greater intensity toward that of smaller intensity. Now the left side of the inequality (144) represents the entropy radiation of two noncoherent plane polarized rays with the intensities K'' and K''', and the right side the entropy radiation of two noncoherent plane polarized rays with the intensities K and K'. But, according to (142), the values of K'' and K''' lie between K and K'; therefore the inequality (144) holds.

At the same time it is apparent that the error committed, when the entropy of two coherent rays is calculated as if they were noncoherent, is always in such a sense that the entropy found is too large. The radiations K'' and K''' are called "partially coherent," since they have some terms in common. In the special case when one of the two principal intensities K and K' vanishes entirely, the radiations K'' and K''' are said to be "completely coherent," since in that case the expression for one radiation may be completely reduced to that for the other. The entropy of two completely coherent plane polarized rays is equal to the entropy of a single plane polarized ray, the energy of which is equal to the sum of the two separate energies.

105. Let us for future use solve also the more general problem of calculating the entropy radiation of a ray consisting of an arbitrary number of plane polarized noncoherent components K_1, K_2, K_3, ... , the planes of vibration (planes of the electric vector) of which are given by the azimuths ψ_1, ψ_2, ψ_3, ... This problem amounts to finding the principal intensities K_0 and K_0' of the whole ray; for the ray behaves in every physical respect as if it consisted of the noncoherent components K_0 and K_0'. For this purpose we begin by establishing the value K_ψ of the component of the ray for an azimuth ψ taken arbitrarily. Denoting by f the electric vector of the ray in the direction ψ, we obtain this value K_ψ from the equation

$$f=f_1 \cos(\psi_1-\psi)+f_2 \cos(\psi_2-\psi)+f_3 \cos(\psi_3-\psi)+ \dots\dots,$$

where the terms on the right side denote the projections of the vectors of the separate components in the direction ψ, by squaring and averaging and taking into account the fact that $f_1, f_2, f_3, \dots$ are noncoherent

$$\mathsf{K}_\psi=\mathsf{K}_1 \cos^2(\psi_1-\psi)+\mathsf{K}_2 \cos^2(\psi_2-\psi)+ \dots\dots$$

or

$$\mathsf{K}_\psi=A \cos^2\psi+B \sin^2\psi+C \sin\psi \cos\psi$$

where

$$\begin{aligned} A&=\mathsf{K}_1 \cos^2\psi_1+\mathsf{K}_2 \cos^2\psi_2+ \dots\dots \\ B&=\mathsf{K}_1 \sin^2\psi_1+\mathsf{K}_2 \sin^2\psi_2+ \dots\dots \\ C&=2(\mathsf{K}_1 \sin\psi_1 \cos\psi_1+\mathsf{K}_2 \sin\psi_2 \cos\psi_2+ \dots\dots). \end{aligned} \tag{145}$$

The principal intensities K_0 and K_0' of the ray follow from this expression as the maximum and the minimum value of K_ψ according to the equation

$$\frac{d\mathsf{K}_\psi}{d\psi}=0 \text{ or, } \tan 2\psi=\frac{C}{A-B}$$

Hence it follows that the principal intensities are

$$\left.\begin{matrix}\mathsf{K}_0\\ K_0'\end{matrix}\right\}=\tfrac{1}{2}(A+B\pm\sqrt{(A-B)^2+C^2}), \tag{146}$$

or, by taking (145) into account,

$$\left.\begin{matrix}\mathsf{K}_0\\ \mathsf{K}_0'\end{matrix}\right\}=\frac{1}{2}(\mathsf{K}_1+\mathsf{K}_2+ \dots \pm\sqrt{(\mathsf{K}_1\cos 2\psi_1+\mathsf{K}_2\cos 2\psi_2+\dots)^2+(\mathsf{K}_1\text{ins } 2\psi_1+\mathsf{K}_2\sin 2\psi_2+\dots)^2}.) \tag{147}$$

Then the entropy radiation required becomes:

$$\mathsf{L}(\mathsf{K}_0)+\mathsf{L}(\mathsf{K}_0'). \tag{148}$$

106. When two ray components K and K', polarized at right angles to each other, are noncoherent, K and K' are also the principal intensities, and the entropy radiation is given by (141). The converse proposition, however, does not hold in general, that is to say, the two components of a ray polarized at right angles to each other, which correspond to the principal intensities K and K', are not necessarily noncoherent, and hence the entropy radiation is not always given by (141).

This is true, *e.g.*, in the case of elliptically polarized light. There the radiations K and K' are completely coherent and their entropy is equal to $\mathsf{L}(\mathsf{K}+\mathsf{K}')$. This is caused by the fact that it is possible to give the two ray components an arbitrary displacement of phase in a reversible manner, say by total reflection. Thereby it is possible to change elliptically polarized light to plane polarized light and *vice versa.*

The entropy of completely or partially coherent rays has been investigated most thoroughly by *M. Laue.*[1] For the significance of optical coherence for thermodynamic probability see the next part, Sec. 119.

[1] *M. Laue,* Annalen d. Phys., **23,** p. 1, 1907.

CHAPTER V

ELECTRODYNAMICAL PROCESSES IN A STATIONARY FIELD OF RADIATION

107. We shall now consider from the standpoint of pure electrodynamics the processes that take place in a vacuum, which is bounded on all sides by reflecting walls and through which heat radiation passes uniformly in all directions, and shall then inquire into the relations between the electrodynamical and the thermodynamic quantities.

The electrodynamical state of the field of radiation is determined at every instant by the values of the electric field-strength E and the magnetic field-strength H at every point in the field, and the changes in time of these two vectors are completely determined by *Maxwell's* field equations (52), which we have already used in Sec. 53, together with the boundary conditions, which hold at the reflecting walls. In the present case, however, we have to deal with a solution of these equations of much greater complexity than that expressed by (54), which corresponds to a plane wave. For a plane wave, even though it be periodic with a wave length lying within the optical or thermal spectrum, can never be interpreted as heat radiation. For, according to Sec. 16, a finite intensity K of heat radiation requires a finite solid angle of the rays and, according to Sec. 18, a spectral interval of finite width. But an absolutely plane, absolutely periodic wave has a zero solid angle and a zero spectral width. Hence in the case of a plane periodic wave there can be no question of either entropy or temperature of the radiation.

108. Let us proceed in a perfectly general way to consider the components of the field-strengths E and H as functions of the time at a definite point, which we may think of as the origin of the coordinate system. Of these components, which are produced by all rays passing through the origin, there are six; we select one of them, say E_z, for closer consideration. However complicated it may be, it may under all circumstances be written as a *Fourier's* series for a limited time interval, say from $t=0$ to $t=\mathsf{T}$; thus

$$\mathsf{E}_z=\sum_{n=1}^{n=\infty} C_n \cos\left(\frac{2\pi nt}{\mathsf{T}}-\theta_n\right) \qquad (149)$$

where the summation is to extend over all positive integers n, while the constants C_n (positive) and θ_n may vary arbitrarily from term to term. The time interval T, the fundamental period of the *Fourier's* series, we shall choose so large that all times t which we shall consider hereafter are included in this time interval, so that $0<t<\mathsf{T}$. Then we may regard E_z as identical in all respects with the *Fourier's* series, *i.e.*, we may regard E_z as consisting of "partial vibrations," which are strictly periodic and of frequencies given by

$$\nu=\frac{n}{\mathsf{T}}$$

Since, according to Sec. 3, the time differential dt required for the definition of the intensity of a heat ray is necessarily large compared with the periods of vibration of all colors contained in the ray, a single time differential dt contains a large number of vibrations, *i.e.*, the product νdt is a large number. Then it follows *a fortiori* that νt and, still more,

$$\nu\mathsf{T}=n \text{ is enormously large} \qquad (150)$$

for all values of ν entering into consideration. From this we must conclude that all amplitudes C_n with a moderately large value for the ordinal number n do not appear at all in the *Fourier's* series, that is to say, they are negligibly small.

109. Though we have no detailed special information about the function E_z, nevertheless its relation to the radiation of heat affords some important information as to a few of its general properties. Firstly, for the space density of radiation in a vacuum we have, according to Maxwell's theory,

$$u=\frac{1}{8\pi}\left(\overline{\mathsf{E}_x^2}+\overline{\mathsf{E}_y^2}+\overline{\mathsf{E}_z^2}+\overline{\mathsf{H}_x^2}+\overline{\mathsf{H}_y^2}+\overline{\mathsf{H}_z^2}\right).$$

Now the radiation is uniform in all directions and in the stationary state, hence the six mean values named are all equal to one another, and it follows that

$$u = \frac{3}{4\pi} \overline{\mathsf{E}_z^2}. \tag{151}$$

Let us substitute in this equation the value of E_z as given by (149). Squaring the latter and integrating term by term through a time interval, from 0 to t, assumed large in comparison with all periods of vibration $\frac{1}{\nu}$ but otherwise arbitrary, and then dividing by t, we obtain, since the radiation is perfectly stationary,

$$u = \frac{3}{8\pi} \sum C_n^2. \tag{152}$$

From this relation we may at once draw an important conclusion as to the nature of E_z as a function of time. Namely, since the *Fourier's* series (149) consists, as we have seen, of a great many terms, the squares, C_n^2, of the separate amplitudes of vibration the sum of which gives the space density of radiation, must have exceedingly small values. Moreover in the integral of the square of the *Fourier's* series the terms which depend on the time t and contain the products of any two different amplitudes all cancel; hence the amplitudes C_n and the phase-constants θ_n must vary from one ordinal number to another in a quite irregular manner. We may express this fact by saying that the separate partial vibrations of the series are very small and in a "chaotic"[1] state.

For the specific intensity of the radiation travelling in any direction whatever we obtain from (21)

$$K = \frac{cu}{4\pi} = \frac{3c}{32\pi^2} \sum C_n^2. \tag{153}$$

110. Let us now perform the spectral resolution of the last two equations. To begin with we have from (22):

$$u = \int_o^\infty \mathsf{u}_\nu d\nu = \frac{3}{8\pi} \sum_1^\infty C_n^2. \tag{154}$$

On the right side of the equation the sum $\sum$ consists of separate

[1] Compare footnote to page 116 (Tr.).

terms, every one of which corresponds to a separate ordinal number n and to a simple periodic partial vibration. Strictly speaking this sum does not represent a continuous sequence of frequencies ν, since n is an integral number. But n is, according to (150), so enormously large for all frequencies which need be considered that the frequencies ν corresponding to the successive values of n lie very close together. Hence the interval $d\nu$, though infinitesimal compared with ν, still contains a large number of partial vibrations, say n', where

$$d\nu=\frac{n'}{\mathsf{T}} \tag{155}$$

If now in (154) we equate, instead of the total energy densities, the energy densities corresponding to the interval $d\nu$ only, which are independent of those of the other spectral regions, we obtain

$$\mathsf{u}_\nu\, d\nu=\frac{3}{8\pi}\sum_n^{n+n'} C_n{}^2,$$

or, according to (155),

$$\mathsf{u}_\nu=\frac{3\mathsf{T}}{8\pi}\cdot\frac{1}{n'}\sum_n^{n+n'} C_n{}^2=\frac{3\mathsf{T}}{8\pi}\cdot\overline{C_n{}^2}, \tag{156}$$

where we denote by $\overline{C_n{}^2}$ the average value of $C_n{}^2$ in the interval from n to $n+n'$. The existence of such an average value, the magnitude of which is independent of n, provided n' be taken small compared with n, is, of course, not self-evident at the outset, but is due to a special property of the function E_z which is peculiar to stationary heat radiation. On the other hand, since many terms contribute to the mean value, nothing can be said either about the magnitude of a separate term $C_n{}^2$, or about the connection of two consecutive terms, but they are to be regarded as perfectly independent of each other.

In a very similar manner, by making use of (24), we find for the specific intensity of a monochromatic plane polarized ray, travelling in any direction whatever,

$$\mathsf{K}_\nu=\frac{3c\mathsf{T}}{64\pi^2}\,\overline{C_n{}^2}. \tag{157}$$

From this it is apparent, among other things, that, according to the electromagnetic theory of radiation, a monochromatic light or heat ray is represented, not by a simple periodic wave, but by a superposition of a large number of simple periodic waves, the mean value of which constitutes the intensity of the ray. In accord with this is the fact, known from optics, that two rays of the same color and intensity but of different origin never interfere with each other, as they would, of necessity, if every ray were a simple periodic one.

Finally we shall also perform the spectral resolution of the mean value of E_z^2, by writing

$$\overline{\mathsf{E}_z^2} = J = \int_0^\infty \mathsf{J}_\nu d\nu \qquad (158)$$

Then by comparison with (151), (154), and (156) we find

$$\mathsf{J}_\nu = \frac{4\pi}{3}\mathsf{u}_\nu = \frac{\mathsf{T}}{2}\overline{C_n^2} \qquad (159)$$

According to (157), J_ν is related to K_ν, the specific intensity of radiation of a plane polarized ray, as follows:

$$\mathsf{K}_\nu = \frac{3c}{32\pi^2}\mathsf{J}_\nu. \qquad (160)$$

111. Black radiation is frequently said to consist of a large number of regular periodic vibrations. This method of expression is perfectly justified, inasmuch as it refers to the resolution of the total vibration in a *Fourier's* series, according to equation (149), and often is exceedingly well adapted for convenience and clearness of discussion. It should, however, not mislead us into believing that such a "regularity" is caused by a special physical property of the elementary processes of vibration. For the resolvability into a Fourier's series is mathematically self-evident and hence, in a physical sense, tells us nothing new. In fact, it is even always possible to regard a vibration which is damped to an arbitrary extent as consisting of a sum of regular periodic partial vibrations with constant amplitudes and constant phases. On the contrary, it may just as correctly be said that in all nature there is no process more complicated than the vibrations of black radiation. In particular, these vibrations do not depend in any characteristic manner on the special processes that take place in the centers of emission of the rays, say on the period or the damping of the emitting particles; for the normal spectrum is distinguished from all other spectra by the very fact that all individual differences caused by the special nature of the emitting substances are perfectly equalized and effaced. Therefore to attempt to draw conclusions concerning the special properties of the particles emitting the rays from the elementary vibrations in the rays of the normal spectrum would be a hopeless undertaking.

In fact, black radiation may just as well be regarded as consisting, not of regular periodic vibrations, but of absolutely irregular separate impulses. The special regularities, which we observe in monochromatic light resolved spectrally, are caused merely by the special properties of the spectral apparatus used, *e.g.*, the dispersing prism (natural periods of the molecules), or the diffraction grating (width of the slits). Hence it is also incorrect to find a characteristic difference between light rays and Roentgen rays (the latter assumed as an electromagnetic process in a vacuum) in the circumstance that in the former the vibrations take place with greater regularity. Roentgen rays may, under certain conditions, possess more selective properties than light rays. The resolvability into a *Fourier's* series of partial vibrations with constant amplitudes and constant phases exists for both kinds of rays in precisely the same manner. What especially distinguishes light vibrations from Roentgen vibrations is the much smaller frequency of the partial vibrations of the former. To this is due the possibility of their spectral resolution, and probably also the far greater regularity of the changes of the radiation intensity in every region of the spectrum in the course of time, which, however, is not caused by a special property of the elementary processes of vibration, but merely by the constancy of the mean values.

112. The elementary processes of radiation exhibit regularities only when the vibrations are restricted to a narrow spectral region, that is to say in the case of spectroscopically resolved light, and especially in the case of the natural spectral lines. If, *e.g.*, the amplitudes C_n of the *Fourier's* series (149) differ from zero only between the ordinal numbers $n=n_0$ and $n=n_1$, where $\frac{n_1-n_0}{n_0}$ is small, we may write

$$\mathsf{E}_z=C_0 \cos\left(\frac{2\pi n_0 t}{\mathsf{T}}-\theta_0\right), \tag{161}$$

where

$$C_0 \cos \theta_0=\sum_{n_0}^{n_1} C_n \cos\left(\frac{2\pi(n-n_0)t}{\mathsf{T}}-\theta_n\right)$$

$$C_0 \sin \theta_0=-\sum_{n_0}^{n_1} C_n \sin\left(\frac{2\pi(n-n_0)t}{\mathsf{T}}-\theta_n\right)$$

and E_z may be regarded as a single approximately periodic vibration of frequency $\nu_0=\frac{n_0}{\mathsf{T}}$ with an amplitude C_0 and a phase-constant θ_0 which vary slowly and irregularly.

The smaller the spectral region, and accordingly the smaller $\frac{n_1-n_0}{n_0}$, the slower are the fluctuations ("Schwankungen") of C_o and θ_o, and the more regular is the resulting vibration and also the larger is the difference of path for which radiation can interfere with itself. If a spectral line were absolutely sharp, the radiation would have the property of being capable of interfering with itself for differences of path of any size whatever. This case, however, according to Sec. 18, is an ideal abstraction, never occurring in reality.

PART III

ENTROPY AND PROBABILITY

CHAPTER I

FUNDAMENTAL DEFINITIONS AND LAWS. HYPOTHESIS OF QUANTA

113. Since a wholly new element, entirely unrelated to the fundamental principles of electrodynamics, enters into the range of investigation with the introduction of probability considerations into the electrodynamic theory of heat radiation, the question arises at the outset, whether such considerations are justifiable and necessary. At first sight we might, in fact, be inclined to think that in a purely electrodynamical theory there would be no room at all for probability calculations. For since, as is well known, the electrodynamic equations of the field together with the initial and boundary conditions determine uniquely the way in which an electrodynamical process takes place in the course of time, considerations which lie outside of the equations of the field would seem, theoretically speaking, to be uncalled for and in any case dispensable. For either they lead to the same results as the fundamental equations of electrodynamics and then they are superfluous, or they lead to different results and in this case they are wrong.

In spite of this apparently unavoidable dilemma, there is a flaw in the reasoning. For on closer consideration it is seen that what is understood in electrodynamics by "initial and boundary" conditions, as well as by the "way in which a process takes place in the course of time," is entirely different from what is denoted by the same words in thermodynamics. In order to make this evident, let us consider the case of radiation *in vacuo*, uniform in all directions, which was treated in the last chapter.

From the standpoint of thermodynamics the state of radiation is completely determined, when the intensity of monochromatic radiation K_ν is given for all frequencies ν. The electrodynamical observer, however, has gained very little by this single statement; because for him a knowledge of the state requires that every one of the six components of the electric and magnetic field-strength be given at all points of the space; and, while from the thermodynamic point of view the question as to the way in which the process takes place in time is settled by the constancy of the intensity of radiation K_ν, from the electrodynamical point of view it would be necessary to know the six components of the field at every point as functions of the time, and hence the amplitudes C_n and the phase-constants θ_n of all the several partial vibrations contained in the radiation would have to be calculated. This, however, is a problem whose solution is quite impossible, for the data obtainable from the measurements are by no means sufficient. The thermodynamically measurable quantities, looked at from the electrodynamical standpoint, represent only certain mean values, as we saw in the special case of stationary radiation in the last chapter.

We might now think that, since in thermodynamic measurements we are always concerned with mean values only, we need consider nothing beyond these mean values, and, therefore, need not take any account of the particular values at all. This method is, however, impracticable, because frequently and that too just in the most important cases, namely, in the cases of the processes of emission and absorption, we have to deal with mean values which cannot be calculated unambiguously by electrodynamical methods from the measured mean values. For example, the mean value of C_n cannot be calculated from the mean value of C_n^2, if no special information as to the particular values of C_n is available.

Thus we see that the electrodynamical state is not by any means determined by the thermodynamic data and that in cases where, according to the laws of thermodynamics and according to all experience, an unambiguous result is to be expected, a purely electrodynamical theory fails entirely, since it admits not one definite result, but an infinite number of different results.

114. Before entering on a further discussion of this fact and of the difficulty to which it leads in the electrodynamical theory of heat radiation, it may be pointed out that exactly the same case and the same difficulty are met with in the mechanical theory of heat, especially in the kinetic theory of gases. For when, for example, in the case of a gas flowing out of an opening at the time

$t=0$, the velocity, the density, and the temperature are given at every point, and the boundary conditions are completely known, we should expect, according to all experience, that these data would suffice for a unique determination of the way in which the process takes place in time. This, however, from a purely mechanical point of view is not the case at all; for the positions and velocities of all the separate molecules are not at all given by the visible velocity, density, and temperature of the gas, and they would have to be known exactly, if the way in which the process takes place in time had to be completely calculated from the equations of motion. In fact, it is easy to show that, with given initial values of the visible velocity, density, and temperature, an infinite number of entirely different processes is mechanically possible, some of which are in direct contradiction to the principles of thermodynamics, especially the second principle.

115. From these considerations we see that, if we wish to calculate the way in which a thermodynamic process takes place in time, such a formulation of initial and boundary conditions as is perfectly sufficient for a unique determination of the process in thermodynamics, does not suffice for the mechanical theory of heat or for the electrodynamical theory of heat radiation. On the contrary, from the standpoint of pure mechanics or electrodynamics the solutions of the problem are infinite in number. Hence, unless we wish to renounce entirely the possibility of representing the thermodynamic processes mechanically or electrodynamically, there remains only one way out of the difficulty, namely, to supplement the initial and boundary conditions by special hypotheses of such a nature that the mechanical or electrodynamical equations will lead to an unambiguous result in agreement with experience. As to how such an hypothesis is to be formulated, no hint can naturally be obtained from the principles of mechanics or electrodynamics, for they leave the question entirely open. Just on that account any mechanical or electrodynamical hypothesis containing some further specialization of the given initial and boundary conditions, which cannot be tested by direct measurement, is admissible *a priori*. What hypothesis is to be preferred can be decided only by testing the results to which it leads in the light of the thermodynamic principles based on experience.

116. Although, according to the statement just made, a decisive test of the different admissible hypotheses can be made only *a posteriori*, it is nevertheless worth while noticing that it is possible to obtain *a priori*, without relying in any way on thermodynamics, a definite hint as to the nature of an admissible hypothesis. Let us again consider a flowing gas as an illustration (Sec. 114). The mechanical state of all the separate gas molecules is not at all completely defined by the thermodynamic state of the gas, as has previously been pointed out. If, however, we consider all conceivable positions and velocities of the separate gas molecules, consistent with the given values of the visible velocity, density, and temperature, and calculate for every combination of them the mechanical process, assuming some simple law for the impact of two molecules, we shall arrive at processes, the vast majority of which agree completely in the mean values, though perhaps not in all details. Those cases, on the other hand, which show appreciable deviations, are vanishingly few, and only occur when certain very special and far-reaching conditions between the coordinates and velocity-components of the molecules are satisfied. Hence, if the assumption be made that such special conditions do not exist, however different the mechanical details may be in other respects, a form of flow of gas will be found, which may be called quite definite with respect to all measurable mean values—and they are the only ones which can be tested experimentally—although it will not, of course, be quite definite in all details. And the remarkable feature of this is that it is just the motion obtained in this manner that satisfies the postulates of the second principle of thermodynamics.

117. From these considerations it is evident that the hypotheses whose introduction was proven above to be necessary completely answer their purpose, if they state nothing more than that exceptional cases, corresponding to special conditions which exist between the separate quantities determining the state and which cannot be tested directly, do not occur in nature. In mechanics this is done by the hypothesis[1] that the heat motion is a "molecular chaos";[2] in electrodynamics the same thing is accomplished

[1] *L. Boltzmann*, Vorlesungen über Gastheorie **1**, p. 21, 1896. Wiener Sitzungsberichte **78**, Juni, 1878, at the end. Compare also *S. H. Burbury*, Nature, **51**, p. 78, 1894.

[2] Hereafter *Boltzmann's* "Unordnung" will be rendered by chaos, "ungeordnet" by chaotic (Tr.).

by the hypothesis of "natural radiation," which states that there exist between the numerous different partial vibrations (149) of a ray no other relations than those caused by the measurable mean values (compare below, Sec. 148). If, for brevity, we denote any condition or process for which such an hypothesis holds as an "elemental chaos," the principle, *that in nature any state or any process containing numerous elements not in themselves measurable is an elemental chaos,* furnishes the necessary condition for a unique determination of the measurable processes in mechanics as well as in electrodynamics and also for the validity of the second principle of thermodynamics. This must also serve as a mechanical or electrodynamical explanation of the conception of entropy, which is characteristic of the second law and of the closely allied concept of temperature.[1] It also follows from this that the significance of entropy and temperature is, according to their nature, connected with the condition of an elemental chaos. The terms entropy and temperature do not apply to a purely periodic, perfectly plane wave, since all the quantities in such a wave are in themselves measurable, and hence cannot be an elemental chaos any more than a single rigid atom in motion can. The necessary condition for the hypothesis of an elemental chaos and with it for the existence of entropy and temperature can consist only in the irregular simultaneous effect of very many partial vibrations of different periods, which are propagated in the different directions in space independent of one another, or in the irregular flight of a multitude of atoms.

118. But what mechanical or electrodynamical quantity represents the entropy of a state? It is evident that this quantity depends in some way on the "probability" of the state. For since an elemental chaos and the absence of a record of any individual element forms an essential feature of entropy, the tendency to neutralize any existing temperature differences, which is connected with an increase of entropy, can mean nothing for the mechanical or electrodynamical observer but that uniform

[1] To avoid misunderstanding I must emphasize that the question, whether the hypothesis of elemental chaos is really everywhere satisfied in nature, is not touched upon by the preceding considerations. I intended only to show at this point that, wherever this hypothesis does not hold, the natural processes, if viewed from the thermodynamic (macroscopic) point of view, do not take place unambiguously.

distribution of elements in a chaotic state is more probable than any other distribution.

Now since the concept of entropy as well as the second principle of thermodynamics are of universal application, and since on the other hand the laws of probability have no less universal validity, it is to be expected that the connection between entropy and probability should be very close. Hence we make the following proposition the foundation of our further discussion: *The entropy of a physical system in a definite state depends solely on the probability of this state.* The fertility of this law will be seen later in several cases. We shall not, however, attempt to give a strict general proof of it at this point. In fact, such an attempt evidently would have no meaning at this point. For, so long as the "probability" of a state is not numerically defined, the correctness of the proposition cannot be quantitatively tested. One might, in fact, suspect at first sight that on this account the proposition has no definite physical meaning. It may, however, be shown by a simple deduction that it is possible by means of this fundamental proposition to determine quite generally the way in which entropy depends on probability, without any further discussion of the probability of a state.

119. For let S be the entropy, W the probability of a physical system in a definite state; then the propositon states that

$$S = f(W) \tag{162}$$

where $f(W)$ represents a universal function of the argument W. In whatever way W may be defined, it can be safely inferred from the mathematical concept of probability that the probability of a system which consists of two entirely independent[1] systems is equal to the product of the probabilities of these two systems separately. If we think, *e.g.*, of the first system as any body whatever on the earth and of the second system as a cavity containing radiation on Sirius, then the probability that the terrestrial body be in a certain state 1 and that simultaneously the radiation in the cavity in a definite state 2 is

$$W = W_1 W_2, \tag{163}$$

[1] It is well known that the condition that the two systems be independent of each other is essential for the validity of the expression (163). That it is also a necessary condition for the additive combination of the entropy was proven first by *M. Laue* in the case of optically coherent rays. Annalen d. Physik, **20**, p. 365, 1906.

where W_1 and W_2 are the probabilities that the systems involved are in the states in question.

If now S_1 and S_2 are the entropies of the separate systems in the two states, then, according to (162), we have

$$S_1 = f(W_1) \qquad S_2 = f(W_2).$$

But, according to the second principle of thermodynamics, the total entropy of the two systems, which are independent (see footnote to preceding page) of each other, is $S = S_1 + S_2$ and hence from (162) and (163)

$$f(W_1 W_2) = f(W_1) + f(W_2).$$

From this functional equation f can be determined. For on differentiating both sides with respect to W_1, W_2 remaining constant, we obtain

$$W_2 \dot{f}(W_1 W_2) = \dot{f}(W_1).$$

On further differentiating with respect to W_2, W_1 now remaining constant, we get

$$\dot{f}(W_1 W_2) + W_1 W_2 \ddot{f}(W_1 W_2) = 0$$

or

$$\dot{f}(W) + W \ddot{f}(W) = 0.$$

The general integral of this differential equation of the second order is

$$f(W) = k \log W + \text{const.}$$

Hence from (162) we get

$$S = k \log W + \text{const.},$$

an equation which determines the general way in which the entropy depends on the probability. The universal constant of integration k is the same for a terrestrial as for a cosmic system, and its value, having been determined for the former, will remain valid for the latter. The second additive constant of integration may, without any restriction as regards generality, be included as a constant multiplier in the quantity W, which here has not yet been completely defined, so that the equation reduces to

$$S = k \log W.$$

120. The logarithmic connection between entropy and probability was first stated by *L. Boltzmann*[1] in his kinetic theory of

[1] *L. Boltzmann*, Vorlesungen über Gastheorie, **1**, Sec. 6.

gases. Nevertheless our equation (164) differs in its meaning from the corresponding one of Boltzmann in two essential points.

Firstly, *Boltzmann's* equation lacks the factor k, which is due to the fact that *Boltzmann* always used gram-molecules, not the molecules themselves, in his calculations. Secondly, and this is of greater consequence, *Boltzmann* leaves an additive constant undetermined in the entropy S as is done in the whole of classical thermodynamics, and accordingly there is a constant factor of proportionality, which remains undetermined in the value of the probability W.

In contrast with this we assign a definite absolute value to the entropy S. This is a step of fundamental importance, which can be justified only by its consequences. As we shall see later, this step leads necessarily to the "hypothesis of quanta" and moreover it also leads, as regards radiant heat, to a definite law of distribution of energy of black radiation, and, as regards heat energy of bodies, to *Nernst's* heat theorem.

From (164) it follows that with the entropy S the probability W is, of course, also determined in the absolute sense. We shall designate the quantity W thus defined as the "thermodynamic probability," in contrast to the "mathematical probability," to which it is proportional but not equal. For, while the mathematical probability is a proper fraction, the thermodynamic probability is, as we shall see, always an integer.

121. The relation (164) contains a general method for calculating the entropy S by probability considerations. This, however, is of no practical value, unless the thermodynamic probability W of a system in a given state can be expressed numerically. The problem of finding the most general and most precise definition of this quantity is among the most important problems in the mechanical or electrodynamical theory of heat. It makes it necessary to discuss more fully what we mean by the "state" of a physical system.

By the state of a physical system at a certain time we mean the aggregate of all those mutually independent quantities, which determine uniquely the way in which the processes in the system take place in the course of time for given boundary conditions. Hence a knowledge of the state is precisely equivalent to a knowledge of the "initial conditions." If we now take into account the considerations stated above in Sec. 113, it is evident that we must distinguish in the theoretical treatment two entirely different kinds of states, which we may denote as "microscopic" and "macroscopic" states. The microscopic state is the state as described by a mechanical or electrodynamical observer; it contains the separate values of all coordinates, velocities, and field-strengths. The microscopic processes, according to the laws of mechanics and electrodynamics, take place in a perfectly unambiguous way; for them entropy and the second principle of thermodynamics have no significance. The macroscopic state, however, is the state as observed by a thermodynamic observer; any macroscopic state contains a large number of microscopic ones, which it unites in a mean value. Macroscopic processes take place in an unambiguous way in the sense of the second principle, when, and only when, the hypothesis of the elemental chaos (Sec. 117) is satisfied.

122. If now the calculation of the probability W of a state is in question, it is evident that the state is to be thought of in the macroscopic sense. The first and most important question is now: How is a macroscopic state defined? An answer to it will dispose of the main features of the whole problem.

For the sake of simplicity, let us first consider a special case, that of a very large number, N, of simple similar molecules. Let the problem be solely the distribution of these molecules in space within a given volume, V, irrespective of their velocities, and further the definition of a certain macroscopic distribution in space. The latter cannot consist of a statement of the coordinates of all the separate molecules, for that would be a definite microscopic distribution. We must, on the contrary, leave the positions of the molecules undetermined to a certain extent, and that can be done only by thinking of the whole volume V as being divided into a number of small but finite *space elements*, G, each containing a specified number of molecules. By any such statement a definite macroscopic distribution in space is defined. The manner in which the molecules are distributed within every separate space element is immaterial, for here the hypothesis of elemental chaos (Sec. 117) provides a supplement, which insures the unambiguity of the macroscopic state, in spite of the microscopic indefiniteness. If we distinguish the space elements in order by the numbers 1, 2, 3, ... and, for any particular macroscopic distribution in space, denote the number of the molecules lying in the separate space elements by N_1, N_2, N_3 . . . . . ., then to every definite system of values N_1, N_2, N_3 . . . . . ., there corresponds a definite macroscopic distribution in space. We have of course always:

$$N_1+N_2+N_3+\ .\ .\ .\ .\ .\ =N \tag{165}$$

or if

$$\frac{N_1}{N}=w_1 \quad \frac{N_2}{N}=w_2,\ .\ .\ .\ .\ . \tag{166}$$

$$w_1+w_2+w_3+\ .\ .\ .\ .\ .\ =1. \tag{167}$$

The quantity w_i may be called the density of distribution of the molecules, or the mathematical probability that any molecule selected at random lies in the ith space element.

If we now had, *e.g.*, only 10 molecules and 7 space elements, a definite space distribution would be represented by the values:

$$N_1=1,\ N_2=2,\ N_3=0,\ N_4=0,\ N_5=1,\ N_6=4,\ N_7=2, \tag{168}$$

which state that in the seven space elements there lie respectively 1, 2, 0, 0, 1, 4, 2 molecules.

123. The definition of a macroscopic distribution in space may now be followed immediately by that of its thermodynamic probability W. The latter is founded on the consideration that a certain distribution in space may be realized in many different ways, namely, by many different individual coordinations or "complexions," according as a certain molecule considered will happen to lie in one or the other space element. For, with a given distribution of space, it is of consequence only how many, not which, molecules lie in every space element.

The number of all complexions which are possible with a given distribution in space we equate to the thermodynamic probability W of the space distribution.

In order to form a definite conception of a certain complexion, we can give the molecules numbers, write these numbers in order from 1 to N, and place below the number of every molecule the number of that space element to which the molecule in question belongs in that particular complexion. Thus the following table represents one particular complexion, selected at random, for the distribution in the preceding illustration

$$\begin{array}{cccccccccc} 1 & 2 & 3 & 4 & 5 & 6 & 7 & 8 & 9 & 10 \\ 6 & 1 & 7 & 5 & 6 & 2 & 2 & 6 & 6 & 7 \end{array} \qquad (169)$$

By this the fact is exhibited that the
Molecule 2 lies in space element 1.
Molecules 6 and 7 lie in space element 2.
Molecule 4 lies in space element 5.
Molecules 1, 5, 8, and 9 lie in space element 6.
Molecules 3 and 10 lie in space element 7.

As becomes evident on comparison with (168), this complexion does, in fact, correspond in every respect to the space distribution given above, and in a similar manner it is easy to exhibit many other complexions, which also belong to the same space distribution. The number of all possible complexions required is now easily found by inspecting the lower of the two lines of figures in (169). For, since the number of the molecules is given, this line of figures contains a definite number of places. Since, moreover, the distribution in space is also given, the number of times that every figure (*i.e.*, every space element) appears in the line is equal to the number of molecules which lie in that particular space element. But every change in the table gives a new particular coordination between molecules and space elements and hence a new complexion. Hence the number of the possible complexions, or the thermodynamic probability, W, of the given space distribution, is equal to the number of "permutations with repetition" possible under the given conditions. In the simple numerical example chosen, we get for W, according to a well-known formula, the expression

$$\frac{10!}{1!\,2!\,0!\,0!\,1!\,4!\,2!} = 37{,}800.$$

The form of this expression is so chosen that it may be applied easily to the general case. The numerator is equal to factorial N, N being the total number of molecules considered, and the denominator is equal to the product of the factorials of the numbers, $N_1, N_2, N_3, \ldots\ldots$ of the molecules, which lie in every separate space element and which, in the general case, must be thought of as large numbers. Hence we obtain for the required probability of the given space distribution

$$W=\frac{N!}{N_1!\,N_2!\,N_3!\,.\,.\,.\,.\,.} \tag{170}$$

Since all the N's are large numbers, we may apply to their factorials Stirling's formula, which for a large number may be abridged[1] to[2]

$$n!=\left(\frac{n}{e}\right)^n \tag{171}$$

Hence, by taking account of (165), we obtain

$$W=\left(\frac{N}{N_1}\right)^{N_1}\left(\frac{N}{N_2}\right)^{N_2}\left(\frac{N}{N_3}\right)^{N_3}\,.\,.\,.\,.\,. \tag{172}$$

124. Exactly the same method as in the case of the space distribution just considered may be used for the definition of a macroscopic state and of the thermodynamic probability in the general case, where not only the coordinates but also the velocities, the electric moments, etc., of the molecules are to be dealt with. Every thermodynamic state of a system of N molecules is, in the macroscopic sense, defined by the statement of the number of molecules, N_1, N_2, N_3, ... , which are contained in the region elements 1, 2, 3, ... of the "state space." This state space, however, is not the ordinary three-dimensional space, but an ideal space of as many dimensions as there are variables for every molecule. In other respects the definition and the calculation of the thermodynamic probability W are exactly the same as above and the entropy of the state is accordingly found from (164), taking (166) also into account, to be

$$S=-kN\Sigma w_1 \log w_1, \tag{173}$$

where the sum Σ is to be taken over all region elements. It is obvious from this expression that the entropy is in every case a *positive quantity.*

125. By the preceding developments the calculation of the

[1] Abridged in the sense that factors which in the logarithmic expression (173) would give rise to small additive terms have been omitted at the outset. A brief derivation of equation (173) may be found on p. 218 (Tr.).

[2] See for example *E. Czuber,* Wahrscheinlichkeitsrechnung (Leipzig, B. G. Teubner) p. 22, 1903; *H. Poincaré,* Calcul des Probabilités (Paris, Gauthier-Villars), p. 85, 1912.

entropy of a system of N molecules in a given thermodynamic state is, in general, reduced to the single problem of finding the magnitude G of the region elements in the state space. That such a definite finite quantity really exists is a characteristic feature of the theory we are developing, as contrasted with that due to *Boltzmann*, and forms the content of the so-called *hypothesis of quanta.* As is readily seen, this is an immediate consequence of the proposition of Sec. 120 that the entropy S has an absolute, not merely a relative, value; for this, according to (164), necessitates also an absolute value for the magnitude of the thermodynamic probability W, which, in turn, according to Sec. 123, is dependent on the number of complexions, and hence also on the number and size of the region elements which are used. Since all different complexions contribute uniformly to the value of the probability W, the region elements of the state space represent also *regions of equal probability.* If this were not so, the complexions would not be all equally probable.

However, not only the magnitude, but also the shape and position of the region elements must be perfectly definite. For since, in general, the distribution density w is apt to vary appreciably from one region element to another, a change in the shape of a region element, the magnitude remaining unchanged, would, in general, lead to a change in the value of w and hence to a change in S. We shall see that only in special cases, namely, when the distribution densities w are very small, may the absolute magnitude of the region elements become physically unimportant, inasmuch as it enters into the entropy only through an additive constant. This happens, *e.g.*, at high temperatures, large volumes, slow vibrations (state of an ideal gas, Sec. 132, *Rayleigh's* radiation law, Sec. 195). Hence it is permissible for such limiting cases to assume, without appreciable error, that G is infinitely small in the macroscopic sense, as has hitherto been the practice in statistical mechanics. As soon, however, as the distribution densities w assume appreciable values, the classical statistical mechanics fail.

126. If now the problem be to determine the magnitude G of the region elements of equal probability, the laws of the classical statistical mechanics afford a certain hint, since in certain limiting cases they lead to correct results.

Let $\phi_1, \phi_2, \phi_3, \ldots\ldots$ be the "generalized coordinates," $\psi_1, \psi_2, \psi_3, \ldots\ldots$ the corresponding "impulse coordinates" or "moments," which determine the microscopic state of a certain molecule; then the state space contains as many dimensions as there are coordinates ϕ and moments ψ for every molecule. Now the region element of probability, according to classical statistical mechanics, is identical with the infinitely small element of the state space (in the macroscopic sense)[1]

$$d\phi_1\, d\phi_2\, d\phi_3 \ldots\ldots d\psi_1\, d\psi_2\, d\psi_3 \ldots\ldots \qquad (174)$$

According to the hypothesis of quanta, on the other hand, every region element of probability has a definite finite magnitude

$$G = \int d\phi_1\, d\phi_2\, d\phi_3 \ldots\ldots d\psi_1\, d\psi_2\, d\psi_3 \ldots\ldots \qquad (175)$$

whose value is the same for all different region elements and, moreover, depends on the nature of the system of molecules considered. The shape and position of the separate region elements are determined by the limits of the integral and must be determined anew in every separate case.

[1] Compare, for example, *L. Boltzmann*, Gastheorie, **2**, p. 62 *et seq.*, 1898, or *J. W. Gibbs*, Elementary principles in statistical mechanics, Chapter I, 1902.

CHAPTER II

IDEAL MONATOMIC GASES

127. In the preceding chapter it was proven that the introduction of probability considerations into the mechanical and electrodynamical theory of heat is justifiable and necessary, and from the general connection between entropy S and probability W, as expressed in equation (164), a method was derived for calculating the entropy of a physical system in a given state. Before we apply this method to the determination of the entropy of radiant heat we shall in this chapter make use of it for calculating the entropy of an ideal monatomic gas in an arbitrarily given state. The essential parts of this calculation are already contained in the investigations of *L. Boltzmann*[1] on the mechanical theory of heat; it will, however, be advisable to discuss this simple case in full, firstly to enable us to compare more readily the method of calculation and physical significance of mechanical entropy with that of radiation entropy, and secondly, what is more important, to set forth clearly the differences as compared with *Boltzmann's* treatment, that is, to discuss the meaning of the universal constant k and of the finite region elements G. For this purpose the treatment of a special case is sufficient.

128. Let us then take N similar monatomic gas molecules in an arbitrarily given thermodynamic state and try to find the corresponding entropy. The state space is six-dimensional, with the three coordinates x, y, z, and the three corresponding moments $m\xi$, $m\eta$, $m\zeta$, of a molecule, where we denote the mass by m and velocity components by ξ, η, ζ. Hence these quantities are to be substituted for the ϕ and ψ in Sec. 126. We thus obtain for the size of a region element G the sextuple integral

$$G = m^3 \int d\sigma, \tag{176}$$

where, for brevity

$$dx\ dy\ dz\ d\xi\ d\eta\ d\zeta = d\sigma \tag{177}$$

[1] *L. Boltzmann*, Sitzungsber. d. Akad. d. Wissensch. zu Wien (II) 76, p. 373, 1877. Compare also Gastheorie, 1, p. 38, 1896.

If the region elements are known, then, since the macroscopic state of the system of molecules was assumed as known, the numbers N_1, N_2, N_3, ... of the molecules which lie in the separate region elements are also known, and hence the distribution densities w_1, w_2, w_3, ... (166) are given and the entropy of the state follows at once from (173).

129. The theoretical determination of G is a problem as difficult as it is important. Hence we shall at this point restrict ourselves from the very outset to the special case in which the distribution density varies but slightly from one region element to the next—the characteristic feature of the state of an ideal gas. Then the summation over all region elements may be replaced by the integral over the whole state space. Thus we have from (176) and (167)

$$\sum w_1 = \sum w_1 \frac{m^3}{G}\int d\sigma = \frac{m^3}{G}\int w d\sigma = 1, \qquad (178)$$

in which w is no longer thought of as a discontinuous function of the ordinal number, i, of the region element, where $i=1$, 2, 3, ... n, but as a continuous function of the variables, $x, y, z, \xi, \eta, \zeta$, of the state space. Since the whole state region contains very many region elements, it follows, according to (167) and from the fact that the distribution density w changes slowly, that w has everywhere a small value.

Similarly we find for the entropy of the gas from (173):

$$S = -kN\sum w_1 \log w_1 = -kN\frac{m^3}{G}\int w \log w \, d\sigma. \qquad (179)$$

Of course the whole energy E of the gas is also determined by the distribution densities w. If w is sufficiently small in every region element, the molecules contained in any one region element are, on the average, so far apart that their energy depends only on the velocities. Hence:

$$E = \sum N_1 \frac{1}{2}m(\xi_1{}^2 + \eta_1{}^2 + \zeta_1{}^2) + E_0$$

$$= N\sum w_1 \frac{1}{2}m(\xi_1{}^2 + \eta_1{}^2 + \zeta_1{}^2) + E_0, \qquad (180)$$

where $\xi_1\eta_1\zeta_1$ denotes any velocity lying within the region element 1 and E_0 denotes the internal energy of the stationary molecules, which is assumed constant. In place of the latter expression we may write, again according to (176),

$$E=\frac{m^4N}{2G}\int(\xi^2+\eta^2+\zeta^2)w\,d\sigma+E_0. \tag{181}$$

130. Let us consider the state of thermodynamic equilibrium. According to the second principle of thermodynamics this state is distinguished from all others by the fact that, for a given volume V and a given energy E of the gas, the entropy S is a maximum. Let us then regard the volume

$$V=\int\int\int dx\;dy\;dz \tag{182}$$

and the energy E of the gas as given. The condition for equilibrium is $\delta S=0$, or, according to (179),

$$\Sigma(\log w_1+1)\delta w_1=0,$$

and this holds for any variations of the distribution densities whatever, provided that, according to (167) and (180), they satisfy the conditions

$$\Sigma\delta w_1=0 \text{ and } \Sigma(\xi_1{}^2+\eta_1{}^2+\zeta_1{}^2)\delta w_1=0.$$

This gives us as the necessary and sufficient condition for thermodynamic equilibrium for every separate distribution density w:

$$\log w+\beta(\xi^2+\eta^2+\zeta^2)+\text{ const. }=0$$

or

$$w=\alpha e^{-\beta(\xi^2+\eta^2+\zeta^2)}, \tag{183}$$

where α and β are constants. Hence in the state of equilibrium the distribution of the molecules in space is independent of x, y, z, that is, macroscopically uniform, and the distribution of velocities is the well-known one of *Maxwell.*

131. The values of the constants α and β may be found from those of V and E. For, on substituting the value of w just found in (178) and taking account of (177) and (182), we get

$$\frac{G}{m^3}=\alpha V\int_{-\infty}^{+\infty}\int\int e^{-\beta(\xi^2+\eta^2+\zeta^2)}\,d\xi\,d\eta\,d\zeta=\alpha V\left(\frac{\pi}{\beta}\right)^{\frac{3}{2}},$$

and on substituting w in (181) we get

$$E=E_o+\frac{\alpha m^4NV}{2G}\int\int\int_{-\infty}^{+\infty}(\xi^2+\eta^2+\zeta^2)e^{-\beta(\xi^2+\eta^2+\zeta^2)}\,d\xi\,d\eta\,d\zeta,$$

or

$$E=E_o+\frac{3\alpha m^4NV}{4G}\,\frac{1}{\beta}\left(\frac{\pi}{\beta}\right)^{\frac{3}{2}}.$$

Solving for α and β we have

$$\alpha=\frac{G}{V}\left(\frac{3N}{4\pi m(E-E_o)}\right)^{\frac{3}{2}} \tag{184}$$

$$\beta=\frac{3}{4}\,\frac{Nm}{E-E_o}. \tag{185}$$

From this finally we find, as an expression for the entropy S of the gas in the state of equilibrium with given values of N, V, and E,

$$S=kN\log\left\{\frac{V}{G}\left(\frac{4\pi\ em\ (E-E_o)}{3N}\right)^{\frac{3}{2}}\right\}. \tag{186}$$

132. This determination of the entropy of an ideal monatomic gas is based solely on the general connection between entropy and probability as expressed in equation (164); in particular, we have at no stage of our calculation made use of any special law of the theory of gases. It is, therefore, of importance to see how the entire thermodynamic behavior of a monatomic gas, especially the equation of state and the values of the specific heats, may be deduced from the expression found for the entropy directly by means of the principles of thermodynamics. From the general thermodynamic equation defining the entropy, namely,

$$dS=\frac{dE+pdV}{T}, \tag{187}$$

the partial differential coefficients of S with respect to E and V are found to be

$$\left(\frac{\partial S}{\partial E}\right)_V=\frac{1}{T},\quad \left(\frac{\partial S}{\partial V}\right)_E=\frac{p}{T}$$

Hence, by using (186), we get for our gas

$$\left(\frac{\partial S}{\partial E}\right)_V = \frac{3}{2}\,\frac{kN}{E-E_o} = \frac{1}{T} \tag{188}$$

and

$$\left(\frac{\partial S}{\partial V}\right)_E = \frac{kN}{V} = \frac{p}{T}. \tag{189}$$

The second of these equations

$$p = \frac{kNT}{V} \tag{190}$$

contains the laws of *Boyle*, *Gay Lussac*, and *Avogadro*, the last named because the pressure depends only on the number N, not on the nature of the molecules. If we write it in the customary form:

$$p = \frac{RnT}{V}, \tag{191}$$

where n denotes the number of gram molecules or mols of the gas, referred to $O_2 = 32g$, and R represents the absolute gas constant

$$R = 831 \times 10^5 \frac{\text{erg}}{\text{degree}}, \tag{192}$$

we obtain by comparison

$$k = \frac{Rn}{N}. \tag{193}$$

If we now call the ratio of the number of mols to the number of molecules ω, or, what is the same thing, the ratio of the mass of a molecule to that of a mol, $\omega = \frac{n}{N}$, we shall have

$$k = \omega R. \tag{194}$$

From this the universal constant k may be calculated, when ω is given, and *vice versa*. According to (190) this constant k is nothing but the absolute gas constant, if it is referred to molecules instead of mols.

From equation (188)

$$E - E_0 = \tfrac{3}{2}\,kNT. \tag{195}$$

Now, since the energy of an ideal gas is also given by

$$E = Anc_vT + E_o \tag{196}$$

where c_v is the heat capacity of a mol at constant volume in calories and A is the mechanical equivalent of heat:

$$A = 419 \times 10^5 \frac{\text{erg}}{\text{cal}} \tag{197}$$

it follows that

$$c_v = \frac{3}{2} \frac{kN}{An}$$

and further, by taking account of (193)

$$c_v = \frac{3}{2} \frac{R}{A} = \frac{3}{2} \frac{831 \times 10^5}{419 \times 10^5} = 3.0 \tag{198}$$

as an expression for the heat capacity per mol of any monatomic gas at constant volume in calories.[1]

For the heat capacity per mol at constant pressure, c_p, we have as a consequence of the first principle of thermodynamics:

$$c_p - c_v = \frac{R}{A}$$

and hence by (198)

$$c_p = \frac{5}{2} \frac{R}{A}, \qquad \frac{c_p}{c_v} = \frac{5}{3}, \tag{199}$$

as is known to be the case for monatomic gases. It follows from (195) that the kinetic energy L of the gas molecules is equal to

$$L = E - E_o = \frac{3}{2} NkT \tag{200}$$

133. The preceding relations, obtained simply by identifying the mechanical expression of the entropy (186) with its thermodynamic expression (187), show the usefulness of the theory developed. In them an additive constant in the expression for the entropy is immaterial and hence the size G of the region element of probability does not matter. The hypothesis of quanta, however, goes further, since it fixes the absolute value of the entropy and thus leads to the same conclusion as the heat theorem

[1] Compare *F. Richarz,* Wiedemann's Annal., **67**, p. 705, 1899.

of *Nernst.* According to this theorem the "characteristic function" of an ideal gas[1] is in our notation

$$\Phi = S - \frac{E+pV}{T} = n\left(Ac_p \log T - R \log p + a - \frac{b}{T}\right),$$

where a denotes *Nernst's* chemical constant, and b the energy constant.

On the other hand, the preceding formulæ (186), (188), and (189) give for the same function Φ the following expression:

$$\Phi = N\left(\frac{5}{2}k \log T - k \log p + a'\right) - \frac{E_o}{T}$$

where for brevity a' is put for:

$$a' = k \log \left\{\frac{kN}{eG}(2\pi mk)^{\frac{3}{2}}\right\}$$

From a comparison of the two expressions for Φ it is seen, by taking account of (199) and (193), that they agree completely, provided

$$a = \frac{N}{n}a' = R \log \left\{\frac{Nk^{\frac{5}{2}}}{eG}(2\pi m)^{\frac{3}{2}}\right\}, \tag{201}$$

$$b = \frac{E_o}{n}$$

This expresses the relation between the chemical constant a of the gas and the region element G of the probability.[2]

It is seen that G is proportional to the total number, N, of the molecules. Hence, if we put $G = Ng$, we see that g, the molecular region element, depends only on the chemical nature of the gas.

Obviously the quantity g must be closely connected with the law, so far unknown, according to which the molecules act microscopically on one another. Whether the value of g varies with the nature of the molecules or whether it is the same for all kinds of molecules, may be left undecided for the present.

[1] *E.g., M. Planck,* Vorlesungen über Thermodynamik, Leipzig, Veit und Comp., 1911, Sec. 287, equation 267.

[2] Compare also *O. Sackur,* Annal. d. Physik, **36,** p. 958, 1911, Nernst-Festschrift, p. 405, 1912, and *H. Tetrode,* Annal. d. Physik, **38,** p. 434, 1912.

If g were known, *Nernst's* chemical constant, a, of the gas could be calculated from (201) and the theory could thus be tested. For the present the reverse only is feasible, namely, to calculate g from a. For it is known that a may be measured directly by the tension of the saturated vapor, which at sufficiently low temperatures satisfies the simple equation[1]

$$\log p = \frac{5}{2}\log T - \frac{A r_o}{RT} + \frac{a}{R} \tag{202}$$

(where r_o is the heat of vaporization of a mol at 0° in calories). When a has been found by measurement, the size g of the molecular region element is found from (201) to be

$$g = (2\pi m)^{\frac{3}{2}} k^{\frac{5}{2}} e^{-\frac{a}{R}-1} \tag{203}$$

Let us consider the dimensions of g.

According to (176) g is of the dimensions [$erg^3 sec^3$]. The same follows from the present equation, when we consider that the dimension of the chemical constant a is not, as might at first be thought, that of R, but, according to (202), that of $R \log \frac{p}{T^{\frac{5}{2}}}$

134. To this we may at once add another quantitative relation. All the preceding calculations rest on the assumption that the distribution density w and hence also the constant α in (183) are small (Sec. 129). Hence, if we take the value of α from (184) and take account of (188), (189) and (201), it follows that

$$\frac{p}{T^{\frac{5}{2}}} e^{-\frac{a}{R}-1} \text{ must be small.}$$

When this relation is not satisfied, the gas cannot be in the ideal state. For the saturated vapor it follows then from (202) that $e^{-\frac{Ar_o}{RT}}$ is small. In order, then, that a saturated vapor may be assumed to be in the state of an ideal gas, the temperature T must certainly be less than $\frac{A}{R} r_o$ or $\frac{r_o}{2}$. Such a restriction is unknown to the classical thermodynamics.

[1] *M. Planck*, l. c., Sec. 288, equation 271.

CHAPTER III

IDEAL LINEAR OSCILLATORS

135. The main problem of the theory of heat radiation is to determine the energy distribution in the normal spectrum of black radiation, or, what amounts to the same thing, to find the function which has been left undetermined in the general expression of *Wien's* displacement law (119), the function which connects the entropy of a certain radiation with its energy. The purpose of this chapter is to develop some preliminary theorems leading to this solution. Now since, as we have seen in Sec. 48, the normal energy distribution in a diathermanous medium cannot be established unless the medium exchanges radiation with an emitting and absorbing substance, it will be necessary for the treatment of this problem to consider more closely the processes which cause the creation and the destruction of heat rays, that is, the processes of emission and absorption. In view of the complexity of these processes and the difficulty of acquiring knowledge of any definite details regarding them, it would indeed be quite hopeless to expect to gain any certain results in this way, if it were not possible to use as a reliable guide in this obscure region the law of *Kirchhoff* derived in Sec. 51. This law states that a vacuum completely enclosed by reflecting walls, in which any emitting and absorbing bodies are scattered in any arrangement whatever, assumes in the course of time the stationary state of black radiation, which is completely determined by one parameter only, namely, the temperature, and in particular does not depend on the number, the nature, and the arrangement of the material bodies present. Hence, for the investigation of the properties of the state of black radiation the nature of the bodies which are assumed to be in the vacuum is perfectly immaterial. In fact, it does not even matter whether such bodies really exist somewhere in nature, provided their existence and their properties are consistent with the laws of thermodynamics and electrodynamics. If, for any special arbitrary assumption regarding the nature and arrangement of emitting and absorbing systems, we can find a state of radiation in the surrounding vacuum which is distinguished by absolute stability, this state can be no other than that of black radiation.

Since, according to this law, we are free to choose any system whatever, we now select from all possible emitting and absorbing systems the simplest conceivable one, namely, one consisting of a large number N of similar stationary oscillators, each consisting of two poles, charged with equal quantities of electricity of opposite sign, which may move relatively to each other on a fixed straight line, the axis of the oscillator.

It is true that it would be more general and in closer accord with the conditions in nature to assume the vibrations to be those of an oscillator consisting of two poles, each of which has three degrees of freedom of motion instead of one, *i.e.*, to assume the vibrations as taking place in space instead of in a straight line only. Nevertheless we may, according to the fundamental principle stated above, restrict ourselves from the beginning to the treatment of one single component, without fear of any essential loss of generality of the conclusions we have in view.

It might, however, be questioned as a matter of principle, whether it is really permissible to think of the centers of mass of the oscillators as stationary, since, according to the kinetic theory of gases, all material particles which are contained in substances of finite temperature and free to move possess a certain finite mean kinetic energy of translatory motion. This objection, however, may also be removed by the consideration that the velocity is not fixed by the kinetic energy alone. We need only think of an oscillator as being loaded, say at its positive pole, with a comparatively large inert mass, which is perfectly neutral electrodynamically, in order to decrease its velocity for a given kinetic energy below any preassigned value whatever. Of course this consideration remains valid also, if, as is now frequently done, all inertia is reduced to electrodynamic action. For this action is at any rate of a kind quite different from the one to be considered in the following, and hence cannot influence it.

Let the state of such an oscillator be completely determined by its moment $f(t)$, that is, by the product of the electric charge of the pole situated on the positive side of the axis and the pole distance, and by the derivative of f with respect to the time or

$$\frac{df(t)}{dt} = \dot{f}(t). \tag{204}$$

Let the energy of the oscillator be of the following simple form:

$$U = \tfrac{1}{2}Kf^2 + \tfrac{1}{2}L\dot{f}^2, \tag{205}$$

where K and L denote positive constants, which depend on the nature of the oscillator in some way that need not be discussed at this point.

If during its vibration an oscillator neither absorbed nor emitted any energy, its energy of vibration, U, would remain constant, and we would have:

$$dU = Kf\,df + L\dot{f}\,d\dot{f} = 0, \tag{205 a}$$

or, on account of (204),

$$Kf(t) + L\ddot{f}(t) = 0. \tag{206}$$

The general solution of this differential equation is found to be a purely periodical vibration:

$$f = C\cos(2\pi\nu t - \theta) \tag{207}$$

where C and θ denote the integration constants and ν the number of vibrations per unit time:

$$\nu = \frac{1}{2\pi}\sqrt{\frac{K}{L}} \tag{208}$$

136. If now the assumed system of oscillators is in a space traversed by heat rays, the energy of vibration, U, of an oscillator will not in general remain constant, but will be always changing by absorption and emission of energy. Without, for the present, considering in detail the laws to which these processes are subject, let us consider any one arbitrarily given thermodynamic state of the oscillators and calculate its entropy, irrespective of the surrounding field of radiation. In doing this we proceed entirely according to the principle advanced in the two preceding chapters, allowing, however, at every stage for the conditions caused by the peculiarities of the case in question.

The first question is: What determines the thermodynamic state of the system considered? For this purpose, according to

Sec. 124, the numbers N_1, N_2, N_3, ... of the oscillators, which lie in the region elements 1, 2, 3, ... of the "state space" must be given. The state space of an oscillator contains those coordinates which determine the microscopic state of an oscillator. In the case in question these are only two in number, namely, the moment f and the rate at which it varies, $\dot{f}$, or instead of the latter the quantity

$$\psi = L\dot{f}, \tag{209}$$

which is of the dimensions of an impulse. The region element of the state plane is, according to the hypothesis of quanta (Sec. 126), the double integral

$$\int\int df\, d\psi = h. \tag{210}$$

The quantity h is the same for all region elements. *A priori*, it might, however, depend also on the nature of the system considered, for example, on the frequency of the oscillators. The following simple consideration, however, leads to the assumption that h is a universal constant. We know from the generalized displacement law of *Wien* (equation 119) that in the universal function, which gives the entropy radiation as dependent on the energy radiation, there must appear a universal constant of the dimension $\frac{c^3 \mathfrak{u}}{\nu^3}$ and this is of the dimension of a quantity of action[1] (erg sec.). Now, according to (210), the quantity h has precisely this dimension, on which account we may denote it as "element of action" or "quantity element of action." Hence, unless a second constant also enters, h cannot depend on any other physical quantities.

137. The principal difference, compared with the calculations for an ideal gas in the preceding chapter, lies in the fact that we do not now assume the distribution densities w_1, w_2, w_3 . . . . . of the oscillators among the separate region elements to vary but little from region to region as was assumed in Sec. 129. Accordingly the w's are not small, but finite proper fractions, and the summation over the region elements cannot be written as an integration.

[1] The quantity from which the principle of *least action* takes its name. (Tr.)

In the first place, as regards the shape of the region elements, the fact that in the case of undisturbed vibrations of an oscillator the phase is always changing, whereas the amplitude remains constant, leads to the conclusion that, for the macroscopic state of the oscillators, the amplitudes only, not the phases, must be considered, or in other words the region elements in the $f\psi$ plane are bounded by the curves $C=\text{const.}$, that is, by ellipses, since from (207) and (209)

$$\left(\frac{f}{C}\right)^2+\left(\frac{\psi}{2\pi\nu LC}\right)^2=1. \tag{211}$$

The semi-axes of such an ellipse are:

$$a=C \text{ and } b=2\pi\nu LC. \tag{212}$$

Accordingly the region elements 1, 2, 3, ... n . . . . . are the concentric, similar, and similarly situated elliptic rings, which are determined by the increasing values of C:

$$0,\ C_1,\ C_2,\ C_3,\ .\ .\ .\ .\ .\ C_{n-1},\ C_n\ .\ .\ .\ .\ . \tag{213}$$

The nth region element is that which is bounded by the ellipses $C=C_{n-1}$ and $C=C_n$. The first region element is the full ellipse C_1. All these rings have the same area h, which is found by subtracting the area of the full ellipse C_{n-1} from that of the full ellipse C_n; hence

$$h=(a_nb_n-a_{n-1}b_{n-1})\pi$$

or, according to (212),

$$h=(C_n{}^2-C_{n-1}{}^2)\,2\pi^2\nu L,$$

where $n=1, 2, 3, \ldots$

From the additional fact that $C_o=0$, it follows that:

$$C_n{}^2=\frac{nh}{2\pi^2\nu L}. \tag{214}$$

Thus the semi-axes of the bounding ellipses are in the ratio of the square roots of the integral numbers.

138. The thermodynamic state of the system of oscillators is fixed by the fact that the values of the distribution densities w_1, w_2, w_3, ... of the oscillators among the separate region elements are given. *Within* a region element the distribution of the oscillators is according to the law of elemental chaos (Sec. 122), *i.e.*, it is approximately *uniform.*

These data suffice for calculating the entropy S as well as the energy E of the system in the given state, the former quantity directly from (173), the latter by the aid of (205). It must be kept in mind in the calculation that, since the energy varies appreciably within a region element, the energy E_n of all those oscillators which lie in the nth region element is to be found by an integration. Then the whole energy E of the system is:

$$E=E_1+E_2+\ .\ .\ .\ .\ .\ E_n+\ .\ .\ .\ .\ . \qquad (215)$$

E_n may be calculated with the help of the law that within every region element the oscillators are uniformly distributed. If the nth region element contains, all told, N_n oscillators, there are per unit area $\frac{N_n}{h}$ oscillators and hence $\frac{N_n}{h}\, df{\cdot}d\psi$ per element of area. Hence we have:

$$E_n=\frac{N_n}{h}\int\int U\ df\ d\psi.$$

In performing the integration, instead of f and ψ we take C and ϕ, as new variables, and since according to (211),

$$f=C\cos\phi \qquad \psi=2\pi\nu LC\sin\phi \qquad (216)$$

we get:

$$E_n=2\pi\nu L\,\frac{N_n}{h}\int\int U\ C\ dC\ d\phi$$

to be integrated with respect to ϕ from 0 to 2π and with respect to C from C_{n-1} to C_n. If we substitute from (205), (209) and (216)

$$U=\tfrac{1}{2}KC^2, \qquad (217)$$

we obtain by integration

$$E_n=\frac{\pi^2}{2}\nu LK\frac{N_n}{h}(C_n{}^4-C_{n-1}{}^4)$$

and from (214) and (208):

$$E_n=N_n(n-\tfrac{1}{2})h\nu=Nw_n(n-\tfrac{1}{2})h\nu,$$

that is, the mean energy of an oscillator in the nth region element is $(n-\frac{1}{2})h\nu$. This is exactly the arithmetic mean of the energies $(n-1)h\nu$ and $nh\nu$ which correspond to the two ellipses $C=C_{n-1}$ and $C=C_n$ bounding the region, as may be seen from (217), if the values of C_{n-1} and C_n are therein substituted from (214).

The total energy E is, according to (215),

$$E = Nh\nu \sum_{n=1}^{n=\infty} (n-\tfrac{1}{2}) w_n. \tag{219}$$

139. Let us now consider the state of thermodynamic equilibrium of the oscillators. According to the second principle of thermodynamics, the entropy S is in that case a maximum for a given energy E. Hence we assume E in (219) as given. Then from (179) we have for the state of equilibrium:

$$\delta S = 0 = \sum_1^\infty (\log w_n + 1)\,\delta w_n,$$

where according to (167) and (219)

$$\sum_1^\infty \delta w_n = 0 \text{ and } \sum_1^\infty (n-\tfrac{1}{2})\,\delta w_n = 0$$

From these relations we find:

$$\log w_n + \beta n + \text{const.} = 0$$

or

$$w_n = \alpha\gamma^n. \tag{220}$$

The values of the constants α and γ follow from equations (167) and (219):

$$\alpha = \frac{2Nh\nu}{2E - Nh\nu} \qquad \gamma = \frac{2E - Nh\nu}{2E + Nh\nu}. \tag{221}$$

Since w_n is essentially positive it follows that equilibrium is not possible in the system of oscillators considered unless the total energy E has a greater value than $\frac{Nh\nu}{2}$, that is unless the mean energy of the oscillators is at least $\frac{h\nu}{2}$. This, according to (218), is the mean energy of the oscillators lying in the first region element. In fact, in this extreme case all N oscillators lie in the first region element, the region of smallest energy; within this element they are arranged uniformly.

The entropy S of the system, which is in thermodynamic equilibrium, is found by combining (173) with (220) and (221)

$$S = kN\left\{\left(\frac{E}{Nh\nu}+\frac{1}{2}\right)\log\left(\frac{E}{Nh\nu}+\frac{1}{2}\right) - \left(\frac{E}{Nh\nu}-\frac{1}{2}\right)\log\left(\frac{E}{Nh\nu}-\frac{1}{2}\right)\right\} \tag{222}$$

140. The connection between energy and entropy just obtained allows furthermore a certain conclusion as regards the temperature. For from the equation of the second principle of thermodynamics, $dS=\frac{dE}{T}$ and from differentiation of (222) with respect to E it follows that

$$E=N\frac{h\nu}{2}\ \frac{1+e^{-\frac{h\nu}{kT}}}{1-e^{-\frac{h\nu}{kT}}}=Nh\nu\left(\frac{1}{2}+\frac{1}{e^{\frac{h\nu}{kT}}-1}\right)$$

Hence, for the zero point of the absolute temperature E becomes, not 0, but $N\frac{h\nu}{2}\cdot$ This is the extreme case discussed in the preceding paragraph, which just allows thermodynamic equilibrium to exist. That the oscillators are said to perform vibrations even at the temperature zero, the mean energy of which is as large as $\frac{h\nu}{2}$ and hence may become quite large for rapid vibrations, may at first sight seem strange. It seems to me, however, that certain facts point to the existence, inside the atoms, of vibrations independent of the temperature and supplied with appreciable energy, which need only a small suitable excitation to become evident externally. For example, the velocity, sometimes very large, of secondary cathode rays produced by Roentgen rays, and that of electrons liberated by photoelectric effect are independent of the temperature of the metal and of the intensity of the exciting radiation. Moreover the radioactive energies are also independent of the temperature. It is also well known that the close connection between the inertia of matter and its energy as postulated by the relativity principle leads to the assumption of very appreciable quantities of intra-atomic energy even at the zero of absolute temperature.

For the extreme case, $T=\infty$, we find from (223) that

$$E=NkT, \tag{224}$$

i.e., the energy is proportional to the temperature and independent of the size of the quantum of action, h, and of the nature of the oscillators. It is of interest to compare this value of the energy of vibration E of the system of oscillators, which holds at high temperatures, with the kinetic energy L of the molecular motion of an ideal monatomic gas at the same temperature as calculated in (200). From the comparison it follows that

$$E=\tfrac{2}{3}L \tag{225}$$

This simple relation is caused by the fact that for high temperatures the contents of the hypothesis of quanta coincide with those of the classical statistical mechanics. Then the absolute magnitude of the region element, G or h respectively, becomes physically unimportant (compare Sec. 125) and we have the simple law of equipartition of the energy among all variables in question (see below Sec. 169). The factor $\frac{2}{3}$ in equation (225) is due to the fact that the kinetic energy of a moving molecule depends on three variables (ξ, η, ζ,) and the energy of a vibrating oscillator on only two (f, ψ).

The heat capacity of the system of oscillators in question is, from (223),

$$\frac{dE}{dT}=Nk\left(\frac{h\nu}{kT}\right)^2 \frac{e^{\frac{h\nu}{kT}}}{\left(e^{\frac{h\nu}{kT}}-1\right)^2} \tag{226}$$

It vanishes for $T=0$ and becomes equal to Nk for $T=\infty$. *A. Einstein*[1] has made an important application of this equation to the heat capacity of solid bodies, but a closer discussion of this would be beyond the scope of the investigations to be made in this book.

For the constants α and γ in the expression (220) for the distribution density w we find from (221):

$$\alpha=e^{\frac{h\nu}{kT}}-1 \qquad \gamma=e^{-\frac{h\nu}{kT}} \tag{227}$$

and finally for the entropy S of our system as a function of temperature:

$$S=kN\left\{\frac{\frac{h\nu}{kT}}{e^{\frac{h\nu}{kT}}-1}-\log\left(1-e^{-\frac{h\nu}{kT}}\right)\right\} \tag{228}$$

[1] *A. Einstein*, Ann. d. Phys. **22,** p. 180, 1907. Compare also *M. Born* und *Th. von Kárman*, Phys. Zeitschr. **13,** p. 297, 1912.

CHAPTER IV

DIRECT CALCULATION OF THE ENTROPY IN THE CASE OF THERMODYNAMIC EQUILIBRIUM

141. In the calculation of the entropy of an ideal gas and of a system of resonators, as carried out in the preceding chapters, we proceeded in both cases, by first determining the entropy for an arbitrarily given state, then introducing the special condition of thermodynamic equilibrium, *i.e.*, of the maximum of entropy, and then deducing for this special case an expression for the entropy.

If the problem is only the determination of the entropy in the case of thermodynamic equilibrium, this method is a roundabout one, inasmuch as it requires a number of calculations, namely, the determination of the separate distribution densities w_1, w_2, w_3, ... which do not enter separately into the final result. It is therefore useful to have a method which leads directly to the expression for the *entropy* of a system in the state of thermodynamic equilibrium, without requiring any consideration of the *state* of thermodynamic equilibrium. This method is based on an important general property of the thermodynamic probability of a state of equilibrium.

We know that there exists between the entropy S and the thermodynamic probability W in any state whatever the general relation (164). In the state of thermodynamic equilibrium both quantities have maximum values; hence, if we denote the maximum values by a suitable index:

$$S_m = k \log W_m. \tag{229}$$

It follows from the two equations that:

$$\frac{W_m}{W} = e^{\frac{S_m - S}{k}}$$

Now, when the deviation from thermodynamic equilibrium is at all appreciable, $\frac{S_m - S}{k}$ is certainly a very large number. Accordingly W_m is not only large but of a very high order large, compared with W, that is to say: The thermodynamic probability of the state of equilibrium is enormously large compared with the thermodynamic probability of all states which, in the course of time, change into the state of equilibrium.

This proposition leads to the possibility of calculating W_m with an accuracy quite sufficient for the determination of S_m, without the necessity of introducing the special condition of equilibrium. According to Sec. 123, *et seq.*, W_m is equal to the number of all different complexions possible in the state of thermodynamic equilibrium. This number is so enormously large compared with the number of complexions of all states deviating from equilibrium that we commit no appreciable error if we think of the number of complexions of all states, which as time goes on change into the state of equilibrium, *i.e.*, all states which are at all possible under the given external conditions, as being included in this number. The total number of all possible complexions may be calculated much more readily and directly than the number of complexions referring to the state of equilibrium only.

142. We shall now use the method just formulated to calculate the entropy, in the state of equilibrium, of the system of ideal linear oscillators considered in the last chapter, when the total energy E is given. The notation remains the same as above.

We put then W_m equal to the number of complexions of all states which are at all possible with the given energy E of the system. Then according to (219) we have the condition:

$$E=h\nu\sum_{n=1}^{\infty}(n-\tfrac{1}{2})N_n. \tag{230}$$

Whereas we have so far been dealing with the number of complexions with given N_n, now the N_n are also to be varied in all ways consistent with the condition (230).

The total number of all complexions is obtained in a simple way by the following consideration. We write, according to (165), the condition (230) in the following form:

$$\frac{E}{h\nu}-\frac{N}{2}=\sum_{n=1}^{\infty}(n-1)N_n$$

or

$$0 \cdot N_1 + 1 \cdot N_2 + 2 \cdot N_3 + \ldots\ldots + (n-1)N_n + \ldots\ldots$$

$$= \frac{E}{h\nu} - \frac{N}{2} = P. \qquad (231)$$

P is a given large positive number, which may, without restricting the generality, be taken as an integer.

According to Sec. 123 a complexion is a definite assignment of every individual oscillator to a definite region element 1, 2, 3, ... of the state plane (f, ψ). Hence we may characterize a certain complexion by thinking of the N oscillators as being numbered from 1 to N and, when an oscillator is assigned to the nth region element, writing down the number of the oscillator $(n-1)$ times. If in any complexion an oscillator is assigned to the first region element its number is not put down at all. Thus every complexion gives a certain row of figures, and *vice versa* to every row of figures there corresponds a certain complexion. The position of the figures in the row is immaterial.

What makes this form of representation useful is the fact that according to (231) the number of figures in such a row is always equal to P. Hence we have "combinations with repetitions of N elements taken P at a time," whose total number is

$$\frac{N(N+1)\ (N+2)\ \ldots\ldots\ (N+P-1)}{1\quad 2\quad\ 3\ \ \ldots\ldots\quad P} = \frac{(N+P-1)!}{(N-1)!P!} \qquad (232)$$

If for example we had $N=3$ and $P=4$ all possible complexions would be represented by the rows of figures:

1111	1133	2222
1112	1222	2223
1113	1223	2233
1122	1233	2333
1123	1333	3333

The first row denotes that complexion in which the first oscillator lies in the 5th region element and the two others in the first. The number of complexions in this case is 15, in agreement with the formula.

143. For the entropy S of the system of oscillators which is in the state of thermodynamic equilibrium we thus obtain from equation (229) since N and P are large numbers:

$$S = k \log \frac{(N+P)!}{N!P!}$$

and by making use of Stirling's formula (171)[1]

$$S = kN \left\{ \left(\frac{P}{N}+1\right) \log \left(\frac{P}{N}+1\right) - \frac{P}{N} \log \frac{P}{N} \right\}.$$

If we now replace P by E from (231) we find for the entropy exactly the same value as given by (222) and thus we have demonstrated in a special case both the admissibility and the practical usefulness of the method employed.[2]

[1] Compare footnote to page 124. See also page 218.

[2] A complete mathematical discussion of the subject of this chapter has been given by *H. A. Lorentz.* Compare, *e. g.*, Nature, **92**, p. 305, Nov. 6, 1913. (Tr.)

PART IV

A SYSTEM OF OSCILLATORS IN A STATIONARY FIELD OF RADIATION

CHAPTER I

THE ELEMENTARY DYNAMICAL LAW FOR THE VIBRATIONS OF AN IDEAL OSCILLATOR. HYPOTHESIS OF EMISSION OF QUANTA

144. All that precedes has been by way of preparation. Before taking the final step, which will lead to the law of distribution of energy in the spectrum of black radiation, let us briefly put together the essentials of the problem still to be solved. As we have already seen in Sec. 93, the whole problem amounts to the determination of the temperature corresponding to a monochromatic radiation of given intensity. For among all conceivable distributions of energy the normal one, that is, the one peculiar to black radiation, is characterized by the fact that in it the rays of all frequencies have the same temperature. But the temperature of a radiation cannot be determined unless it be brought into thermodynamic equilibrium with a system of molecules or oscillators, the temperature of which is known from other sources. For if we did not consider any emitting and absorbing matter there would be no possibility of defining the entropy and temperature of the radiation, and the simple propagation of free radiation would be a reversible process, in which the entropy and temperature of the separate pencils would not undergo any change. (Compare below Sec. 166.)

Now we have deduced in the preceding section all the characteristic properties of the thermodynamic equilibrium of a system of ideal oscillators. Hence, if we succeed in indicating a state of radiation which is in thermodynamic equilibrium with the system of oscillators, the temperature of the radiation can be no other than that of the oscillators, and therewith the problem is solved.

145. Accordingly we now return to the considerations of Sec. 135 and assume a system of ideal linear oscillators in a stationary field of radiation. In order to make progress along the line proposed, it is necessary to know the elementary dynamical law, according to which the mutual action between an oscillator and the incident radiation takes place, and it is moreover easy to see that this law cannot be the same as the one which the classical electrodynamical theory postulates for the vibrations of a linear Hertzian oscillator. For, according to this law, all the oscillators, when placed in a stationary field of radiation, would, since their properties are exactly similar, assume the same energy of vibration, if we disregard certain irregular variations, which, however, will be smaller, the smaller we assume the damping constant of the oscillators, that is, the more pronounced their natural vibration is. This, however, is in direct contradiction to the definite discrete values of the distribution densities w_1, w_2, w_3, ... which we have found in Sec. 139 for the stationary state of the system of oscillators. The latter allows us to conclude with certainty that in the dynamical law to be established the quantity element of action h must play a characteristic part. Of what nature this will be cannot be predicted *a priori;* this much, however, is certain, that the only type of dynamical law admissible is one that will give for the stationary state of the oscillators exactly the distribution densities w calculated previously. It is in this problem that the question of the dynamical significance of the quantum of action h stands for the first time in the foreground, a question the answer to which was unnecessary for the calculations of the preceding sections, and this is the principal reason why in our treatment the preceding section was taken up first.

146. In establishing the dynamical law, it will be rational to proceed in such a way as to make the deviation from the laws of classical electrodynamics, which was recognized as necessary, as slight as possible. Hence, as regards the influence of the field of radiation on an oscillator, we follow that theory closely. If the oscillator vibrates under the influence of any external electromagnetic field whatever, its energy U will not in general remain constant, but the energy equation (205 a) must be extended to include the work which the external electromagnetic field does on the oscillator, and, if the axis of the electric doublet coincides with the z-axis, this work is expressed by the term $\mathsf{E}_z\, df = \mathsf{E}_z\, \dot{f}\, dt$. Here E_z denotes the z component of the external electric field-strength at the position of the oscillator, that is, that electric field-strength which would exist at the position of the oscillator, if the latter were not there at all. The other components of the external field have no influence on the vibrations of the oscillator.

Hence the complete energy equation reads:

$$Kf\,df + L\dot{f}\,d\dot{f} = \mathsf{E}_z df$$

or:

$$Kf + L\ddot{f} = \mathsf{E}_z, \tag{233}$$

and the energy absorbed by the oscillator during the time element *dt* is:

$$\mathsf{E}_z\,\dot{f}\,dt \tag{234}$$

147. While the oscillator is absorbing it must also be emitting, for otherwise a stationary state would be impossible. Now, since in the law of absorption just assumed the hypothesis of quanta has as yet found no room, it follows that it must come into play in some way or other in the emission of the oscillator, and this is provided for by the introduction of the hypothesis of emission of quanta. That is to say, we shall assume that the emission does not take place continuously, as does the absorption, but that it occurs only at certain definite times, suddenly, in pulses, and in particular we assume that an oscillator can emit energy only at the moment when its energy of vibration, U, is an integral multiple n of the quantum of energy, $\epsilon = h\nu$. Whether it then really emits or whether its energy of vibration increases further by absorption will be regarded as a matter of chance. This will not be regarded as implying that there is no causality for emission; but the processes which cause the emission will be assumed to be of such a concealed nature that for the present their laws cannot be obtained by any but statistical methods. Such an assumption is not at all foreign to physics; it is, *e.g.*, made in the atomistic theory of chemical reactions and the disintegration theory of radioactive substances.

It will be assumed, however, that if emission does take place, the entire energy of vibration, U, is emitted, so that the vibration of the oscillator decreases to zero and then increases again by further absorption of radiant energy.

It now remains to fix the law which gives the probability that an oscillator will or will not emit at an instant when its energy has reached an integral multiple of ϵ. For it is evident that the statistical state of equilibrium, established in the system of oscillators by the assumed alternations of absorption and emission will depend on this law; and evidently the mean energy U of the oscillators will be larger, the larger the probability that in such a critical state no emission takes place. On the other hand, since the mean energy U will be larger, the larger the intensity of the field of radiation surrounding the oscillators, we shall state the law of emission as follows: *The ratio of the probability that no emission takes place to the probability that emission does take place is proportional to the intensity* I of the vibration which excites the oscillator and which was defined in equation (158). The value of the constant of proportionality we shall determine later on by the application of the theory to the special case in which the energy of vibration is very large. For in this case, as we know, the familiar formulæ of the classical dynamics hold for any period of the oscillator whatever, since the quantity element of action h may then, without any appreciable error, be regarded as infinitely small.

These statements define completely the way in which the radiation processes considered take place, as time goes on, and the properties of the stationary state. We shall now, in the first place, consider in the second chapter the absorption, and, then, in the third chapter the emission and the stationary distribution of energy, and, lastly, in the fourth chapter we shall compare the stationary state of the system of oscillators thus found with the thermodynamic state of equilibrium which was derived directly from the hypothesis of quanta in the preceding part. If we find them to agree, the hypothesis of emission of quanta may be regarded as admissible.

It is true that we shall not thereby prove that this hypothesis represents the only possible or even the most adequate expression of the elementary dynamical law of the vibrations of the oscillators. On the contrary I think it very probable that it may be greatly improved as regards form and contents. There is, however, no method of testing its admissibility except by the investigation of its consequences, and as long as no contradiction in itself or with experiment is discovered in it, and as long as no more adequate hypothesis can be advanced to replace it, it may justly claim a certain importance.

CHAPTER II

ABSORBED ENERGY

148. Let us consider an oscillator which has just completed an emission and which has, accordingly, lost all its energy of vibration. If we reckon the time t from this instant then for $t=0$ we have $f=0$ and $df/dt=0$, and the vibration takes place according to equation (233). Let us write E_z as in (149) in the form of a Fourier's series:

$$\mathsf{E}_z=\sum_{n=1}^{n=\infty}\left[A_n\cos\frac{2\pi nt}{\mathsf{T}}+B_n\sin\frac{2\pi nt}{\mathsf{T}}\right], \tag{235}$$

where T may be chosen very large, so that for all times t considered $t<\mathsf{T}$. Since we assume the radiation to be stationary, the constant coefficients A_n and B_n depend on the ordinal numbers n in a wholly irregular way, according to the hypothesis of natural radiation (Sec. 117). The partial vibration with the ordinal number n has the frequency ν, where

$$\omega=2\pi\nu=\frac{2\pi n}{\mathsf{T}}, \tag{236}$$

while for the frequency ν_o of the natural period of the oscillator

$$\omega_o=2\pi\nu_o=\sqrt{\frac{K}{L}}.$$

Taking the initial condition into account, we now obtain as the solution of the differential equation (233) the expression

$$f=\sum_1^\infty\left[a_n(\cos\omega t-\cos\omega_o t)+b_n\left(\sin\omega t-\frac{\omega}{\omega_o}\sin\omega_o t\right)\right], \tag{237}$$

where

$$a_n=\frac{A_n}{L(\omega_o{}^2-\omega^2)},\quad b_n=\frac{B_n}{L(\omega_o{}^2-\omega^2)}. \tag{238}$$

This represents the vibration of the oscillator up to the instant when the next emission occurs.

The coefficients a_n and b_n attain their largest values when ω is nearly equal to ω_o. (The case $\omega=\omega_o$ may be excluded by assuming at the outset that $\nu_o\mathsf{T}$ is not an integer.)

149. Let us now calculate the total energy which is absorbed by the oscillator in the time from $t=0$ to $t=\tau$, where

$$\omega_o\,\tau \text{ is large.} \tag{239}$$

According to equation (234), it is given by the integral

$$\int_o^\tau \mathsf{E}_z \frac{df}{dt}dt, \tag{240}$$

the value of which may be obtained from the known expression for E_z (235) and from

$$\frac{df}{dt}=\sum_1^\infty[a_n(-\omega\sin\omega t+\omega_o\sin\omega_o t)+b_n(\omega\cos\omega t-\omega\cos\omega_o t)]. \tag{241}$$

By multiplying out, substituting for a_n and b_n their values from (238), and leaving off all terms resulting from the multiplication of two constants A_n and B_n, this gives for the absorbed energy the following value:

$$\frac{1}{L}\int_o^\tau dt\sum_1^\infty\left[\frac{A_n^2}{\omega_o^2-\omega^2}\cos\omega t(-\omega\sin\omega t+\omega_o\sin\omega_o t)+\right.$$
$$\left.\frac{B_n^2}{\omega_o^2-\omega^2}\sin\omega t(\omega\cos\omega t-\omega\cos\omega_o t)\right]. \tag{241a}$$

In this expression the integration with respect to t may be performed term by term. Substituting the limits τ and 0 it gives

$$\frac{1}{L}\sum_1^\infty\frac{A_n^2}{\omega_o^2-\omega^2}\left[-\frac{\sin^2\omega\tau}{2}+\omega_o\left(\frac{\sin^2\frac{\omega_o+\omega}{2}\tau}{\omega_o+\omega}+\frac{\sin^2\frac{\omega_o-\omega}{2}\tau}{\omega_o-\omega}\right)\right]$$
$$+\frac{1}{L}\sum_1^\infty\frac{B_n^2}{\omega_o^2-\omega^2}\left[\frac{\sin^2\omega\tau}{2}-\omega\left(\frac{\sin^2\frac{\omega_o+\omega}{2}\tau}{\omega_o+\omega}-\frac{\sin^2\frac{\omega_o-\omega}{2}\tau}{\omega_o-\omega}\right)\right].$$

In order to separate the terms of different order of magnitude, this expression is to be transformed in such a way that the difference $\omega_o - \omega$ will appear in all terms of the sum. This gives

$$\frac{1}{L}\sum_{1}^{\infty}\frac{A_n^2}{\omega_o^2-\omega^2}\left[\frac{\omega_o-\omega}{2(\omega_o+\omega)}\sin^2\omega\tau+\frac{\omega_o}{\omega_o+\omega}\sin\frac{\omega_o-\omega}{2}\tau\cdot\sin\frac{\omega_o+3\omega}{2}\tau\right.$$
$$\left.+\frac{\omega_o}{\omega_o-\omega}\sin^2\frac{\omega_o-\omega}{2}\tau\right]$$
$$+\frac{1}{L}\sum_{1}^{\infty}\frac{B_n^{\ 2}}{\omega_o^2-\omega^2}\left[\frac{\omega_o-\omega}{2(\omega_o+\omega)}\sin^2\omega\tau\right.$$
$$\left.-\frac{\omega}{\omega_o+\omega}\sin\frac{\omega_o-\omega}{2}\tau\cdot\sin\frac{\omega_o+3\omega}{2}\tau+\frac{\omega}{\omega_o-\omega}\sin^2\frac{\omega_o-\omega}{2}\tau\right].$$

The summation with respect to the ordinal numbers n of the Fourier's series may now be performed. Since the fundamental period T of the series is extremely large, there corresponds to the difference of two consecutive ordinal numbers, $\Delta n = 1$ only a very small difference of the corresponding values of ω, $d\omega$, namely, according to (236),

$$\Delta n = 1 = \mathsf{T}d\nu = \frac{\mathsf{T}d\omega}{2\pi}, \tag{242}$$

and the summation with respect to n becomes an integration with respect to ω.

The last summation with respect to A_n may be rearranged as the sum of three series, whose orders of magnitude we shall first compare. So long as only the order is under discussion we may disregard the variability of the A_n^2 and need only compare the three integrals

$$\int_o^\infty d\omega\frac{\sin^2\omega\tau}{2(\omega_o+\omega)^2} = J_1,$$

$$\int_o^\infty d\omega\frac{\omega_o}{(\omega_o+\omega)^2(\omega_o-\omega)}\sin\frac{\omega_o-\omega}{2}\tau\cdot\sin\frac{\omega_o+3\omega}{2}\tau = J_2,$$

and

$$\int_o^\infty d\omega\frac{\omega_o}{(\omega_o+\omega)(\omega_o-\omega)^2}\sin^2\frac{\omega_o-\omega}{2}\tau = J_3.$$

The evaluation of these integrals is greatly simplified by the fact that, according to (239), $\omega_o\tau$ and therefore also $\omega\tau$ are large numbers, at least for all values of ω which have to be considered. Hence it is possible to replace the expression $\sin^2\omega\tau$ in the integral J_1 by its mean value $\frac{1}{2}$ and thus we obtain:

$$J_1=\frac{1}{4\omega_o}$$

It is readily seen that, on account of the last factor, we obtain

$$J_2=0$$

for the second integral.

In order finally to calculate the third integral J_3 we shall lay off in the series of values of ω on both sides of ω_o an interval extending from $\omega_1(<\omega_o)$ to $\omega_2(>\omega_o)$ such that

$$\frac{\omega_o-\omega_1}{\omega_o} \text{ and } \frac{\omega_2-\omega_o}{\omega_o} \text{ are small,} \tag{243}$$

and simultaneously

$$(\omega_o-\omega_1)\tau \text{ and } (\omega_2-\omega_o)\tau \text{ are large.} \tag{244}$$

This can always be done, since $\omega_o\tau$ is large. If we now break up the integral J_3 into three parts, as follows:

$$J_3=\int_o^\infty=\int_o^{\omega_1}+\int_{\omega_1}^{\omega_2}+\int_{\omega_2}^{\infty},$$

it is seen that in the first and third partial integral the expression $\sin^2\frac{\omega_o-\omega}{2}\tau$ may, because of the condition (244), be replaced by its mean value $\frac{1}{2}$. Then the two partial integrals become:

$$\int_o^{\omega_1}\frac{\omega_o d\omega}{2(\omega_o+\omega)(\omega_o-\omega)^2} \text{ and } \int_{\omega_2}^{\infty}\frac{\omega_o d\omega}{2(\omega_o+\omega)(\omega_o-\omega)^2}. \tag{245}$$

These are certainly smaller than the integrals:

$$\int_o^{\omega_1}\frac{d\omega}{2(\omega_o-\omega)^2} \text{ and } \int_{\omega_2}^{\infty}\frac{d\omega}{2(\omega_o-\omega)^2}$$

which have the values

$$\frac{1}{2}\frac{\omega_1}{\omega_o(\omega_o-\omega_1)} \quad \text{and} \quad \frac{1}{2(\omega_2-\omega_o)} \tag{246}$$

respectively. We must now consider the middle one of the three partial integrals:

$$\int_{\omega_1}^{\omega_2} d\omega \frac{\omega_o}{(\omega_o+\omega)(\omega_o-\omega)^2}\cdot \sin^2\frac{\omega_o-\omega}{2}\tau.$$

Because of condition (243) we may write instead of this:

$$\int_{\omega_1}^{\omega_2} d\omega \cdot \frac{\sin^2\frac{\omega_o-\omega}{2}\tau}{2(\omega_o-\omega)^2}$$

and by introducing the variable of integration x, where

$$x=\frac{\omega-\omega_o}{2}\tau$$

and taking account of condition (244) for the limits of the integral, we get:

$$\frac{\tau}{4}\int_{-\infty}^{+\infty}\frac{\sin^2 x\, dx}{x^2}=\frac{\tau}{4}\pi.$$

This expression is of a higher order of magnitude than the expressions (246) and hence of still higher order than the partial integrals (245) and the integrals J_1 and J_2 given above. Thus for our calculation only those values of ω will contribute an appreciable part which lie in the interval between ω_1 and ω_2, and hence we may, because of (243), replace the separate coefficients $A_n{}^2$ and $B_n{}^2$ in the expression for the total absorbed energy by their mean values $A_o{}^2$ and $B_o{}^2$ in the neighborhood of ω_o and thus, by taking account of (242), we shall finally obtain for the total value of the energy absorbed by the oscillator in the time τ:

$$\frac{1}{L}\frac{\tau}{8}(A_o{}^2+B_o{}^2)\ \mathsf{T} \tag{247}$$

If we now, as in (158), define I, the "intensity of the vibration exciting the oscillator," by spectral resolution of the mean value of the square of the exciting field-strength E_z:

$$\overline{\mathsf{E}_z^2} = \int_o^\infty \mathsf{I}_\nu \, d\nu \tag{248}$$

we obtain from (235) and (242):

$$\overline{\mathsf{E}_z^2} = \tfrac{1}{2} \sum_1^\infty (A_n^2 + B_n^2) = \tfrac{1}{2} \int_o^\infty (A_n^2 + B_n^2)\, \mathsf{T}\, d\nu,$$

and by comparison with (248):

$$\mathsf{I} = \tfrac{1}{2} (A_o^2 + B_o^2)\, \mathsf{T}.$$

Accordingly from (247) the energy absorbed in the time τ becomes:

$$\frac{\mathsf{I}}{4L}\tau,$$

that is, *in the time between two successive emissions, the energy U of the oscillator increases uniformly with the time,* according to the law

$$\frac{dU}{dt} = \frac{\mathsf{I}}{4L} = a. \tag{249}$$

Hence the energy absorbed by all N oscillators in the time dt is:

$$\frac{N\mathsf{I}}{4L}\, dt = Na \, dt. \tag{250}$$

CHAPTER III

EMITTED ENERGY. STATIONARY STATE

150. Whereas the absorption of radiation by an oscillator takes place in a perfectly continuous way, so that the energy of the oscillator increases continuously and at a constant rate, for its emission we have, in accordance with Sec. 147, the following law: The oscillator emits in irregular intervals, subject to the laws of chance; it emits, however, only at a moment when its energy of vibration is just equal to an integral multiple n of the elementary quantum $\epsilon = h\nu$, and then it always emits its whole energy of vibration $n\epsilon$.

We may represent the whole process by the following figure in which the abscissæ represent the time t and the ordinates the energy

$$U = n\epsilon + \rho, \ (\rho < \epsilon) \tag{251}$$

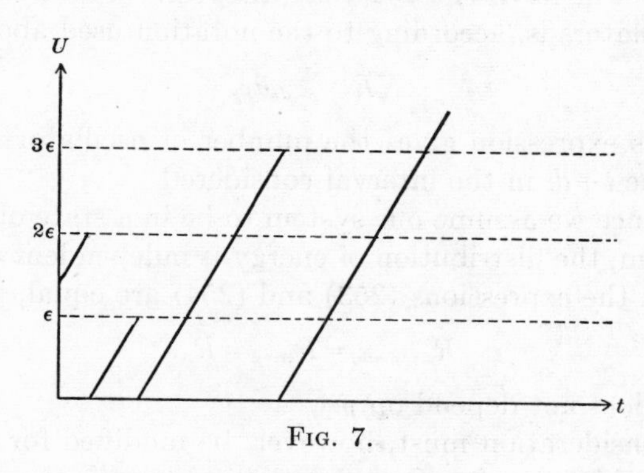

FIG. 7.

of a definite oscillator under consideration. The oblique parallel lines indicate the continuous increase of energy at a constant rate.

$$\frac{dU}{dt} = \frac{d\rho}{dt} = a, \tag{252}$$

which is, according to (249), caused by absorption at a constant rate. Whenever this straight line intersects one of the parallels to the axis of abscissæ $U=\epsilon$, $U=2\epsilon$, ... emission may possibly take place, in which case the curve drops down to zero at that point and immediately begins to rise again.

151. Let us now calculate the most important properties of the state of statistical equilibrium thus produced. Of the N oscillators situated in the field of radiation the number of those whose energy at the time t lies in the interval between $U=n\epsilon+\rho$ and $U+dU=n\epsilon+\rho+d\rho$ may be represented by

$$NR_{n,\rho}d\rho, \tag{253}$$

where R depends in a definite way on the integer n and the quantity ρ which varies continuously between 0 and ϵ.

After a time $dt=\frac{d\rho}{a}$ all the oscillators will have their energy increased by $d\rho$ and hence they will all now lie outside of the energy interval considered. On the other hand, during the same time dt, all oscillators whose energy at the time t was between $n\epsilon+\rho-d\rho$ and $n\epsilon+\rho$ will have entered that interval. The number of all these oscillators is, according to the notation used above,

$$NR_{n,\ \rho-d\rho}d\rho. \tag{254}$$

Hence this expression gives the number of oscillators which are at the time $t+dt$ in the interval considered.

Now, since we assume our system to be in a state of statistical equilibrium, the distribution of energy is independent of the time and hence the expressions (253) and (254) are equal, *i.e.*,

$$R_{n,\ \rho-d\rho}=R_{n,\ \rho}=R_n. \tag{255}$$

Thus R_n does not depend on ρ.

This consideration must, however, be modified for the special case in which $\rho=0$. For, in that case, of the oscillators, $N=R_{n-1}d\rho$ in number, whose energy at the time t was between $n\epsilon$ and $n\epsilon-d\rho$, during the time $dt=\frac{d\rho}{a}$ some enter into the energy interval (from $U=n\epsilon$ to $U+dU=n\epsilon+d\rho$) considered; but all of them do not necessarily enter, for an oscillator may possibly emit all its energy on passing through the value $U=n\epsilon$. If the probability that emission takes place be denoted by $\eta(<1)$ the number of oscillators which pass through the critical value without emitting will be

$$NR_{n-1}(1-\eta)d\rho, \tag{256}$$

and by equating (256) and (253) it follows that

$$R_n = R_{n-1}(1-\eta),$$

and hence, by successive reduction,

$$R_n = R_o(1-\eta)^n. \tag{257}$$

To calculate R_o we repeat the above process for the special case when $n=0$ and $\rho=0$. In this case the energy interval in question extends from $U=0$ to $dU=d\rho$. Into this interval enter in the time $dt=\frac{d\rho}{a}$ all the oscillators which perform an emission during this time, namely, those whose energy at the time t was between $\epsilon-d\rho$ and ϵ, $2\epsilon-d\rho$ and 2ϵ, $3\epsilon-d\rho$ and 3ϵ . . . . .
The numbers of these oscillators are respectively

$$NR_0d\rho,\ NR_1d\rho,\ NR_2d\rho,$$

hence their sum multiplied by η gives the desired number of emitting oscillators, namely,

$$N\eta(R_o+R_1+R_2+\ .\ .\ .\ .\ .\ )\ d\rho, \tag{258}$$

and this number is equal to that of the oscillators in the energy interval between 0 and $d\rho$ at the time $t+dt$, which is $NR_od\rho$. Hence it follows that

$$R_o=\eta(R_o+R_1+R_2+\ .\ .\ .\ .\ .). \tag{259}$$

Now, according to (253), the whole number of all the oscillators is obtained by integrating with respect to ρ from 0 to ϵ, and summing up with respect to n from 0 to ∞. Thus

$$N=N\sum_{n=0}^{n=\infty}\int_o^\epsilon R_{n,\rho}\ d\rho=N\ \Sigma\ R_n\epsilon \tag{260}$$

and

$$\Sigma\ R_n=\frac{1}{\epsilon}. \tag{261}$$

Hence we get from (257) and (259)

$$R_o=\frac{\eta}{\epsilon}\ ,\ R_n=\frac{\eta}{\epsilon}\ (1-\eta)^n. \tag{262}$$

152. The total energy emitted in the time element $dt=\frac{d\rho}{a}$ is found from (258) by considering that every emitting oscillator expends all its energy of vibration and is

$$\begin{aligned} &N\eta\, d\rho(R_o+2R_1+3R_2+\ .\ .\ .\ .\ .)\epsilon \\ &=N\eta\, d\rho\ \eta(1+2(1-\eta)+3(1-\eta)^2+\ .\ .\ .\ .\ .) \\ &=N\, d\rho=Na\, dt. \end{aligned}$$

It is therefore equal to the energy absorbed in the same time by all oscillators (250), as is necessary, since the state is one of statistical equilibrium.

Let us now consider the *mean energy* $\overline{U}$ of an oscillator. It is evidently given by the following relation, which is derived in the same way as (260):

$$N\overline{U}=N\sum_0^\infty\int_o^\epsilon(n\epsilon+\rho)R_n\, d\rho. \tag{263}$$

From this it follows by means of (262), that

$$\overline{U}=\left(\frac{1}{\eta}-\frac{1}{2}\right)\epsilon=\left(\frac{1}{\eta}-\frac{1}{2}\right)h\nu \tag{264}$$

Since $\eta<1$, $\overline{U}$ lies between $\frac{h\nu}{2}$ and ∞. Indeed, it is immediately evident that $\overline{U}$ can never become less than $\frac{h\nu}{2}$ since the energy of *every* oscillator, however small it may be, will assume the value $\epsilon=h\nu$ within a time limit, which can be definitely stated.

153. The probability constant η contained in the formulæ for the stationary state is determined by the law of emission enunciated in Sec. 147. According to this, the ratio of the probability that no emission takes place to the probability that emission does take place is proportional to the intensity I of the vibration exciting the oscillator, and hence

$$\frac{1-\eta}{\eta}=p\mathsf{I} \tag{265}$$

where the constant of proportionality is to be determined in such a way that for very large energies of vibration the familiar formulæ of classical dynamics shall hold.

Now, according to (264), η becomes small for large values of $\overline{U}$ and for this special case the equations (264) and (265) give

$$\overline{U} = ph\nu I,$$

and the energy emitted or absorbed respectively in the time dt by all N oscillators becomes, according to (250),

$$\frac{NI}{4L}\,dt = \frac{N\overline{U}}{4Lph\nu}\,dt. \tag{266}$$

On the other hand, *H. Hertz* has already calculated from *Maxwell's* theory the energy emitted by a linear oscillator vibrating periodically. For the energy emitted in the time of one-half of one vibration he gives the expression[1]

$$\frac{\pi^4 E^2 l^2}{3\lambda^3}$$

where λ denotes half the wave length, and the product El (the C of our notation) denotes the amplitude of the moment f (Sec. 135) of the vibrations. This gives for the energy emitted in the time of a whole vibration

$$\frac{16\pi^4 C^2}{3\lambda^3}$$

where λ denotes the whole wave length, and for the energy emitted by N similar oscillators in the time dt

$$N\,\frac{16\pi^4 C^2 \nu^4}{3c^3}\,dt$$

since $\lambda = \frac{c}{\nu}$. On introducing into this expression the energy U of an oscillator from (205), (207), and (208), namely

$$U = 2\pi^2\nu^2 L C^2,$$

we have for the energy emitted by the system of oscillators

$$N\frac{8\pi^2\nu^2 U}{3c^3 L}dt \tag{267}$$

[1] *H. Hertz,* Wied. Ann. 36, p. 12, 1889.

and by equating the expressions (266) and (267) we find for the factor of proportionality p

$$p=\frac{3c^3}{32\pi^2 h\nu^3}. \tag{268}$$

154. By the determination of p the question regarding the properties of the state of statistical equilibrium between the system of the oscillators and the vibration exciting them receives a general answer. For from (265) we get

$$\eta=\frac{1}{1+p\mathsf{I}}$$

and further from (262)

$$R_n=\frac{1}{\epsilon}\frac{(p\mathsf{I})^n}{(1+p\mathsf{I})^{n+1}}. \tag{269}$$

Hence in the state of stationary equilibrium the number of oscillators whose energy lies between $nh\nu$ and $(n+1)h\nu$ is, from equation (253),

$$N\int_0^\epsilon R_n d\rho = NR_n\epsilon = N\frac{(p\mathsf{I})^n}{(1+p\mathsf{I})^{n+1}} \tag{270}$$

where $n=0, 1, 2, 3, \ldots\ldots$

CHAPTER IV

THE LAW OF THE NORMAL DISTRIBUTION OF ENERGY. ELEMENTARY QUANTA OF MATTER AND ELECTRICITY

155. In the preceding chapter we have made ourselves familiar with all the details of a system of oscillators exposed to uniform radiation. We may now develop the idea put forth at the end of Sec. 144. That is to say, we may identify the stationary state of the oscillators just found with the state of maximum entropy of the system of oscillators which was derived directly from the hypothesis of quanta in the preceding part, and we may then equate the temperature of the radiation to the temperature of the oscillators. It is, in fact, possible to obtain perfect agreement of the two states by a suitable coordination of their corresponding quantities.

According to Sec. 139, the "distribution density" w of the oscillators in the state of statistical equilibrium changes abruptly from one region element to another, while, according to Sec. 138, the distribution within a single region element is uniform. The region elements of the state plane $(f\psi)$ are bounded by concentric similar and similarly situated ellipses which correspond to those values of the energy U of an oscillator which are integral multiples of $h\nu$. We have found exactly the same thing for the stationary state of the oscillators when they are exposed to uniform radiation, and the distribution density w_n in the nth region element may be found from (270), if we remember that the nth region element contains the energies between $(n-1)h\nu$ and $nh\nu$. Hence:

$$w_n = \frac{(p\mathsf{l})^{n-1}}{(1+p\mathsf{l})^n} = \frac{1}{p\mathsf{l}}\left(\frac{p\mathsf{l}}{1+p\mathsf{l}}\right)^n. \tag{271}$$

This is in perfect agreement with the previous value (220) of w_n if we put

$$\alpha = \frac{1}{p\mathsf{l}} \text{ and } \gamma = \frac{p\mathsf{l}}{1+p\mathsf{l}},$$

and each of these two equations leads, according to (221), to the following relation between the intensity of the exciting vibration $\mathfrak{I}$ and the total energy E of the N oscillators:

$$p\mathfrak{I} = \frac{E}{Nh\nu} - \frac{1}{2} \ . \tag{272}$$

156. If we finally introduce the temperature T from (223), we get from the last equation, by taking account of the value (268) of the factor of proportionality p,

$$\mathfrak{I} = \frac{32\pi^2 h\nu^3}{3c^3} \frac{1}{e^{\frac{h\nu}{kT}} - 1} \tag{273}$$

Moreover the specific intensity $\mathfrak{K}$ of a monochromatic plane polarized ray of frequency ν is, according to equation (160),

$$\mathfrak{K} = \frac{h\nu^3}{c^2} \frac{1}{e^{\frac{h\nu}{kT}} - 1} \tag{274}$$

and the space density of energy of uniform monochromatic unpolarized radiation of frequency ν is, from (159),

$$\mathfrak{u} = \frac{8\pi h\nu^3}{c^3} \frac{1}{e^{\frac{h\nu}{kT}} - 1} \tag{275}$$

Since, among all the forms of radiation of differing constitutions, black radiation is distinguished by the fact that all monochromatic rays contained in it have the same temperature (Sec. 93) these equations also give the law of distribution of energy in the normal spectrum, *i.e.*, in the emission spectrum of a body which is black with respect to the vacuum.

If we refer the specific intensity of a monochromatic ray not to the frequency ν but, as is usually done in experimental physics, to the wave length λ, by making use of (15) and (16) we obtain the expression

$$E_\lambda = \frac{c^2 h}{\lambda^5} \frac{1}{e^{\frac{ch}{k\lambda T}} - 1} = \frac{c_1}{\lambda^5} \frac{1}{e^{\frac{c_2}{\lambda T}} - 1} \tag{276}$$

This is the specific intensity of a monochromatic plane polarized ray of the wave length λ which is emitted from a black body at the temperature T into a vacuum in a direction perpendicular to the surface. The corresponding space density of unpolarized radiation is obtained by multiplying E_λ by $\frac{8\pi}{c}$.

Experimental tests have so far confirmed equation (276).[1] According to the most recent measurements made in the Physikalisch-technische Reichsanstalt[2] the value of the second radiation constant c_2 is approximately

$$c_2 = \frac{ch}{k} = 1.436 \text{ cm degree.}$$

More detailed information regarding the history of the equation of radiation is to be found in the original papers and in the first edition of this book. At this point it may merely be added that equation (276) was not simply extrapolated from radiation measurements, but was originally found in a search after a connection between the entropy and the energy of an oscillator vibrating in a field, a connection which would be as simple as possible and consistent with known measurements.

157. The entropy of a ray is, of course, also determined by its temperature. In fact, by combining equations (138) and (274) we readily obtain as an expression for the entropy radiation L of a monochromatic plane polarized ray of the specific intensity of radiation K and the frequency ν,

$$\mathsf{L} = \frac{k\nu^2}{c^2}\left\{\left(1+\frac{c^2\mathsf{K}}{h\nu^3}\right)\log\left(1+\frac{c^2\mathsf{K}}{h\nu^3}\right) - \frac{c^2\mathsf{K}}{h\nu^3}\log\frac{c^2\mathsf{K}}{h\nu^3}\right\} \quad (278)$$

which is a more definite statement of equation (134) for *Wien's* displacement law.

Moreover it follows from (135), by taking account of (273), that the space density of the entropy s of uniform monochromatic unpolarized radiation as a function of the space density of energy u is

$$\mathsf{s} = \frac{8\pi k\nu^2}{c^3}\left\{\left(1+\frac{c^3\mathsf{u}}{8\pi h\nu^3}\right)\log\left(1+\frac{c^3\mathsf{u}}{8\pi h\nu^3}\right) - \frac{c^3\mathsf{u}}{8\pi h\nu^3}\log\frac{c^3\mathsf{u}}{8\pi h\nu^3}\right\} \quad (279)$$

This is a more definite statement of equation (119).

[1] See among others *H. Rubens* und *F. Kurlbaum*, Sitz. Ber. d. Akad. d. Wiss. zu Berlin vom 25. Okt., 1900, p. 929. Ann. d. Phys. **4**, p. 649, 1901. *F. Paschen*, Ann. d. Phys. **4**, p. 277, 1901. *O. Lummer* und *E. Pringsheim*, Ann. d. Phys. **6**, p. 210, 1901. Tätigkeitsbericht der Phys.-Techn. Reichsanstalt vom J. 1911, Zeitschr. f. Instrumentenkunde, 1912, April, p. 134 ff.

[2] According to private information kindly furnished by the president, *Mr. Warburg*.

158. For *small* values of λT (*i.e.*, small compared with the constant $\left.\frac{ch}{k}\right)$ equation (276) becomes

$$E_\lambda = \frac{c^2 h}{\lambda^5} e^{-\frac{ch}{k\lambda T}} \tag{280}$$

an equation which expresses *Wien's*[1] law of energy distribution.

The specific intensity of radiation K then becomes, according to (274),

$$\mathsf{K} = \frac{h\nu^3}{c^2} e^{-\frac{h\nu}{kT}} \tag{281}$$

and the space density of energy u is, from (275),

$$\mathsf{u} = \frac{8\pi h\nu^3}{c^3} e^{-\frac{h\nu}{kT}} \tag{282}$$

159. On the other hand, for *large* values of λT (276) becomes

$$E_\lambda = \frac{ckT}{\lambda^4} \tag{283}$$

a relation which was established first by *Lord Rayleigh*[2] and which we may, therefore, call "*Rayleigh's* law of radiation."

We then find for the specific intensity of radiation K from (274)

$$\mathsf{K} = \frac{k\nu^2 T}{c^2} \tag{284}$$

and from (275) for the space density of monochromatic radiation we get

$$\mathsf{u} = \frac{8\pi k\nu^2 T}{c^3} \tag{285}$$

Rayleigh's law of radiation is of very great theoretical interest, since it represents that distribution of energy which is obtained for radiation in statistical equilibrium with material molecules by means of the classical dynamics, and without introducing the hypothesis of quanta.[3] This may also be seen from the fact that for a vanishingly small value of the quantity element of action, h, the general formula (276) degenerates into *Rayleigh's* formula (283). See also below, Sec. 168 *et seq.*

[1] *W. Wien*, Wied. Ann. **58**, p. 662, 1896.

[2] *Lord Rayleigh*, Phil. Mag. **49**, p. 539, 1900.

[3] *J. H. Jeans*, Phil. Mag. Febr., 1909, p. 229, *H. A. Lorentz*, Nuovo Cimento V, vol. **16**, 1908.

160. For the total space density, u, of black radiation at any temperature T we obtain, from (275),

$$u=\int_0^\infty \mathsf{u}\,d\nu=\frac{8\pi h}{c^3}\int_0^\infty \frac{\nu^3 d\nu}{e^{\frac{h\nu}{kT}}-1}$$

or

$$u=\frac{8\pi h}{c^3}\int_0^\infty\left(e^{-\frac{h\nu}{kT}}+e^{-\frac{2h\nu}{kT}}+e^{-\frac{3h\nu}{kT}}+\ldots\ldots\right)\nu^3 d\nu$$

and, integrating term by term,

$$u=\frac{48\pi h}{c^3}\left(\frac{kT}{h}\right)^4\alpha \qquad (286)$$

where α is an abbreviation for

$$\alpha=1+\frac{1}{2^4}+\frac{1}{3^4}+\frac{1}{4^4}+\ldots\ldots=1.0823. \qquad (287)$$

This relation expresses the *Stefan-Boltzmann* law (75) and it also tells us that the constant of this law is given by

$$a=\frac{48\pi\alpha k^4}{c^3h^3}. \qquad (288)$$

161. For that wave length λ_m to which the maximum of the intensity of radiation corresponds in the spectrum of black radiation, we find from (276)

$$\left(\frac{dE_\lambda}{d\lambda}\right)_{\lambda=\lambda_m}=0.$$

On performing the differentiation and putting as an abbreviation

$$\frac{ch}{k\lambda_m T}=\beta,$$

we get

$$e^{-\beta}+\frac{\beta}{5}-1=0.$$

The root of this transcendental equation is

$$\beta=4.9651, \qquad (289)$$

and accordingly $\lambda_m T=\frac{ch}{\beta k}$, and this is a constant, as demanded by *Wien's* displacement law. By comparison with (109) we find the meaning of the constant b, namely,

$$b=\frac{ch}{\beta k}, \tag{290}$$

and, from (277),

$$b=\frac{c_2}{\beta}=\frac{1.436}{4.9651}=0.289 \text{ cm} \cdot \text{degree}, \tag{291}$$

while *Lummer* and *Pringsheim* found by measurements 0.294 and *Paschen* 0.292.

162. By means of the measured values[1] of a and c_2 the universal constants h and k may be readily calculated. For it follows from equations (277) and (288) that

$$h=\frac{ac_2{}^4}{48\pi\alpha c} \qquad k=\frac{ac_2{}^3}{48\pi\alpha} \tag{292}$$

Substituting the values of the constants a, c_2, α, c, we get

$$h=6.415\cdot 10^{-27} \text{ erg sec.}, \qquad k=1.34\cdot 10^{-16}\frac{\text{erg}}{\text{degree}} \tag{293}$$

163. To ascertain the full physical significance of the quantity element of action, h, much further research work will be required. On the other hand, the value obtained for k enables us readily to state numerically in the C. G. S. system the general connection between the entropy S and the thermodynamic probability W as expressed by the universal equation (164). The general expression for the entropy of a physical system is

$$S=1.34\cdot 10^{-16} \log W \frac{\text{erg}}{\text{degree}} \tag{294}$$

This equation may be regarded as the most general definition of entropy. Herein the thermodynamic probability W is an integral number, which is completely defined by the macroscopic state of the system. Applying the result expressed in (293) to the kinetic

[1] Here as well as later on the value given above (79) has been replaced by $a=7.39\cdot 10^{-15}$, obtained from $\sigma=a\,c/4=5.54\cdot 10^{-5}$. This is the final result of the newest measurements made by *W. Westphal*, according to information kindly furnished by him and Mr. *H. Rubens*. (Nov., 1912). [Compare p. 64, footnote. Tr.]

theory of gases, we obtain from equation (194) for the ratio of the mass of a molecule to that of a mol,

$$\omega=\frac{k}{R}=\frac{1.34\times10^{-16}}{831\times10^{5}}=1.61\times10^{-24}, \qquad (295)$$

that is to say, there are in one mol

$$\frac{1}{\omega}=6.20\times10^{23}$$

molecules, where the mol of oxygen, O_2, is always assumed as 32 gr. Hence, for example, the absolute mass of a hydrogen atom ($\frac{1}{2}H_2=1\ 008$) equals 1.62×10^{-24} gr. With these numerical values the number of molecules contained in 1 cm.^{3} of an ideal gas at 0° C. and 1 atmosphere pressure becomes

$$\mathbf{N}=\frac{76\cdot13.6\cdot981}{831\cdot10^{5}\cdot273\omega}=2.77\cdot10^{19}. \qquad (296)$$

The mean kinetic energy of translatory motion of a molecule at the absolute temperature $T=1$ is, in the absolute C. G. S. system, according to (200),

$$\frac{3}{2}k=2.01\cdot10^{-16} \qquad (297)$$

In general the mean kinetic energy of translatory motion of a molecule is expressed by the product of this number and the absolute temperature T.

The elementary quantity of electricity or the free charge of a monovalent ion or electron is, in electrostatic units,

$$e=\omega\cdot9654\cdot3\cdot10^{10}=4.67\cdot10^{-10}. \qquad (298)$$

Since absolute accuracy is claimed for the formulæ here employed, the degree of approximation to which these numbers represent the corresponding physical constants depends only on the accuracy of the measurements of the two radiation constants a and c_2.

164. Natural Units.—All the systems of units which have hitherto been employed, including the so-called absolute C. G. S. system, owe their origin to the coincidence of accidental circumstances, inasmuch as the choice of the units lying at the base of every system has been made, not according to general points of view which would necessarily retain their importance for all places and all times, but essentially with reference to the special needs of our terrestrial civilization.

Thus the units of length and time were derived from the present dimensions and motion of our planet, and the units of mass and temperature from the density and the most important temperature points of water, as being the liquid which plays the most important part on the surface of the earth, under a pressure which corresponds to the mean properties of the atmosphere surrounding us. It would be no less arbitrary if, let us say, the invariable wave length of Na-light were taken as unit of length. For, again, the particular choice of Na from among the many chemical elements could be justified only, perhaps, by its common occurrence on the earth, or by its double line, which is in the range of our vision, but is by no means the only one of its kind. Hence it is quite conceivable that at some other time, under changed external conditions, every one of the systems of units which have so far been adopted for use might lose, in part or wholly, its original natural significance.

In contrast with this it might be of interest to note that, with the aid of the two constants h and k which appear in the universal law of radiation, we have the means of establishing units of length, mass, time, and temperature, which are independent of special bodies or substances, which necessarily retain their significance for all times and for all environments, terrestrial and human or otherwise, and which may, therefore, be described as "natural units."

The means of determining the four units of length, mass, time, and temperature, are given by the two constants h and k mentioned, together with the magnitude of the velocity of propagation of light in a vacuum, c, and that of the constant of gravitation, f. Referred to centimeter, gram, second, and degrees Centigrade, the numerical values of these four constants are as follows:

$$h = 6.415 \cdot 10^{-27} \frac{g\,\mathrm{cm}^2}{\mathrm{sec}}$$

$$k = 1.34 \cdot 10^{-16} \frac{g\,\mathrm{cm}^2}{\mathrm{sec}^2\,\mathrm{degree}}$$

$$c = 3 \cdot 10^{10} \frac{\mathrm{cm}}{\mathrm{sec}}$$

$$f = 6.685 \cdot 10^{-8} \frac{\mathrm{cm}^3}{g\,\mathrm{sec}^2}$$ [1]

If we now choose the natural units so that in the new system of measurement each of the four preceding constants assumes the value 1, we obtain, as unit of length, the quantity

$$\sqrt{\frac{fh}{c^3}} = 3.99 \cdot 10^{-33}\ \mathrm{cm},$$

as unit of mass

$$\sqrt{\frac{ch}{f}} = 5.37 \cdot 10^{-5}\, g,$$

as unit of time

$$\sqrt{\frac{fh}{c^5}} = 1.33 \cdot 10^{-43}\ \mathrm{sec},$$

as unit of temperature

$$\frac{1}{k}\sqrt{\frac{c^5 h}{f}} = 3.60 \cdot 10^{32}\ \mathrm{degree}.$$

These quantities retain their natural significance as long as the law of gravitation and that of the propagation of light in a vacuum and the two principles of thermodynamics remain valid; they therefore must be found always the same, when measured by the most widely differing intelligences according to the most widely differing methods.

165. The relations between the intensity of radiation and the temperature expressed in Sec. 156 hold for radiation in a pure vacuum. If the radiation is in a medium of refractive index n, the way in which the intensity of radiation depends on the frequency and the temperature is given by the proposition of Sec. 39, namely, the product of the specific intensity of radiation K_ν and the square of the velocity of propagation of the radiation

[1] *F. Richarz* and *O. Krigar-Menzel,* Wied. Ann. **66,** p. 190, 1898.

has the same value for all substances. The form of this universal function (42) follows directly from (274)

$$\mathsf{K}q^2 = \frac{\epsilon_\nu}{\alpha_\nu} q^2 = \frac{h\nu^3}{e^{\frac{h\nu}{kT}} - 1} \tag{299}$$

Now, since the refractive index n is inversely proportional to the velocity of propagation, equation (274) is, in the case of a medium with the index of refraction n, replaced by the more general relation

$$\mathsf{K}_\nu = \frac{h\nu^3 n^2}{c^2} \frac{1}{e^{\frac{h\nu}{kT}} - 1} \tag{300}$$

and, similarly, in place of (275) we have the more general relation

$$\mathsf{u} = \frac{8\pi h\nu^3 n^3}{c^3} \frac{1}{e^{\frac{h\nu}{kT}} - 1} \tag{301}$$

These expressions hold, of course, also for the emission of a body which is black with respect to a medium with an index of refraction n.

166. We shall now use the laws of radiation we have obtained to calculate the temperature of a monochromatic unpolarized radiation of given intensity in the following case. Let the light pass normally through a small area (slit) and let it fall on an arbitrary system of diathermanous media separated by spherical surfaces, the centers of which lie on the same line, the axis of the system. Such radiation consists of homocentric pencils and hence forms behind every refracting surface a real or virtual image of the emitting surface, the image being likewise normal to the axis. To begin with, we assume the last as well as the first medium to be a pure vacuum. Then, for the determination of the temperature of the radiation according to equation (274), we need calculate only the specific intensity of radiation K_ν in the last medium, and this is given by the total intensity of the monochromatic radiation I_ν, the size of the area of the image F, and the solid angle Ω of the cone of rays passing through a point of the image. For the specific intensity of radiation K_ν is, according to (13), determined by the fact that an amount

$$2\mathsf{K}_\nu \, d\sigma \, d\Omega \, d\nu \, dt$$

of energy of unpolarized light corresponding to the interval of frequencies from ν to $\nu+d\nu$ is, in the time dt, radiated in a normal direction through an element of area $d\sigma$ within the conical element $d\Omega$. If now $d\sigma$ denotes an element of the area of the surface image in the last medium, then the total monochromatic radiation falling on the image has the intensity

$$I_\nu = 2\mathsf{K}_\nu \int d\sigma \int d\Omega.$$

I_ν is of the dimensions of energy, since the product $d\nu\, dt$ is a mere number. The first integral is the whole area, F, of the image, the second is the solid angle, Ω, of the cone of rays passing through a point of the surface of the image. Hence we get

$$I_\nu = 2\mathsf{K}_\nu F\Omega, \tag{302}$$

and, by making use of (274), for the temperature of the radiation

$$T = \frac{h\nu}{k} \cdot \frac{1}{\log\left(\dfrac{2h\nu^3 F\Omega}{c^2 I_\nu}+1\right)} \tag{303}$$

If the diathermanous medium considered is not a vacuum but has an index of refraction n, (274) is replaced by the more general relation (300), and, instead of the last equation, we obtain

$$T = \frac{h\nu}{k} \cdot \frac{1}{\log\left(\dfrac{2h\nu^3 F\Omega n^2}{c^2 I_\nu}+1\right)} \tag{304}$$

or, on substituting the numerical values of c, h, and k,

$$T = \frac{0.479 \cdot 10^{-10}\nu}{\log\left(\dfrac{1.43 \cdot 10^{-47}\nu^3 F\Omega n^2}{I_\nu}+1\right)} \text{ degree Centigrade.}$$

In this formula the natural logarithm is to be taken, and I_ν is to be expressed in ergs, ν in "reciprocal seconds," *i.e.*, (seconds)$^{-1}$, F in square centimeters. In the case of visible rays the second term, 1, in the denominator may usually be omitted.

The temperature thus calculated is retained by the radiation considered, so long as it is propagated without any disturbing influence in the diathermanous medium, however great the distance to which it is propagated or the space in which it spreads. For, while at larger distances an ever decreasing amount of energy is radiated through an element of area of given size, this is contained in a cone of rays starting from the element, the angle of the cone continually decreasing in such a way that the value of K remains entirely unchanged. Hence the free expansion of radiation is a perfectly reversible process. (Compare above, Sec. 144.) It may actually be reversed by the aid of a suitable concave mirror or a converging lens.

Let us next consider the temperature of the radiation in the other media, which lie between the separate refracting or reflecting spherical surfaces. In every one of these media the radiation has a definite temperature, which is given by the last formula when referred to the real or virtual image formed by the radiation in that medium.

The frequency ν of the monochromatic radiation is, of course, the same in all media; moreover, according to the laws of geometrical optics, the product $n^2F\Omega$ is the same for all media. Hence, if, in addition, the total intensity of radiation I_ν remains constant on refraction (or reflection), T also remains constant, or in other words: The temperature of a homocentric pencil is not changed by regular refraction or reflection, unless a loss in energy of radiation occurs. Any weakening, however, of the total intensity I_ν by a subdivision of the radiation, whether into two or into many different directions, as in the case of diffuse reflection, leads to a lowering of the temperature of the pencil. In fact, a certain loss of energy by refraction or reflection does occur, in general, on a refraction or reflection, and hence also a lowering of the temperature takes place. In these cases a fundamental difference appears, depending on whether the radiation is weakened merely by free expansion or by subdivision or absorption. In the first case the temperature remains constant, in the second it decreases.[1]

167. The laws of emission of a black body having been deter-

[1] Nevertheless regular refraction and reflection are not irreversible processes; for the refracted and the reflected rays are coherent and the entropy of two coherent rays is not equal to the sum of the entropies of the separate rays. (Compare above, Sec. 104.) On the other hand, diffraction is an irreversible process. *M. Laue*, Ann. d. Phys. **31**, p. 547, 1910.

mined, it is possible to calculate, with the aid of *Kirchhoff's* law (48), the emissive power E of any body whatever, when its absorbing power A or its reflecting power $1-A$ is known. In the case of metals this calculation becomes especially simple for long waves, since *E. Hagen* and *H. Rubens*[1] have shown experimentally that the reflecting power and, in fact, the entire optical behavior of the metals in the spectral region mentioned is represented by the simple equations of *Maxwell* for an electromagnetic field with homogeneous conductors and hence depends only on the specific conductivity for steady electric currents. Accordingly, it is possible to express completely the emissive power of a metal for long waves by its electric conductivity combined with the formulæ for black radiation.[2]

168. There is, however, also a method, applicable to the case of long waves, for the direct theoretical determination of the electric conductivity and, with it, of the absorbing power, A, as well as the emissive power, E, of metals. This is based on the ideas of the electron theory, as they have been developed for the thermal and electrical processes in metals by *E. Riecke*[3] and especially by *P. Drude*.[4] According to these, all such processes are based on the rapid irregular motions of the negative electrons, which fly back and forth between the positively charged molecules of matter (here of the metal) and rebound on impact with them as well as with one another, like gas molecules when they strike a rigid obstacle or one another. The velocity of the heat motions of the material molecules may be neglected compared with that of the electrons, since in the stationary state the mean kinetic energy of motion of a material molecule is equal to that of an electron, and since the mass of a material molecule is more than a thousand times as large as that of an electron. Now, if there is an electric field in the interior of the metal, the oppositely charged particles are driven in opposite directions with average velocities depending on the mean free path, among other factors, and this explains the conductivity of the metal for the electric current. On the other hand, the emissive power of the metal for the radiant heat follows from the calculation of the impacts of the electrons. For.

[1] *E. Hagen* und *H. Rubens*, Ann. d. Phs.y**11**, p. 873, 1903.
[2] *E. Aschkinass*, Ann. d. Phys. **17**, p. 960, 1905.
[3] *E. Riecke*, Wied. Ann. **66**, p. 353, 1898.
[4] *P. Drude*, Ann. d. Phys. **1**, p. 566, 1900.

so long as an electron flies with constant speed in a constant direction, its kinetic energy remains constant and there is no radiation of energy; but, whenever it suffers by impact a change of its velocity components, a certain amount of energy, which may be calculated from electrodynamics and which may always be represented in the form of a *Fourier's* series, is radiated into the surrounding space, just as we think of *Roentgen rays* as being caused by the impact on the anticathode of the electrons ejected from the cathode. From the standpoint of the hypothesis of quanta this calculation cannot, for the present, be carried out without ambiguity except under the assumption that, during the time of a partial vibration of the *Fourier* series, a large number of impacts of electrons occurs, *i.e.*, for comparatively long waves, for then the fundamental law of impact does not essentially matter.

Now this method may evidently be used to derive the laws of black radiation in a new way, entirely independent of that previously employed. For if the emissive power, E, of the metal, thus calculated, is divided by the absorbing power, A, of the same metal, determined by means of its electric conductivity, then, according to *Kirchhoff's* law (48), the result must be the emissive power of a black body, irrespective of the special substance used in the determination. In this manner *H. A. Lorentz*[1] has, in a profound investigation, derived the law of radiation of a black body and has obtained a result the contents of which agree exactly with equation (283), and where also the constant k is related to the gas constant R by equation (193). It is true that this method of establishing the laws of radiation is, as already said, restricted to the range of long waves, but it affords a deeper and very important insight into the mechanism of the motions of the electrons and the radiation phenomena in metals caused by them. At the same time the point of view described above in Sec. 111, according to which the normal spectrum may be regarded as consisting of a large number of quite irregular processes as elements, is expressly confirmed.

169. A further interesting confirmation of the law of radiation of black bodies for long waves and of the connection of the radiation constant k with the absolute mass of the material

[1] *H. A. Lorentz,* Proc. Kon. Akad. v. Wet. Amsterdam, 1903, p. 666.

molecules was found by *J. H. Jeans*[1] by a method previously used by *Lord Rayleigh*,[2] which differs essentially from the one pursued here, in the fact that it entirely avoids making use of any special mutual action between matter (molecules, oscillators) and the ether and considers essentially only the processes in the vacuum through which the radiation passes. The starting point for this method of treatment is given by the following proposition of statistical mechanics. (Compare above, Sec. 140.) When irreversible processes take place in a system, which satisfies *Hamilton's* equations of motion, and whose state is determined by a large number of independent variables and whose total energy is found by addition of different parts depending on the squares of the variables of state, they do so, on the average, in such a sense that the partial energies corresponding to the separate independent variables of state tend to equality, so that finally, on reaching statistical equilibrium, their mean values have become equal. From this proposition the stationary distribution of energy in such a system may be found, when the independent variables which determine the state are known.

Let us now imagine a perfect vacuum, cubical in form, of edge l, and with metallically reflecting sides. If we take the origin of coordinates at one corner of the cube and let the axes of coordinates coincide with the adjoining edges, an electromagnetic process which may occur in this cavity is represented by the following system of equations:

$$\mathsf{E}_x = \cos\frac{\mathfrak{a}\pi x}{l}\sin\frac{\mathfrak{b}\pi y}{l}\sin\frac{\mathfrak{c}\pi z}{l}(e_1\cos 2\pi\nu t + e'_1\sin 2\pi\nu t),$$

$$\mathsf{E}_y = \sin\frac{\mathfrak{a}\pi x}{l}\cos\frac{\mathfrak{b}\pi y}{l}\sin\frac{\mathfrak{c}\pi z}{l}(e_2\cos 2\pi\nu t + e'_2\sin 2\pi\nu t),$$

$$\mathsf{E}_z = \sin\frac{\mathfrak{a}\pi x}{l}\sin\frac{\mathfrak{b}\pi y}{l}\cos\frac{\mathfrak{c}\pi z}{l}(e_3\cos 2\pi\nu t + e'_3\sin 2\pi\nu t),$$

$$\mathsf{H}_x = \sin\frac{\mathfrak{a}\pi x}{l}\cos\frac{\mathfrak{b}\pi y}{l}\cos\frac{\mathfrak{c}\pi z}{l}(h_1\sin 2\pi\nu t - h'_1\cos 2\pi\nu t),$$

[1] *J. H. Jeans*, Phil. Mag. **10**, p. 91, 1905.
[2] *Lord Rayleigh*, Nature **72**, p. 54 and p. 243, 1905.

$$\mathsf{H}_y = \cos\frac{\mathsf{a}\pi x}{l}\sin\frac{\mathsf{b}\pi y}{l}\cos\frac{\mathsf{c}\pi z}{l}(h_2 \sin 2\pi\nu t - h'_2 \cos 2\pi\nu t),$$

$$\mathsf{H}_z = \cos\frac{\mathsf{a}\pi x}{l}\cos\frac{\mathsf{b}\pi y}{l}\sin\frac{\mathsf{c}\pi z}{l}(h_3 \sin 2\pi\nu t - h'_3 \cos 2\pi\nu t),$$

where a, b, c represent any three positive integral numbers. The boundary conditions in these expressions are satisfied by the fact that for the six bounding surfaces $x=0$, $x=l$, $y=0$, $y=l$, $z=0$, $z=l$ the tangential components of the electric field-strength E vanish. Maxwell's equations of the field (52) are also satisfied, as may be seen on substitution, provided there exist certain conditions between the constants which may be stated in a single proposition as follows: Let a be a certain positive constant, then there exist between the nine quantities written in the following square:

$$\begin{matrix} \frac{\mathsf{a}c}{2l\nu} & \frac{\mathsf{b}c}{2l\nu} & \frac{\mathsf{c}c}{2l\nu} \\ \\ \frac{h_1}{a} & \frac{h_2}{a} & \frac{h_3}{a} \\ \\ \frac{e_1}{a} & \frac{e_2}{a} & \frac{e_3}{a} \end{matrix}$$

all the relations which are satisfied by the nine so-called "direction cosines" of two orthogonal right-handed coordinate systems, *i.e.*, the cosines of the angles of any two axes of the systems.

Hence the sum of the squares of the terms of any horizontal or vertical row equals 1, for example,

$$\frac{c^2}{4l^2\nu^2}(\mathsf{a}^2+\mathsf{b}^2+\mathsf{c}^2)=1 \tag{306}$$

$$h_1^2+h_2^2+h_3^2=a^2=e_1^2+e_2^2+e_3^2.$$

Moreover the sum of the products of corresponding terms in any two parallel rows is equal to zero, for example,

$$\begin{aligned} \mathsf{a}e_1+\mathsf{b}e_2+\mathsf{c}e_3&=0 \\ \mathsf{a}h_1+\mathsf{b}h_2+\mathsf{c}h_3&=0. \end{aligned} \tag{307}$$

Moreover there are relations of the following form:

$$\frac{h_1}{a}=\frac{e_2}{a}\cdot\frac{\mathrm{c}c}{2l\nu}-\frac{e_3}{a}\,\frac{\mathrm{b}c}{2l\nu},$$

and hence

$$h_1=\frac{c}{2l\nu}(\mathrm{c}e_2-\mathrm{b}e_3), \text{ etc.} \tag{308}$$

If the integral numbers a, b, c are given, then the frequency ν is immediately determined by means of (306). Then among the six quantities e_1, e_2, e_3, h_1, h_2, h_3, only two may be chosen arbitrarily, the others then being uniquely determined by them by linear homogeneous relations. If, for example, we assume e_1 and e_2 arbitrarily, e_3 follows from (307) and the values of h_1, h_2, h_3 are then found by relations of the form (308). Between the quantities with accent e_1', e_2', e_3', h_1', h_2', h_3' there exist exactly the same relations as between those without accent, of which they are entirely independent. Hence two also of them, say h_1' and h_2', may be chosen arbitrarily so that in the equations given above for given values of a, b, c four constants remain undetermined. If we now form, for all values of a b c whatever, expressions of the type (305) and add the corresponding field components, we again obtain a solution for *Maxwell's* equations of the field and the boundary conditions, which, however, is now so general that it is capable of representing any electromagnetic process possible in the hollow cube considered. For it is always possible to dispose of the constants e_1, e_2, h_1', h_2' which have remained undetermined in the separate particular solutions in such a way that the process may be adapted to any initial state ($t=0$) whatever.

If now, as we have assumed so far, the cavity is entirely void of matter, the process of radiation with a given initial state is uniquely determined in all its details. It consists of a set of stationary vibrations, every one of which is represented by one of the particular solutions considered, and which take place entirely independent of one another. Hence in this case there can be no question of irreversibility and hence also none of any tendency to equality of the partial energies corresponding to the separate partial vibrations. As soon, however, as we assume the presence in the cavity of only the slightest trace of matter which can influence the electrodynamic vibrations, *e.g.*, a few gas molecules, which emit or absorb radiation, the process becomes chaotic and a passage from less to more probable states will take place, though perhaps slowly. Without considering any further details of the electromagnetic constitution of the molecules, we may from the law of statistical mechanics quoted above draw the conclusion that, among all possible processes, that one in which the energy is distributed uniformly among all the independent variables of the state has the stationary character.

From this let us determine these independent variables. In the first place there are the velocity components of the gas molecules. In the stationary state to every one of the three mutually independent velocity components of a molecule there corresponds on the average the energy $\frac{1}{3}\bar{L}$ where $\bar{L}$ represents the mean energy of a molecule and is given by (200). Hence the partial energy, which on the average corresponds to any one of the independent variables of the electromagnetic system, is just as large.

Now, according to the above discussion, the electro-magnetic state of the whole cavity for every stationary vibration corresponding to any one system of values of the numbers a b c is determined, at any instant, by four mutually independent quantities. Hence for the radiation processes the number of independent variables of state is four times as large as the number of the possible systems of values of the positive integers a, b, c.

We shall now calculate the number of the possible systems of values a, b, c, which correspond to the vibrations within a certain small range of the spectrum, say between the frequencies ν and $\nu+d\nu$. According to (306), these systems of values satisfy the inequalities

$$\left(\frac{2l\nu}{c}\right)^2 < \mathsf{a}^2+\mathsf{b}^2+\mathsf{c}^2 < \left(\frac{2l(\nu+d\nu)}{c}\right)^2, \qquad (309)$$

where not only $\frac{2l\nu}{c}$ but also $\frac{2ld\nu}{c}$ is to be thought of as a large number. If we now represent every system of values of a, b, c graphically by a point, taking a, b, c as coordinates in an orthogonal coordinate system, the points thus obtained occupy one octant of the space of infinite extent, and condition (309) is equivalent to requiring that the distance of any one of these points from the origin of the coordinates shall lie between $\frac{2l\nu}{c}$ and $\frac{2l(\nu+d\nu)}{c}$. Hence the required number is equal to the number of points which lie between the two spherical surface-octants corresponding to the radii $\frac{2l\nu}{c}$ and $\frac{2l(\nu+d\nu)}{c}$. Now since to every point there corresponds a cube of volume 1 and *vice versa,* that number is simply equal to the space between the two spheres mentioned, and hence equal to

$$\frac{1}{8}4\pi\left(\frac{2l\nu}{c}\right)^2\frac{2ld\nu}{c},$$

and the number of the independent variables of state is four times as large or

$$\frac{16\pi l^3\nu^2\,d\nu}{c^3}$$

Since, moreover, the partial energy $\frac{\overline{L}}{3}$ corresponds on the average to every independent variable of state in the state of equilibrium, the total energy falling in the interval from ν to $\nu+d\nu$ becomes

$$\frac{16\pi l^3\nu^2 d\nu}{3c^3}\,\overline{L}.$$

Since the volume of the cavity is l^3, this gives for the space density of the energy of frequency ν

$$\mathfrak{u}d\nu=\frac{16\pi\nu^2 d\nu}{3c^3}\,\overline{L},$$

and, by substitution of the value of $\overline{L}=\frac{L}{N}$ from (200),

$$\mathfrak{u}=\frac{8\pi\nu^2 kT}{c^3}, \tag{310}$$

which is in perfect agreement with *Rayleigh's* formula (285).

If the law of the equipartition of energy held true in all

cases, *Rayleigh's* law of radiation would, in consequence, hold for all wave lengths and temperatures. But since this possibility is excluded by the measurements at hand, the only possible conclusion is that the law of the equipartition of energy and, with it, the system of *Hamilton's* equations of motion does not possess the general importance attributed to it in classical dynamics. Therein lies the strongest proof of the necessity of a fundamental modification of the latter.

PART V

IRREVERSIBLE RADIATION PROCESSES

CHAPTER I

FIELDS OF RADIATION IN GENERAL

170. According to the theory developed in the preceding section, the nature of heat radiation within an isotropic medium, when the state is one of stable thermodynamic equilibrium, may be regarded as known in every respect. The intensity of the radiation, uniform in all directions, depends for all wave lengths only on the temperature and the velocity of propagation, according to equation (300), which applies to black radiation in any medium whatever. But there remains another problem to be solved by the theory. It is still necessary to explain how and by what processes the radiation which is originally present in the medium and which may be assigned in any way whatever, passes gradually, when the medium is bounded by walls impermeable to heat, into the stable state of black radiation, corresponding to the maximum of entropy, just as a gas which is enclosed in a rigid vessel and in which there are originally currents and temperature differences assigned in any way whatever gradually passes into the state of rest and of uniform distribution of temperature.

To this much more difficult question only a partial answer can, at present, be given. In the first place, it is evident from the extensive discussion in the first chapter of the third part that, since irreversible processes are to be dealt with, the principles of pure electrodynamics alone will not suffice. For the second principle of thermodynamics or the principle of increase of entropy is foreign to the contents of pure electrodynamics as well as of pure mechanics. This is most immediately shown by the fact that the fundamental equations of mechanics as well as those of electrodynamics allow the direct reversal of every process as regards time, which contradicts the principle of increase of entropy. Of course all kinds of friction and of electric conduction of currents must be assumed to be excluded; for these processes, since they are always connected with the production of heat, do not belong to mechanics or electrodynamics proper.

This assumption being made, the time t occurs in the fundamental equations of mechanics only in the components of acceleration; that is, in the form of the square of its differential. Hence, if instead of t the quantity $-t$ is introduced as time variable in the equations of motion, they retain their form without change, and hence it follows that if in any motion of a system of material points whatever the velocity components of all points are suddenly reversed at any instant, the process must take place in the reverse direction. For the electrodynamic processes in a homogeneous non-conducting medium a similar statement holds. If in *Maxwell's* equations of the electrodynamic field $-t$ is written everywhere instead of t, and if, moreover, the sign of the magnetic field-strength H is reversed, the equations remain unchanged, as can be readily seen, and hence it follows that if in any electrodynamic process whatever the magnetic field-strength is everywhere suddenly reversed at a certain instant, while the electric field-strength keeps its value, the whole process must take place in the opposite sense.

If we now consider any radiation processes whatever, taking place in a perfect vacuum enclosed by reflecting walls, it is found that, since they are completely determined by the principles of classical electrodynamics, there can be in their case no question of irreversibility of any kind. This is seen most clearly by considering the perfectly general formulæ (305), which hold for a cubical cavity and which evidently have a periodic, *i.e.*, reversible character. Accordingly we have frequently (Sec. 144 and 166) pointed out that the simple propagation of free radiation represents a reversible process. An irreversible element is introduced by the addition of emitting and absorbing substance.

171. Let us now try to define for the general case the state of radiation in the thermodynamic-macroscopic sense as we did above in Sec. 107, *et seq.*, for a stationary radiation. Every one of the three components of the electric field-strength, *e.g.*, E_z may, for the long time interval from $t=0$ to $t=\mathsf{T}$, be represented at every point, *e.g.*, at the origin of coordinates, by a *Fourier's* integral, which in the present case is somewhat more convenient than the *Fourier's* series (149):

$$\mathsf{E}_z = \int_0^\infty d\nu C_\nu \cos(2\pi\nu t - \theta_\nu), \tag{311}$$

where C_ν (positive) and θ_ν denote certain functions of the positive variable of integration ν. The values of these functions are not wholly determined by the behavior of E_z in the time interval mentioned, but depend also on the manner in which E_z varies as a function of the time beyond both ends of that interval. Hence the quantities C_ν and θ_ν possess separately no definite physical significance, and it would be quite incorrect to think of the vibration E_z as, say, a continuous spectrum of periodic vibrations with the constant amplitudes C_ν. This may, by the way, be seen at once from the fact that the character of the vibration E_z may vary with the time in any way whatever. How the spectral resolution of the vibration E_z is to be performed and to what results it leads will be shown below (Sec. 174).

172. We shall, as heretofore (158), define J, the "intensity of the exciting vibration,"[1] as a function of the time to be the mean value of E_z^2 in the time interval from t to $t+\tau$, where τ is taken as large compared with the time $1/\nu$, which is the duration of one of the periodic partial vibrations contained in the radiation, but as small as possible compared with the time T. In this statement there is a certain indefiniteness, from which results the fact that J will, in general, depend not only on t but also on τ. If this is the case one cannot speak of the intensity of the exciting vibration at all. For it is an essential feature of the conception of the intensity of a vibration that its value should change but unappreciably within the time required for a single vibration. (Compare above, Sec. 3.) Hence we shall consider in future only those processes for which, under the conditions mentioned, there exists a mean value of E_z^2 depending only on t. We are then obliged to assume that the quantities C_ν in (311) are negligible for all values of ν which are of the same order of magnitude as $\frac{1}{\tau}$ or smaller, *i.e.*,

$$\nu\tau \text{ is large.} \tag{312}$$

[1] Not to be confused with the "field intensity" (field-strength) E_z of the exciting vibration.

In order to calculate J we now form from (311) the value of E_z^2 and determine the mean value $\overline{\mathsf{E}_z^2}$ of this quantity by integrating with respect to t from t to $t+\tau$, then dividing by τ and passing to the limit by decreasing τ sufficiently. Thus we get

$$\mathsf{E}_z^2 = \int_o^\infty \int_o^\infty d\nu' \, d\nu \, C_{\nu'} \, C_\nu \cos(2\pi\nu' t - \theta_{\nu'}) \cos(2\pi\nu t - \theta_\nu).$$

If we now exchange the values of ν and ν', the function under the sign of integration does not change; hence we assume

$$\nu' > \nu$$

and write:

$$\mathsf{E}_z^2 = 2 \int\int d\nu' \, d\nu \, C_{\nu'} \, C_\nu \cos(2\pi\nu' t - \theta_{\nu'}) \cos(2\pi\nu t - \theta_\nu),$$

or

$$\mathsf{E}_z^2 = \int\int d\nu' \, d\nu \, C_{\nu'} \, C_\nu \{\cos[2\pi(\nu' - \nu)t - \theta_{\nu'} + \theta_\nu] + \cos[2\pi(\nu' + \nu)t - \theta_{\nu'} - \theta_\nu]\}.$$

And hence

$$J = \overline{\mathsf{E}_z^2} = \frac{1}{\tau} \int_t^{t+\tau} \mathsf{E}_z^2 \, dt$$

$$= \int\int d\nu' \, d\nu \, C_{\nu'} C_\nu \left\{ \frac{\sin \pi(\nu' - \nu)\tau \cdot \cos[\pi(\nu' - \nu)(2t + \tau) - \theta_{\nu'} + \theta_\nu]}{\pi(\nu' - \nu)\tau} + \frac{\sin \pi(\nu' + \nu)\tau \cdot \cos[\pi(\nu' + \nu)(2t + \tau) - \theta_{\nu'} - \theta_\nu]}{\pi(\nu' + \nu)\tau} \right\}.$$

If we now let τ become smaller and smaller, since $\nu\tau$ remains large, the denominator $(\nu' + \nu)\tau$ of the second fraction remains large under all circumstances, while that of the first fraction $(\nu' - \nu)\tau$ may decrease with decreasing value of τ to less than any finite value. Hence for sufficiently small values of $\nu' - \nu$ the integral reduces to

$$\int\int d\nu' \, d\nu \, C_{\nu'} \, C_\nu \cos[2\pi(\nu' - \nu)t - \theta_{\nu'} + \theta_\nu]$$

which is in fact independent of τ. The remaining terms of the double integral, which correspond to larger values of $\nu' - \nu$, *i.e.*, to more rapid changes with the time, depend in general on τ and therefore must vanish, if the intensity J is not to depend on τ. Hence in our case on introducing as a second variable of integration instead of ν

$$\mu = \nu' - \nu (> 0)$$

we have

$$J = \int\int d\mu \, d\nu \, C_{\nu+\mu} C_{\nu} \cos (2\pi\mu t - \theta_{\nu+\mu} + \theta_{\nu}) \tag{313}$$

or

$$J = \int d\mu (A_{\mu} \cos 2\pi\mu t + B_{\mu} \sin 2\pi\mu t)$$

$$\text{where } A_{\mu} = \int d\nu C_{\nu+\mu} C_{\nu} \cos (\theta_{\nu+\mu} - \theta_{\nu}) \tag{314}$$

$$B_{\mu} = \int d\nu C_{\nu+\mu} C_{\nu} \sin (\theta_{\nu+\mu} - \theta_{\nu})$$

By this expression the intensity J of the exciting vibration, if it exists at all, is expressed by a function of the time in the form of a *Fourier's* integral.

173. The conception of the intensity of vibration J necessarily contains the assumption that this quantity varies much more slowly with the time t than the vibration E_z itself. The same follows from the calculation of J in the preceding paragraph. For there, according to (312), $\nu\tau$ and $\nu'\tau$ are large, but $(\nu' - \nu)\tau$ is small for all pairs of values C_{ν} and $C_{\nu'}$ that come into consideration; hence, *a fortiori*,

$$\frac{\nu' - \nu}{\nu} = \frac{\mu}{\nu} \text{ is small,} \tag{315}$$

and accordingly the *Fourier's* integrals E_z in (311) and J in (314) vary with the time in entirely different ways. Hence in the following we shall have to distinguish, as regards dependence on time, two kinds of quantities, which vary in different ways: Rapidly varying quantities, as E_z, and slowly varying quantities as J and I the spectral intensity of the exciting vibration, whose value we shall calculate in the next paragraph. Nevertheless this difference in the variability with respect to time of the quantities named is only relative, since the absolute value of the differential coefficient of J with respect to time depends on the value of the unit of time and may, by a suitable choice of this unit, be made as large as we please. It is, therefore, not proper to speak of $J(t)$ simply as a slowly varying function of t. If, in the following, we nevertheless employ this mode of expression for the sake of brevity, it will always be in the relative sense, namely, with respect to the different behavior of the function $\mathsf{E}_z(t)$.

On the other hand, as regards the dependence of the phase constant θ_ν on its index ν it necessarily possesses the property of rapid variability in the *absolute* sense. For, although μ is small compared with ν, nevertheless the difference $\theta_{\nu+\mu}-\theta_\nu$ is in general not small, for if it were, the quantities A_μ and B_μ in (314) would have too special values and hence it follows that $(\partial\theta_\nu/\partial\nu)\cdot\nu$ must be large. This is not essentially modified by changing the unit of time or by shifting the origin of time.

Hence the rapid variability of the quantities θ_ν and also C_ν with ν is, in the absolute sense, a necessary condition for the existence of a definite intensity of vibration J, or, in other words, for the possibility of dividing the quantities depending on the time into those which vary rapidly and those which vary slowly—a distinction which is also made in other physical theories and upon which all the following investigations are based.

174. The distinction between rapidly variable and slowly variable quantities introduced in the preceding section has, at the present stage, an important physical aspect, because in the following we shall assume that only slow variability with time is capable of direct measurement. On this assumption we approach conditions as they actually exist in optics and heat radiation. Our problem will then be to establish relations between slowly variable quantities exclusively; for these only can be compared with the results of experience. Hence we shall now determine the most important one of the slowly variable quantities to be considered here, namely, the "spectral intensity" I of the exciting vibration. This is effected as in (158) by means of the equation

$$J=\int_0^\infty \mathsf{I}\,d\nu.$$

By comparison with 313 we obtain:

$$\left\{\begin{array}{l} \mathsf{I} = \int d\mu(\mathsf{A}_\mu \cos 2\pi\mu t + \mathsf{B}_\mu \sin 2\pi\mu t) \\ \text{where} \\ \mathsf{A}_\mu = \overline{C_{\nu+\mu} C_\nu \cos\ (\theta_{\nu+\mu} - \theta_\nu)} \\ \mathsf{B}_\mu = \overline{C_{\nu+\mu} C_\nu \sin\ (\theta_{\nu+\mu} - \theta_\nu)}\ . \end{array}\right. \tag{316}$$

By this expression the spectral intensity, I, of the exciting vibration at a point in the spectrum is expressed as a slowly variable function of the time t in the form of a *Fourier's* integral. The dashes over the expressions on the right side denote the mean values extended over a narrow spectral range for a given value of μ. If such mean values do not exist, there is no definite spectral intensity.

CHAPTER II

ONE OSCILLATOR IN THE FIELD OF RADIATION

175. If in any field of radiation whatever we have an ideal oscillator of the kind assumed above (Sec. 135), there will take place between it and the radiation falling on it certain mutual actions, for which we shall again assume the validity of the elementary dynamical law introduced in the preceding section. The question is then, how the processes of emission and absorption will take place in the case now under consideration.

In the first place, as regards the emission of radiant energy by the oscillator, this takes place, as before, according to the hypothesis of emission of quanta (Sec. 147), where the probability quantity η again depends on the corresponding spectral intensity I through the relation (265).

On the other hand, the absorption is calculated, exactly as above, from (234), where the vibrations of the oscillator also take place according to the equation (233). In this way, by calculations analogous to those performed in the second chapter of the preceding part, with the difference only that instead of the Fourier's series (235) the Fourier's integral (311) is used, we obtain for the energy absorbed by the oscillator in the time τ the expression

$$\frac{\tau}{4L}\int d\mu(\mathsf{A}_\mu \cos 2\pi\mu t + \mathsf{B}_\mu \sin 2\pi\mu t),$$

where the constants A_μ and B_μ denote the mean values expressed in (316), taken for the spectral region in the neighborhood of the natural frequency ν_o of the oscillator. Hence the law of absorption will again be given by equation (249), which now holds also for an intensity of vibration I varying with the time.

176. There now remains the problem of deriving the expression for I, the spectral intensity of the vibration exciting the oscillator, when the thermodynamic state of the field of radiation at the oscillator is given in accordance with the statements made in Sec. 17.

Let us first calculate the total intensity $J=\overline{\mathsf{E}_z^2}$ of the vibration exciting an oscillator, from the intensities of the heat rays striking the oscillator from all directions.

For this purpose we must also allow for the polarization of the monochromatic rays which strike the oscillator. Let us begin by considering a pencil which strikes the oscillator within a conical element whose vertex lies in the oscillator and whose solid angle, $d\Omega$, is given by (5), where the angles θ and ϕ, polar coordinates, designate the direction of the propagation of the rays. The whole pencil consists of a set of monochromatic pencils, one of which may have the principal values of intensity K and K' (Sec. 17). If we now denote the angle which the plane of vibration belonging to the principal intensity K makes with the plane through the direction of the ray and the z-axis (the axis of the oscillator) by ψ, no matter in which quadrant it lies, then, according to (8), the specific intensity of the monochromatic pencil may be resolved into the two plane polarized components at right angles with each other,

$$\mathsf{K}\cos^2\psi + \mathsf{K}'\sin^2\psi$$
$$\mathsf{K}\sin^2\psi + \mathsf{K}'\cos^2\psi,$$

the first of which vibrates in a plane passing through the z-axis and the second in a plane perpendicular thereto.

The latter component does not contribute anything to the value of E_z^2, since its electric field-strength is perpendicular to the axis of the oscillator. Hence there remains only the first component whose electric field-strength makes the angle $\frac{\pi}{2}-\theta$ with the z-axis. Now according to *Poynting's* law the intensity of a plane polarized ray in a vacuum is equal to the product of $\frac{c}{4\pi}$ and the mean square of the electric field-strength. Hence the mean square of the electric field-strength of the pencil here considered is

$$\frac{4\pi}{c}(\mathsf{K}\cos^2\psi+\mathsf{K}'\sin^2\psi)\,d\nu\,d\Omega,$$

and the mean square of its component in the direction of the z-axis is

$$\frac{4\pi}{c}(\mathsf{K}\cos^2\psi+\mathsf{K}'\sin^2\psi)\sin^2\theta\,d\nu\,d\Omega. \tag{317}$$

By integration over all frequencies and all solid angles we then obtain the value required

$$\overline{\mathsf{E}_z^2}=\frac{4\pi}{c}\int\sin^2\theta\,d\Omega\int d\nu(\mathsf{K}_\nu\cos^2\psi+\mathsf{K}_\nu'\sin^2\psi)=J. \tag{318}$$

The space density u of the electromagnetic energy at a point of the field is

$$u=\frac{1}{8\pi}(\overline{\mathsf{E}_x^2}+\overline{\mathsf{E}_y^2}+\overline{\mathsf{E}_z^2}+\overline{\mathsf{H}_x^2}+\overline{\mathsf{H}_y^2}+\overline{\mathsf{H}_z^2}),$$

where E_x^2, E_y^2, E_z^2, H_x^2, H_y^2, H_z^2 denote the squares of the field-strengths, regarded as "slowly variable" quantities, and are hence supplied with the dash to denote their mean value. Since for every separate ray the mean electric and magnetic energies are equal, we may always write

$$u=\frac{1}{4\pi}(\overline{\mathsf{E}_x^2}+\overline{\mathsf{E}_y^2}+\overline{\mathsf{E}_z^2}). \tag{319}$$

If, in particular, all rays are unpolarized and if the intensity of radiation is constant in all directions, $\mathsf{K}_\nu=\mathsf{K}_\nu'$ and, since

$$\int\sin^2\theta\,d\Omega=\iint\sin^3\theta\,d\theta\,d\phi=\frac{8\pi}{3} \tag{319a}$$

$$\overline{\mathsf{E}_z^2}=\frac{32\pi^2}{3c}\int\mathsf{K}_\nu\,d\nu=\overline{\mathsf{E}_x^2}=\overline{\mathsf{E}_y^2}$$

and, by substitution in (319),

$$u=\frac{8\pi}{c}\int\mathsf{K}_\nu\,d\nu,$$

which agrees with (22) and (24).

177. Let us perform the spectral resolution of the intensity J according to Sec. 174; namely,

$$J=\int\mathsf{I}_\nu d\nu.$$

Then, by comparison with (318), we find for the intensity of a definite frequency ν contained in the exciting vibration the value

$$\mathsf{I}=\frac{4\pi}{c}\int \sin^2\theta\, d\Omega(\mathsf{K}_\nu \cos^2\psi+\mathsf{K}_\nu' \sin^2\psi). \qquad (320)$$

For radiation which is unpolarized and uniform in all directions we obtain again, in agreement with (160),

$$\mathsf{I}=\frac{32\pi^2}{3c}\mathsf{K}.$$

178. With the value (320) obtained for I the total energy absorbed by the oscillator in an element of time dt from the radiation falling on it is found from (249) to be

$$\frac{\pi dt}{cL}\int \sin^2\theta\, d\Omega(\mathsf{K}\cos^2\psi+\mathsf{K}'\sin^2\psi).$$

Hence the oscillator absorbs in the time dt from the pencil striking it within the conical element $d\Omega$ an amount of energy equal to

$$\frac{\pi dt}{cL}\sin^2\theta(\mathsf{K}\cos^2\psi+\mathsf{K}'\sin^2\psi)d\Omega. \qquad (321)$$

CHAPTER III

A SYSTEM OF OSCILLATORS

179. Let us suppose that a large number N of similar oscillators with parallel axes, acting quite independently of one another, are distributed irregularly in a volume-element of the field of radiation, the dimensions of which are so small that within it the intensities of radiation K do not vary appreciably. We shall investigate the mutual action between the oscillators and the radiation which is propagated freely in space.

As before, the state of the field of radiation may be given by the magnitude and the azimuth of vibration ψ of the principal intensities K_ν and K_ν' of the pencils which strike the system of oscillators, where K_ν and K_ν' depend in an arbitrary way on the direction angles θ and ϕ. On the other hand, let the state of the system of oscillators be given by the densities of distribution $w_1, w_2, w_3, \ldots\ldots$ (166), with which the oscillators are distributed among the different region elements, $w_1, w_2, w_3, \ldots\ldots$ being any proper fractions whose sum is 1. Herein, as always, the nth region element is supposed to contain the oscillators with energies between $(n-1)h\nu$ and $nh\nu$.

The energy absorbed by the system in the time dt within the conical element $d\Omega$ is, according to (321),

$$\frac{\pi N dt}{cL} \sin^2 \theta(\mathsf{K} \cos^2 \psi + \mathsf{K}' \sin^2 \psi) d\Omega. \tag{322}$$

Let us now calculate also the energy emitted within the same conical element.

180. The total energy emitted in the time element dt by all N oscillators is found from the consideration that a single oscillator, according to (249), takes up an energy element $h\nu$ during the time

$$\frac{4h\nu L}{\mathsf{I}} = \tau, \tag{323}$$

and hence has a chance to emit once, the probability being η. We shall assume that the intensity I of the exciting vibration does not change appreciably in the time τ. Of the Nw_n oscillators which at the time t are in the nth region element a number $Nw_n\eta$ will emit during the time τ, the energy emitted by each being $nh\nu$. From (323) we see that the energy emitted by all oscillators during the time element dt is

$$\sum Nw_n\,\eta\,nh\nu\frac{dt}{\tau}=\frac{N\eta\mathsf{I}dt}{4L}\Sigma nw_n,$$

or, according to (265),

$$\frac{N(1-\eta)dt}{4pL}\Sigma nw_n. \tag{324}$$

From this the energy emitted within the conical element $d\Omega$ may be calculated by considering that, in the state of thermodynamic equilibrium, the energy emitted in every conical element is equal to the energy absorbed and that, in the general case, the energy emitted in a certain direction is independent of the energy simultaneously absorbed. For the stationary state we have from (160) and (265)

$$\mathsf{K}=\mathsf{K}'=\frac{3c}{32\pi^2}\mathsf{I}=\frac{3c}{32\pi^2}\,\frac{1-\eta}{p\eta} \tag{325}$$

and further from (271) and (265)

$$w_n=\frac{1}{p\mathsf{I}}\left(\frac{p\mathsf{I}}{1+p\mathsf{I}}\right)^n=\eta(1-\eta)^{n-1}, \tag{326}$$

and hence

$$\Sigma nw_n=\eta\,\Sigma n(1-\eta)^{n-1}=\frac{1}{\eta}. \tag{327}$$

Thus the energy emitted (324) becomes

$$\frac{N(1-\eta)dt}{4Lp\eta}. \tag{328}$$

This is, in fact, equal to the total energy absorbed, as may be found by integrating the expression (322) over all conical elements $d\Omega$ and taking account of (325).

Within the conical element $d\Omega$ the energy emitted or absorbed will then be

$$\frac{\pi N dt}{cL} \sin^2\theta \; \mathsf{K} d\Omega,$$

or, from (325), (327) and (268),

$$\frac{\pi h \nu^3 (1-\eta) N}{c^3 L} \sum n w_n \sin^2 \theta \; d\Omega \; dt, \tag{329}$$

and this is the general expression for the energy emitted by the system of oscillators in the time element dt within the conical element $d\Omega$, as is seen by comparison with (324).

181. Let us now, as a preparation for the following deductions, consider more closely the properties of the different pencils passing the system of oscillators. From all directions rays strike the volume-element that contains the oscillators; if we again consider those which come toward it in the direction (θ, ϕ) within the conical element $d\Omega$, the vertex of which lies in the volume-element, we may in the first place think of them as being resolved into their monochromatic constituents, and then we need consider further only that one of these constituents which corresponds to the frequency ν of the oscillators; for all other rays simply pass the oscillators without influencing them or being influenced by them. The specific intensity of a monochromatic ray of frequency ν is

$$\mathsf{K} + \mathsf{K}'$$

where K and K' represent the principal intensities which we assume as non-coherent. This ray is now resolved into two components according to the directions of its principal planes of vibration (Sec. 176).

The first component,

$$\mathsf{K} \sin^2 \psi + \mathsf{K}' \cos^2 \psi,$$

passes by the oscillators and emerges on the other side with no change whatever. Hence it gives a plane polarized ray, which starts from the system of oscillators in the direction (θ, ϕ) within the solid angle $d\Omega$ and whose vibrations are perpendicular to the axis of the oscillators and whose intensity is

$$\mathsf{K} \sin^2 \psi + \mathsf{K}' \cos^2 \psi = \mathsf{K}''. \tag{330}$$

The second component,

$$\mathsf{K}\cos^2\psi+\mathsf{K}'\sin^2\psi,$$

polarized at right angles to the first consists again, according to Sec. 176, of two parts

$$(\mathsf{K}\cos^2\psi+\mathsf{K}'\sin^2\psi)\cos^2\theta \tag{331}$$

and

$$(\mathsf{K}\cos^2\psi+\mathsf{K}'\sin^2\psi)\sin^2\theta, \tag{332}$$

of which the first passes by the system without any change, since its direction of vibration is at right angles to the axes of the oscillators, while the second is weakened by absorption, say by the small fraction β. Hence on emergence this component has only the intensity

$$(1-\beta)\,(\mathsf{K}\cos^2\psi+\mathsf{K}'\sin^2\psi)\sin^2\theta. \tag{333}$$

It is, however, strengthened by the radiation emitted by the system of oscillators (329), which has the value

$$\beta'(1-\eta)\;\Sigma n w_n\sin^2\theta, \tag{334}$$

where β' denotes a certain other constant, which depends only on the nature of the system and whose value is obtained at once from the condition that, in the state of thermodynamic equilibrium, the loss is just compensated by the gain.

For this purpose we make use of the relations (325) and (327) corresponding to the stationary state, and thus find that the sum of the expressions (333) and (334) becomes just equal to (332); and thus for the constant β' the following value is found:

$$\beta'=\beta\frac{3c}{32\pi^2 p}=\beta\,\frac{h\nu^3}{c^2}.$$

Then by addition of (331), (333) and (334) the total specific intensity of the radiation which emanates from the system of oscillators within the conical element $d\Omega$, and whose plane of vibration is parallel to the axes of the oscillators, is found to be

$$\begin{aligned}\mathsf{K}'''=\mathsf{K}\cos^2\psi+\mathsf{K}'\sin^2\psi+&\\ \beta\sin^2\theta(\mathsf{K}_e-(\mathsf{K}\cos^2\psi+\mathsf{K}'\sin^2\psi))&\end{aligned} \tag{335}$$

where for the sake of brevity the term referring to the emission is written

$$\frac{h\nu^3}{c^2}(1-\eta)\;\Sigma n w_n=\mathsf{K}_e. \tag{336}$$

Thus we finally have a ray starting from the system of oscillators in the direction (θ,ϕ) within the conical element $d\Omega$ and consisting of two components K'' and K''' polarized perpendicularly to each other, the first component vibrating at right angles to the axes of the oscillators.

In the state of thermodynamic equilibrium

$$\mathsf{K}=\mathsf{K}'=\mathsf{K}''=\mathsf{K}'''=\mathsf{K}_e,$$

a result which follows in several ways from the last equations.

182. The constant β introduced above, a small positive number, is determined by the spacial and spectral limits of the radiation influenced by the system of oscillators. If q denotes the cross-section at right angles to the direction of the ray, $\triangle\nu$ the spectral width of the pencil cut out of the total incident radiation by the system, the energy which is capable of absorption and which is brought to the system of oscillators within the conical element $d\Omega$ in the time dt is, according to (332) and (11),

$$q\triangle\nu(\mathsf{K}\cos^2\psi+\mathsf{K}'\sin^2\psi)\sin^2\theta\, d\Omega\, dt. \tag{337}$$

Hence the energy actually absorbed is the fraction β of this value. Comparing this with (322) we get

$$\beta=\frac{\pi N}{q\cdot\triangle\nu\cdot cL}. \tag{338}$$

CHAPTER IV

CONSERVATION OF ENERGY AND INCREASE OF ENTROPY. CONCLUSION

183. It is now easy to state the relation of the two principles of thermodynamics to the irreversible processes here considered. Let us consider first the *conservation of energy*. If there is no oscillator in the field, every one of the elementary pencils, infinite in number, retains, during its rectilinear propagation, both its specific intensity K and its energy without change, even though it be reflected at the surface, assumed as plane and reflecting, which bounds the field (Sec. 166). The system of oscillators, on the other hand, produces a change in the incident pencils and hence also a change in the energy of the radiation propagated in the field. To calculate this we need consider only those monochromatic rays which lie close to the natural frequency ν of the oscillators, since the rest are not altered at all by the system.

The system is struck in the direction (θ, ϕ) within the conical element $d\Omega$ which converges toward the system of oscillators by a pencil polarized in some arbitrary way, the intensity of which is given by the sum of the two principal intensities K and K'. This pencil, according to Sec. 182, conveys the energy

$$q\triangle\nu(\mathsf{K}+\mathsf{K}')d\Omega\, dt$$

to the system in the time dt; hence this energy is taken from the field of radiation on the side of the rays arriving within $d\Omega$. As a compensation there emerges from the system on the other side in the same direction (θ, ϕ) a pencil polarized in some definite way, the intensity of which is given by the sum of the two components K'' and K'''. By it an amount of energy

$$q\triangle\nu(\mathsf{K}''+\mathsf{K}''')d\Omega\, dt,$$

is added to the field of radiation. Hence, all told, the change in energy of the field of radiation in the time dt is obtained by subtracting the first expression from the second and by integrating with respect to $d\Omega$. Thus we get

$$dt \, \triangle\nu \int (\mathsf{K}'' + \mathsf{K}''' - \mathsf{K} - \mathsf{K}') q \, d\Omega,$$

or by taking account of (330), (335), and (338)

$$\frac{\pi N dt}{cL} \int d\Omega \, \sin^2\theta \, (\mathsf{K}_e - (\mathsf{K} \cos^2 \psi + \mathsf{K}' \sin^2 \psi)). \qquad (339)$$

184. Let us now calculate the change in energy of the system of oscillators which has taken place in the same time dt. According to (219), this energy at the time t is

$$E = Nh\nu \sum_1^\infty (n - \frac{1}{2}) w_n,$$

where the quantities w_n whose total sum is equal to 1 represent the densities of distribution characteristic of the state. Hence the energy change in the time dt is

$$dE = Nh\nu \sum_1^\infty (n - \frac{1}{2}) dw_n = Nh\nu \sum_1^\infty n dw_n. \qquad (340)$$

To calculate dw_n we consider the nth region element. All of the oscillators which lie in this region at the time t have, after the lapse of time τ, given by (323), left this region; they have either passed into the $(n+1)$st region, or they have performed an emission at the boundary of the two regions. In compensation there have entered $(1-\eta)Nw_{n-1}$ oscillators during the time τ, that is, all oscillators which, at the time t, were in the $(n-1)$st region element, excepting such as have lost their energy by emission. Thus we obtain for the required change in the time dt

$$N dw_n = \frac{dt}{\tau} N((1-\eta) w_{n-1} - w_n). \qquad (341)$$

A separate discussion is required for the first region element $n=1$. For into this region there enter in the time τ all those oscillators which have performed an emission in this time. Their number is

$$\eta(w_1 + w_2 + w_3 + \ . \ . \ . \ . \ . \ . \ )N = \eta N.$$

Hence we have

$$N\,dw_1 = \frac{dt}{\tau} N(\eta - w_1).$$

We may include this equation in the general one (341) if we introduce as a new expression

$$w_o = \frac{\eta}{1-\eta}. \tag{342}$$

Then (341) gives, substituting τ from (323),

$$dw_n = \frac{\mathsf{I}\,dt}{4h\nu L}((1-\eta)w_{n-1} - w_n), \tag{343}$$

and the energy change (340) of the system of oscillators becomes

$$dE = \frac{N\mathsf{I}\,dt}{4L} \sum_1^\infty n((1-\eta)w_{n-1} - w_n).$$

The sum Σ may be simplified by recalling that

$$\sum_1^\infty n w_{n-1} = \sum_1^\infty (n-1)w_{n-1} + \sum_1^\infty w_{n-1}$$

$$= \sum_1^\infty n w_n + w_o + 1 = \sum_1^\infty n w_n + \frac{1}{1-\eta}.$$

Then we have

$$dE = \frac{N\mathsf{I}\,dt}{4L}(1 - \eta \sum_1^\infty n w_n). \tag{344}$$

This expression may be obtained more readily by considering that dE is the difference of the total energy absorbed and the total energy emitted. The former is found from (250), the latter from (324), by taking account of (265).

The principle of the conservation of energy demands that the sum of the energy change (339) of the field of radiation and the energy change (344) of the system of oscillators shall be zero, which, in fact, is quite generally the case, as is seen from the relations (320) and (336).

185. We now turn to the discussion of the second principle, the principle of the *increase of entropy*, and follow closely the above discussion regarding the energy. When there is no oscillator in the field, every one of the elementary pencils, infinite in number, retains during rectilinear propagation both its specific intensity and its entropy without change, even when reflected at the surface, assumed as plane and reflecting, which bounds the field. The system of oscillators, however, produces a change in the incident pencils and hence also a change in the entropy of the radiation propagated in the field. For the calculation of this change we need to investigate only those monochromatic rays which lie close to the natural frequency ν of the oscillators, since the rest are not altered at all by the system.

The system of oscillators is struck in the direction (θ,ϕ) within the conical element $d\Omega$ converging toward the system by a pencil polarized in some arbitrary way, the spectral intensity of which is given by the sum of the two principal intensities K and K' with the azimuth of vibration ψ and $\frac{\pi}{2}+\psi$ respectively, which are assumed to be non-coherent. According to (141) and Sec. 182 this pencil conveys the entropy

$$q\Delta\nu[\mathsf{L}(\mathsf{K})+\mathsf{L}(\mathsf{K}')]\,d\Omega\,dt \tag{345}$$

to the system of oscillators in the time dt, where the function $\mathsf{L}(\mathsf{K})$ is given by (278). Hence this amount of entropy is taken from the field of radiation on the side of the rays arriving within $d\Omega$. In compensation a pencil starts from the system on the other side in the same direction (θ,ϕ) within $d\Omega$ having the components K'' and K''' with the azimuth of vibration $\frac{\pi}{2}$ and 0 respectively, but its entropy radiation is not represented by $\mathsf{L}(\mathsf{K}'')+\mathsf{L}(\mathsf{K}''')$, since K'' and K''' are not non-coherent, but by

$$\mathsf{L}(\mathsf{K}_o)+\mathsf{L}(\mathsf{K}_o') \tag{346}$$

where K_o and K_o' represent the principal intensities of the pencil.

For the calculation of K_o and K_o' we make use of the fact that, according to (330) and (335), the radiation K'' and K''', of which the component K''' vibrates in the azimuth 0, consists of the following three components, non-coherent with one another:

$$\mathsf{K}_1=\mathsf{K}\sin^2\psi+\mathsf{K}\cos^2\psi\,(1-\beta\sin^2\theta)=\mathsf{K}(1-\beta\sin^2\theta\cos^2\psi)$$

$$\text{with the azimuth of vibration } tg^2\,\psi_1=\frac{\mathrm{tg}^2\,\psi}{1-\beta\sin^2\theta},$$

$$\mathsf{K}_2=\mathsf{K}'\cos^2\psi+\mathsf{K}'\sin^2\psi(1-\beta\sin^2\theta)=\mathsf{K}'(1-\beta\sin^2\theta\sin^2\psi)$$

with the azimuth of vibration $\operatorname{tg}^2\psi_2=\dfrac{\cot^2\psi}{1-\beta\sin^2\theta}$,

and,

$$\mathsf{K}_3=\beta\sin^2\theta\,\mathsf{K}_e$$

with the azimuth of vibration $\operatorname{tg}\psi_3=0$.

According to (147) these values give the principal intensities K_o and K_o' required and hence the entropy radiation (346). Thereby the amount of entropy

$$q\Delta\nu[\mathsf{L}(\mathsf{K}_o)+\mathsf{L}(\mathsf{K}_o')]d\Omega\,dt \tag{347}$$

is added to the field of radiation in the time dt. All told, the entropy change of the field of radiation in the time dt, as given by subtraction of the expression (345) from (347) and integration with respect to $d\Omega$, is

$$dt\Delta\nu\int qd\Omega[\mathsf{L}(\mathsf{K}_o)+\mathsf{L}(\mathsf{K}_o')-\mathsf{L}(\mathsf{K})-\mathsf{L}(\mathsf{K}')]. \tag{348}$$

Let us now calculate the entropy change of the system of oscillators which has taken place in the same time dt. According to (173) the entropy at the time t is

$$S=-kN\sum_1^\infty w_n\log w_n.$$

Hence the entropy change in the time dt is

$$dS=-kN\sum_1^\infty\log w_n\,dw_n,$$

and, by taking account of (343), we have:

$$dS=\frac{Nk\mathsf{I}dt}{4h\nu L}\sum_1^\infty\Big(w_n-(1-\eta)\,w_{n-1}\Big)\log w_n. \tag{349}$$

186. The principle of increase of entropy requires that the sum of the entropy change (348) of the field of radiation and the entropy change (349) of the system of oscillators be always positive, or zero in the limiting case. That this condition is in fact satisfied we shall prove only for the special case when all rays falling on the oscillators are unpolarized, *i.e.*, when $\mathsf{K}'=\mathsf{K}$.

In this case we have from (147) and Sec. 185.

$$\left.\begin{matrix}\mathsf{K}_o \\ \mathsf{K}_o'\end{matrix}\right\} = \tfrac{1}{2}\left\{ 2\mathsf{K}+\beta \sin^2\theta(\mathsf{K}_e-\mathsf{K}) \pm \beta \sin^2\theta(\mathsf{K}_e-\mathsf{K}) \right\},$$

and hence

$$\mathsf{K}_o = \mathsf{K}+\beta\sin^2\theta(\mathsf{K}_e-\mathsf{K}),\quad \mathsf{K}_o' = \mathsf{K}.$$

The entropy change (348) of the field of radiation becomes

$$dt\triangle\nu\int q\,d\Omega\{\mathsf{L}(\mathsf{K}_o)-\mathsf{L}(\mathsf{K})\}$$

$$= dt\triangle\nu\int q\,d\Omega\ \beta\sin^2\theta(\mathsf{K}_e-\mathsf{K})\frac{d\mathsf{L}(\mathsf{K})}{d\mathsf{K}}$$

or, by (338) and (278),

$$= \frac{\pi kN\,dt}{hc\nu L}\int d\Omega\ \sin^2\theta(\mathsf{K}_e-\mathsf{K})\log\left(1+\frac{h\nu^3}{c^2\mathsf{K}}\right).$$

On adding to this the entropy change (349) of the system of oscillators and taking account of (320), the total increase in entropy in the time dt is found to be equal to the expression

$$\frac{\pi kN\,dt}{ch\nu L}\int d\Omega\ \sin^2\theta\left\{\mathsf{K}\sum_1^\infty(w_n-\zeta w_{n-1})\log w_n+(\mathsf{K}_e-\mathsf{K})\log\left(1+\frac{h\nu^3}{c^2\mathsf{K}}\right)\right\}$$

where

$$\zeta = 1-\eta. \tag{350}$$

We now must prove that the expression

$$F = \int d\Omega\ \sin^2\theta\left\{\mathsf{K}\sum_1^\infty(w_n-\zeta w_{n-1})\log w_n + (\mathsf{K}_e-\mathsf{K})\log\left(1+\frac{h\nu^3}{c^2\mathsf{K}}\right)\right\} \tag{351}$$

is always positive and for that purpose we set down once more the meaning of the quantities involved. K is an arbitrary positive function of the polar angles θ and ϕ. The positive proper fraction ζ is according to (350), (265), and (320) given by

$$\frac{\zeta}{1-\zeta} = \frac{3c^2}{8\pi h\nu^3}\int\mathsf{K}\sin^2\theta\,d\Omega. \tag{352}$$

The quantities w_1, w_2, w_3, ... are any positive proper fractions whatever which, according to (167), satisfy the condition

$$\sum_{1}^{\infty} w_n = 1 \tag{353}$$

while, according to (342),

$$w_o = \frac{1-\zeta}{\zeta}. \tag{354}$$

Finally we have from (336)

$$\mathsf{K}_e = \frac{h\nu^3\zeta}{c^2} \sum_{1}^{\infty} n w_n. \tag{355}$$

187. To give the proof required we shall show that the least value which the function F can assume is positive or zero. For this purpose we consider first that positive function, K, of θ and ϕ, which, with fixed values of ζ, w_1, w_2, w_3, ... and K_e, will make F a minimum. The necessary condition for this is $\delta F = 0$, where according to (352)

$$\int \delta \mathsf{K} \sin^2 \theta \, d\,\Omega = 0.$$

This gives, by considering that the quantities w and ζ do not depend on θ and ϕ, as a necessary condition for the minimum,

$$\delta F = 0 = \int d\Omega \sin^2\theta \, \delta \mathsf{K} \left\{ -\log\left(1+\frac{h\nu^3}{c^2\mathsf{K}}\right) - \frac{\mathsf{K}_e - \mathsf{K}}{\frac{c^2\mathsf{K}}{h\nu^3}+1} : \frac{1}{\mathsf{K}} \right\}$$

and it follows, therefore, that the quantity in brackets, and hence also K itself is independent of θ and ϕ. That in this case F really has a minimum value is readily seen by forming the second variation

$$\delta^2 F = \int d\Omega \sin^2\theta \, \delta \mathsf{K} \delta \left\{ -\log\left(1+\frac{h\nu^3}{c^2\mathsf{K}}\right) - \frac{\mathsf{K}_e - \mathsf{K}}{\frac{c^2\mathsf{K}}{h\nu^3}+1} \cdot \frac{1}{\mathsf{K}} \right\}$$

which may by direct computation be seen to be positive under all circumstances.

In order to form the minimum value of F we calculate the value of K, which, from (352), is independent of θ and ϕ. Then it follows, by taking account of (319a), that

$$\mathsf{K} = \frac{h\nu^3}{c^2} \; \frac{\zeta}{1-\zeta}$$

and, by also substituting K_e from (355),

$$F = \frac{8\pi h\nu^3}{3c^2} \frac{\zeta}{1-\zeta} \sum_1^\infty (w_n - \zeta w_{n-1}) \log w_n - [(1-\zeta)n-1]\, w_n \log \zeta.$$

188. It now remains to prove that the sum

$$\Phi = \sum_1^\infty (w_n - \zeta w_{n-1}) \log w_n - [(1-\zeta)n-1]\, w_n \log \zeta, \tag{356}$$

where the quantities w_n are subject only to the restrictions that (353) and (354) can never become negative. For this purpose we determine that system of values of the w's which, with a fixed value of ζ, makes the sum Φ a minimum. In this case $\delta\Phi = 0$, or

$$\sum_1^\infty (\delta w_n - \zeta\ \delta w_{n-1}) \log w_n + (w_n - \zeta w_{n-1}) \frac{\delta w_n}{w_n} \tag{357}$$

$$-[(1-\zeta)n-1]\ \delta w_n \log \zeta = 0,$$

where, according to (353) and (354),

$$\sum_1^\infty \delta w_n = 0 \text{ and } \delta w_o = 0. \tag{358}$$

If we suppose all the separate terms of the sum to be written out, the equation may be put into the following form:

$$\sum_1^\infty \delta w_n \{\log w_n - \zeta \log w_{n+1} + \frac{w_n - \zeta w_{n-1}}{w_n} - [(1-\zeta)n-1] \log \zeta\} = 0. \tag{359}$$

From this, by taking account of (358), we get as the condition for a minimum, that

$$\log w_n - \zeta \log w_{n+1} + \frac{w_n - \zeta w_{n-1}}{w_n} - [(1-\zeta)\, n-1] \log \zeta \tag{360}$$

must be independent of n.

The solution of this functional equation is

$$w_n = (1-\zeta)\zeta^{n-1} \tag{361}$$

for it satisfies (360) as well as (353) and (354). With this value (356) becomes

$$\Phi = 0. \tag{362}$$

189. In order to show finally that the value (362) of Φ is really the minimum value, we form from (357) the second variation

$$\delta^2\Phi = \sum_1^\infty (\delta w_n - \zeta\delta w_{n-1})\frac{\delta w_n}{w_n} - \frac{\zeta\delta w_{n-1}}{w_n}\delta w_n + \frac{\zeta w_{n-1}}{w_n^2}\delta w_n^2,$$

where all terms containing the second variation $\delta^2 w_n$ have been omitted since their coefficients are, by (360), independent of n and since

$$\sum_1^\infty \delta^2 w_n = 0.$$

This gives, taking account of (361),

$$\delta^2\Phi = \sum_1^\infty \frac{2\delta w_n^2}{(1-\zeta)\zeta^{n-1}} - \frac{2\zeta\delta w_{n-1}\delta w_n}{(1-\zeta)\zeta^{n-1}}$$

or

$$\delta^2\Phi = \frac{2\zeta}{1-\zeta}\sum_1^\infty \frac{\delta w_n^2}{\zeta^n} - \frac{\delta w_{n-1}\delta w_n}{\zeta^{n-1}}.$$

That the sum which occurs here, namely,

$$\frac{\delta w_1^2}{\zeta} - \frac{\delta w_1\delta w_2}{\zeta} + \frac{\delta w_2^2}{\zeta^2} - \frac{\delta w_2\delta w_3}{\zeta^2} + \frac{\delta w_3^2}{\zeta^3} - \frac{\delta w_3\delta w_4}{\zeta^3} + \dots\dots \quad (363)$$

is essentially positive may be seen by resolving it into a sum of squares. For this purpose we write it in the form

$$\sum_1^\infty \frac{1-\alpha_n}{\zeta^n}\delta w_n^2 - \frac{\delta w_n \delta w_{n+1}}{\zeta^n} + \frac{\alpha_{n+1}}{\zeta^{n+1}}\delta w_{n+1}^2,$$

which is identical with (363) provided $\alpha_1 = 0$. Now the α's may be so determined that every term of the last sum is a perfect square, *i.e.*, that

$$4\cdot\frac{1-\alpha_n}{\zeta^n}\cdot\frac{\alpha_{n+1}}{\zeta^{n+1}} = \left(\frac{1}{\zeta^n}\right)^2$$

or

$$\alpha_{n+1} = \frac{\zeta}{4(1-\alpha_n)}. \quad (364)$$

By means of this formula the α's may be readily calculated. The first values are:

$$\alpha_1 = 0, \quad \alpha_2 = \frac{\zeta}{4}, \quad \alpha_3 = \frac{\zeta}{4-\zeta}, \quad \dots\dots$$

Continuing the procedure α_n remains always positive and less than $\alpha' = \frac{1}{2}\left(1 - \sqrt{1-\zeta}\right)$. To prove the correctness of this statement we show that, if it holds for α_n, it holds also for α_{n+1}. We assume, therefore, that α_n is positive and $< \alpha'$. Then from

(364) α_{n+1} is positive and $< \frac{\zeta}{4(1-\alpha')}$. But $\frac{\zeta}{4(1-\alpha')} = \alpha'$.

Hence $\alpha_{n+1} < \alpha'$. Now, since the assumption made does actually hold for $n = 1$, it holds in general. The sum (363) is thus essentially positive and hence the value (362) of Φ really is a minimum, so that the increase of entropy is proven generally.

The limiting case (361), in which the increase of entropy vanishes, corresponds, of course, to the case of thermodynamic equilibrium between radiation and oscillators, as may also be seen directly by comparison of (361) with (271), (265), and (360).

190. Conclusion.—The theory of irreversible radiation processes here developed explains how, with an arbitrarily assumed initial state, a stationary state is, in the course of time, established in a cavity through which radiation passes and which contains oscillators of all kinds of natural vibrations, by the intensities and polarizations of all rays equalizing one another as regards magnitude and direction. But the theory is still incomplete in an important respect. For it deals only with the mutual actions of rays and vibrations of oscillators of the same period. For a definite frequency the increase of entropy in every time element until the maximum value is attained, as demanded by the second principle of thermodynamics, has been proven directly. But, for all frequencies taken together, the maximum thus attained does not yet represent the absolute maximum of the entropy of the system and the corresponding state of radiation does not, in general, represent the absolutely stable equilibrium (compare Sec. 27). For the theory gives no information as to the way in which the intensities of radiation corresponding to different frequencies equalize one another, that is to say, how from any arbitrary initial spectral distribution of energy the normal energy distribution corresponding to black radiation is, in the course of time, developed. For the oscillators on which the consideration was based influence only the intensities of rays which correspond to their natural vibration, but they are not capable of changing their frequencies, so long as they exert or suffer no other action than emitting or absorbing radiant energy.[1]

To get an insight into those processes by which the exchange of energy between rays of different frequencies takes place in nature would require also an investigation of the influence which the motion of the oscillators and of the electrons flying back and forth between them exerts on the radiation phenomena. For, if the oscillators and electrons are in motion, there will be impacts between them, and, at every impact, actions must come into play which influence the energy of vibration of the oscillators in a quite different and much more radical way than the simple emission and absorption of radiant energy. It is true that the final result of all such impact actions may be anticipated by the aid of the probability considerations discussed in the third section, but to show in detail how and in what time intervals this result is arrived at will be the problem of a future theory. It is certain that, from such a theory, further information may be expected as to the nature of the oscillators which really exist in nature, for the very reason that it must give a closer explanation of the physical significance of the universal elementary quantity of action, a significance which is certainly not second in importance to that of the elementary quantity of electricity.

[1] Compare *P. Ehrenfest*, Wien. Ber. **114** [2a], p. 1301, 1905. Ann. d. Phys. **36**, p. 91, 1911. *H. A. Lorentz*, Phys. Zeitschr. **11**, p. 1244, 1910. *H. Poincaré*, Journ. de Phys. (5) **2**, p. 5, p. 347, 1912.

AUTHOR'S BIBLIOGRAPHY

List of the papers published by the author on heat radiation and the hypothesis of quanta, with references to the sections of this book where the same subject is treated.

Absorption und Emission elektrischer Wellen durch Resonanz. Sitzungsber. d. k. preuss. Akad. d. Wissensch. vom 21. März 1895, p. 289–301. WIED. Ann. **57**, p. 1–14, 1896.

Ueber elektrische Schwingungen, welche durch Resonanz erregt und durch Strahlung gedämpft werden. Sitzungsber. d. k. preuss. Akad. d. Wissensch. vom 20. Februar 1896, p. 151–170. WIED. Ann. **60**, p. 577–599, 1897.

Ueber irreversible Strahlungsvorgänge. (Erste Mitteilung.) Sitzungsber. d. k. preuss. Akad. d. Wissensch. vom 4. Februar 1897, p. 57–68.

Ueber irreversible Strahlungsvorgänge. (Zweite Mitteilung.) Sitzungsber. d. k. preuss. Akad. d. Wissensch. vom 8. Juli 1897, p. 715–717.

Ueber irreversible Strahlungsvorgänge. (Dritte Mittelung.) Sitzungsber. d. k. preuss. Akad. d. Wissensch. vom 16. Dezember 1897, p. 1122–1145.

Ueber irreversible Strahlungsvorgänge. (Vierte Mitteilung.) Sitzungsber. d. k. preuss. Akad. d. Wissensch. vom 7. Juli 1898, p. 449–476.

Ueber irreversible Strahlungsvorgänge. (Fünfte Mitteilung.) Sitzungsber. d. k. preuss. Akad. d. Wissensch. vom 18. Mai 1899, p. 440–480. (§§ 144 bis 190. § 164.)

Ueber irreversible Strahlungsvorgänge. Ann. d. Phys. **1**, p. 69–122, 1900. (§§ 144–190. § 164.)

Entropie und Temperatur strahlender Wärme. Ann. d. Phys. **1**, p. 719 bis 737, 1900. (§ 101. § 166.)

Ueber eine Verbesserung der WIENschen Spektralgleichung. Verhandlungen der Deutschen Physikalischen Gesellschaft **2**, p. 202–204, 1900. (§ 156.)

Ein vermeintlicher Widerspruch des magneto-optischen FARADAY-Effektes mit der Thermodynamik. Verhandlungen der Deutschen Physikalischen Gesellschaft **2**, p. 206–210, 1900.

Kritik zweier Sätze des Herrn W. WIEN. Ann. d. Phys. **3**, p. 764–766, 1900.

Zur Theorie des Gesetzes der Energieverteilung im Normalspektrum. Verhandlungen der Deutschen Physikalischen Gesellschaft **2**, p. 237–245, 1900. (§§ 141–143. § 156 f. § 163.)

Ueber das Gesetz der Energieverteilung im Normalspektrum. Ann. d. Phys. **4**, p. 553–563, 1901. (§§ 141–143. §§ 156–162.)

Ueber die Elementarquanta der Materie und der Elektrizität. Ann. d. Phys. **4**, p. 564–566, 1901. (§ 163.)

Ueber irreversible Strahlungsvorgänge (Nachtrag). Sitzungsber. d. k. preuss. Akad. d. Wissensch. vom 9. Mai 1901, p. 544–555. Ann. d. Phys. **6**, p. 818–831, 1901. (§§ 185–189.)

Vereinfachte Ableitung der Schwingungsgesetze eines linearen Resonators im stationär durchstrahlten Felde. Physikalische Zeitschrift **2**, p. 530 bis p. 534, 1901.

Ueber die Natur des weissen Lichtes. Ann. d. Phys. **7**, p. 390–400, 1902. (§§ 107–112. §§ 170–174.)

Ueber die von einem elliptisch schwingenden Ion emittierte und absorbierte Energie. Archives Néerlandaises, Jubelband für H. A. LORENTZ, 1900, p. 164–174. Ann. d. Phys. **9,** p. 619–628, 1902.

Ueber die Verteilung der Energie zwischen Aether und Materie. Archives Néerlandaises, Jubelband für J. BOSSCHA, 1901, p. 55–66. Ann. d. Phys. **9,** p. 629–641, 1902. (§§ 121–132.)

Bemerkung über die Konstante des WIENschen Verschiebungsgesetzes. Verhandlungen der Deutschen Physikalischen Gesellschaft **8,** p. 695–696, 1906. (§ 161.)

Zur Theorie der Wärmestrahlung. Ann. d. Phys. **31,** p. 758–768, 1910. Eine neue Strahlungshypothese. Verhandlungen der Deutschen Physikalischen Gesellschaft **13,** p. 138–148, 1911. (§ 147.)

Zur Hypothese der Quantenemission. Sitzungsber. d. k. preuss. Akad. d. Wissensch. vom 13. Juli 1911, p. 723–731. (§§ 150–152.)

Ueber neuere thermodynamische Theorien (NERNSTsches Wärmetheorem und Quantenhypothese). Ber. d. Deutschen Chemischen Gesellschaft **45,** p. 5–23, 1912. Physikalische Zeitschrift **13,** p. 165–175, 1912. Akademische Verlagsgesellschaft m. b. H., Leipzig 1912. (§§ 120–125.)

Ueber die Begründung des Gesetzes der schwarzen Strahlung. Ann. d. Phys. **37,** p. 642–656, 1912. (§§ 145–156.)

APPENDIX I

On Deductions from Stirling's Formula.

The formula is

(a) $$\lim_{n=\infty} \frac{n!}{n^n e^{-n}\sqrt{2\pi n}} = 1,$$

or, to an approximation quite sufficient for all practical purposes, provided that n is larger than 7

(b) $$n! = \left(\frac{n}{e}\right)^n \sqrt{2\pi n}.$$

For a proof of this relation and a discussion of its limits of accuracy a treatise on probability must be consulted.

On substitution in (170) this gives

$$W = \frac{\left(\frac{N}{e}\right)^N}{\left(\frac{N_1}{e}\right)^{N_1} \cdot \left(\frac{N_2}{e}\right)^{N_2} \ldots} \cdot \frac{\sqrt{2\pi N}}{\sqrt{2\pi N_1}\ \sqrt{2\pi N_2} \ldots}$$

On account of (165) this reduces at once to

$$\frac{N^N}{N_1^{N_1}\ N_2^{N_2} \ldots} \cdot \frac{\sqrt{2\pi N}}{\sqrt{2\pi N_1} \cdot \sqrt{2\pi N_2} \ldots}$$

Passing now to the logarithmic expression we get

$$S = k \log W = k[N \log N - N_1 \log N_1 - N_2 \log N_2 - \ldots\ldots + \log \sqrt{2\pi N} - \log \sqrt{2\pi N_1} - \log \sqrt{2\pi N_2} - \ldots],$$

or,

$$S = k \log W = k[(N \log N - \log \sqrt{2\pi N}) + (N_1 \log N_1 - \log \sqrt{2\pi N_1}) + (N_2 \log N_2 - \log \sqrt{2\pi N_2}) + \ldots].$$

Now, for a large value of N_i, the term $N_i \log N_i$ is very much larger than $\log \sqrt{2\pi N_i}$, as is seen by writing the latter in the form $\frac{1}{2} \log 2\pi + \frac{1}{2} \log N_i$. Hence the last expression will, with a fair approximation, reduce to

$$S = k \log W = k[N \log N - N_1 \log N_1 - N_2 \log N_2 - \ldots\ldots].$$

Introducing now the values of the densities of distribution w by means of the relation

$$N_i = w_i N$$

we obtain

$$S = k \log W = kN[\log N - w_1 \log N_1 - w_2 \log N_2 - \ . \ . \ . \ ],$$

or, since

$$w_1 + w_2 + w_3 + \ . \ . \ . \ = 1,$$

and hence

$$(w_1 + w_2 + w_3 + \ . \ . \ . \ ) \log N = \log N,$$

and

$$\log N - \log N_1 = \log \frac{N}{N_1} = \log \frac{1}{w_1} = -\log w_1,$$

we obtain by substitution, after one or two simple transformations

$$S = k \log W = -kN \Sigma \, w_1 \log w_1,$$

a relation which is identical with (173).

The statements of Sec. 143 may be proven in a similar manner. From (232) we get at once

$$S = k \log W_m = k \log \frac{(N+P-1)!}{(N-1)! \, P!}$$

Now $\qquad \log (N-1)! = \log N! - \log N,$

and, for large values of N, $\log N$ is negligible compared with $\log N!$ Applying the same reasoning to the numerator we may without appreciable error write

$$S = k \log W_m = k \log \frac{(N+P)!}{N! \, P!}$$

Substituting now for $(N+P)!$, $N!$, and $P!$ their values from (b) and omitting, as was previously shown to be approximately correct, the terms arising from the $\sqrt{2\pi(N+P)}$ *etc.*, we get, since the terms containing e cancel out

$$S = k[(N+P) \log (N+P) - N \log N - P \log P]$$

$$= k\left[(N+P) \log \frac{N+P}{N} + P \log N - P \log P\right]$$

$$= kN\left[\left(\frac{P}{N}+1\right) \log \left(\frac{P}{N}+1\right) - \frac{P}{N} \log \frac{P}{N}\right].$$

This is the relation of Sec. 143.

APPENDIX II

REFERENCES

Among general papers treating of the application of the theory of quanta to different parts of physics are:

1. *A. Sommerfeld*, Das Planck'sche Wirkungsquantum und seine allgemeine Bedeutung für die Molekularphysik, Phys. Zeitschr., **12,** p. 1057. Report to the Versammlung Deutscher Naturforscher und Aerzte. Deals especially with applications to the theory of specific heats and to the photoelectric effect. Numerous references are quoted.

2. Meeting of the British Association, Sept., 1913. See Nature, **92,** p. 305, Nov. 6, 1913, and Phys. Zeitschr., **14,** p. 1297. Among the principal speakers were *J. H. Jeans* and *H. A. Lorentz.*

(Also American Phys. Soc., Chicago Meeting, 1913.[1])

3. *R. A. Millikan,* Atomic Theories of Radiation, Science, **37,** p. 119, Jan. 24, 1913. A non-mathematical discussion.

4. *W. Wien,* Neuere Probleme der Theoretischen Physik, 1913. (*Wien's* Columbia Lectures, in German.) This is perhaps the most complete review of the entire theory of quanta.

H. A. Lorentz, Alte und Neue Probleme der Physik, Phys. Zeitschr., **11,** p. 1234. Address to the Versammlung Deutscher Naturforscher und Aerzte, Königsberg, 1910, contains also some discussion of the theory of quanta.

Among the papers on radiation are:

E. Bauer, Sur la théorie du rayonnement, Comptes Rendus, **153,** p. 1466. Adheres to the quantum theory in the original form, namely, that emission and absorption both take place in a discontinuous manner.

E. Buckingham, Calculation of c_2 in Planck's equation, Bull. Bur. Stand. **7,** p. 393.

E. Buckingham, On *Wien's* Displacement Law, Bull. Bur. Stand. **8,** p. 543. Contains a very simple and clear proof of the displacement law.

[1] Not yet published (Jan. 26, 1914. Tr.)

P. Ehrenfest, Strahlungshypothesen, Ann. d. Phys., **36,** p. 91.

A. Joffé, Theorie der Strahlung, Ann. d. Phys., **36,** p. 534.

Discussions of the method of derivation of the radiation formula are given in many papers on the subject. In addition to those quoted elsewhere may be mentioned:

C. Benedicks, Ueber die Herleitung von *Planck's* Energieverteilungsgesetz, Ann. d. Phys., **42,** p. 133. Derives *Planck's* law without the help of the quantum theory. The law of equipartition of energy is avoided by the assumption that solids are not always monatomic, but that, with decreasing temperature, the atoms form atomic complexes, thus changing the number of degrees of freedom. The equipartition principle applies only to the free atoms.

P. Debye, Planck's Strahlungsformel, Ann. d. Phys., **33,** p. 1427. This method is fully discussed by *Wien* (see 4, above). It somewhat resembles *Jeans'* method (Sec. 169) since it avoids all reference to resonators of any particular kind and merely establishes the most probable energy distribution. It differs, however, from *Jeans'* method by the assumption of discrete energy quanta $h\nu$. The physical nature of these units is not discussed at all and it is also left undecided whether it is a property of matter or of the ether or perhaps a property of the energy exchange between matter and the ether that causes their existence. (Compare also some remarks of *Lorentz* in 2.)

P. Frank, Zur Ableitung der Planckschen Strahlungsformel, Phys. Zeitschr., **13,** p. 506.

L. Natanson, Statistische Theorie der Strahlung, Phys. Zeitschr., **12,** p. 659.

W. Nernst, Zur Theorie der Specifischen Wärme und über die Anwendung, der Lehre von den Energiequanten auf Physikalisch-chemische Fragen überhaupt, Zeitschr. f. Elektochemie, **17,** p. 265.

The experimental facts on which the recent theories of specific heat (quantum theories) rely, were discovered by *W. Nernst* and his fellow workers. The results are published in a large number of papers that have appeared in different periodicals. See, *e.g., W. Nernst,* Der Energieinhalt fester Substanzen, Ann. d. Phys., **36,** p. 395, where also numerous other papers are quoted. (See also references given in 1.) These experimental facts give very strong support to the heat theorem of *Nernst* (Sec. 120), according to which the entropy approaches a definite limit (perhaps the value zero, see *Planck's* Thermodynamics, 3. ed., sec. 282, *et seq.*) at the absolute zero of temperature, and which is consistent with the quantum theory. This work is in close connection with the recent attempts to develop an equation of state applicable to the solid state of matter. In addition to the papers by *Nernst* and his school there may be mentioned:

K. Eisenmann, Canonische Zustandsgleichung einatomiger fester Körper und die Quantentheorie, Verhandlungen der Deutschen Physikalischen Gesellschaft, **14,** p. 769.

W. H. Keesom, Entropy and the Equation of State, Konink. Akad. Wetensch. Amsterdam Proc., **15,** p. 240.

L. Natanson, Energy Content of Bodies, Acad. Science Cracovie Bull. Ser. A, p. 95. In *Einstein's* theory of specific heats (Sec. 140) the atoms of actual bodies in nature are apparently identified with the ideal resonators of *Planck*. In this paper it is pointed out that this is implying too special features for the atoms of real bodies, and also, that such far-reaching specializations do not seem necessary for deriving the laws of specific heat from the quantum theory.

L. S. Ornstein, Statistical Theory of the Solid State, Konink. Akad. Wetensch. Amsterdam Proc., **14,** p. 983.

S. Ratnowsky, Die Zustandsgleichung einatomiger fester Körper und die Quantentheorie, Ann. d. Phys., **38,** p. 637.

Among papers on the law of equipartition of energy (Sec. 169) are:

J. H. Jeans, *Planck's* Radiation Theory and *Non-Newtonian* Mechanics, Phil. Mag., **20,** p. 943.

S. B. McLaren, Partition of Energy between Matter and Radiation, Phil. Mag., **21,** p. 15.

S. B. McLaren, Complete Radiation, Phil. Mag. **23,** p. 513. This paper and the one of Jeans deal with the fact that from Newtonian Mechanics (Hamilton's Principle) the equipartition principle necessarily follows, and that hence either Planck's law or the fundamental principles of mechanics need a modification.

For the law of equipartition compare also the discussion at the meeting of the British Association (see 2).

In many of the papers cited so far deductions from the quantum theory are compared with experimental facts. This is also done by:

F. Haber, Absorptionsspectra fester Körper und die Quantentheorie, Verhandlungen der Deutschen Physikalischen Gesellschaft, **13,** p. 1117.

J. Franck und G. Hertz, Quantumhypothese und Ionisation, Ibid., **13,** p. 967.

Attempts of giving a concrete physical idea of Planck's constant h are made by:

A. Schidlof, Zur Aufklärung der universellen electrodynamischen Bedeutung der Planckschen Strahlungsconstanten h, Ann. d. Phys., **35,** p. 96.

D. A. Goldhammer, Ueber die Lichtquantenhypothese, Phys. Zeitschr., **13,** p. 535.

J. J. Thomson, On the Structure of the Atom, Phil. Mag., **26,** p. 792.

N. Bohr, On the Constitution of the Atom, Phil. Mag., **26,** p. 1.

S. B. McLaren, The Magneton and Planck's Universal Constant, Phil. Mag., **26,** p. 800.

The line of reasoning may be briefly stated thus: Find some quantity of the same dimension as h, and then construct a model of an atom where this property plays an important part and can be made, by a simple hypothesis, to vary by finite amounts instead of continuously. The simplest of these is *Bohr's,* where h is interpreted as angular momentum.

The logical reason for the quantum theory is found in the fact that the *Rayleigh-Jeans* radiation formula does not agree with experiment. Formerly *Jeans* attempted to reconcile theory and experiment by the assumption that the equilibrium of radiation and a black body observed and agreeing with *Planck's* law rather than his own, was only apparent, and that the true state of equilibrium which really corresponds to his law and the equipartition of energy among all variables, is so slowly reached that it is never actually observed. This standpoint, which was strongly objected to by authorities on the experimental side of the question (see, *e.g.*, *E. Pringsheim* in 2), he has recently abandoned. *H. Poincaré,* in a profound mathematical investigation (*H. Poincaré,* Sur. la Théorie des Quanta,

Journal de Physique (5), **2,** p. 1, 1912) reached the conclusion that whatever the law of radiation may be, it must always, if the total radiation is assumed as finite, lead to a function presenting similar discontinuites as the one obtained from the hypothesis of quanta.

While most authorities have accepted the quantum theory for good (see *J. H. Jeans* and *H. A. Lorentz* in 2), a few still entertain doubts as to the general validity of Poincaré's conclusion (see above *C. Benedicks* and *R. A Millikan* 3). Others still reject the quantum theory on account of the fact that the experimental evidence in favor of *Planck's* law is not absolutely conclusive (see *R. A. Millikan* 3); among these is *A. E. H. Love* (2), who suggests that *Korn's* (*A. Korn*, Neue Mechanische Vorstellungen uber die Schwarze Strahlung und eine sich aus denselben ergebende Modification des Planckschen Verteilungsgesetzes, Phys. Zeitschr., **14,** p. 632) radiation formula fits the facts as well as that of Planck.

H. A. Callendar, Note on Radiation and Specific Heat, Phil. Mag., **26,** p. 787, has also suggested a radiation formula that fits the data well. Both Korn's and Callendar's formulæ conform to *Wien's* displacement law and degenerate for large values of λT into the Rayleigh-Jeans, and for small values of λT into Wien's radiation law. Whether Planck's law or one of these is the correct law, and whether, if either of the others should prove to be right, it would eliminate the necessity of the adoption of the quantum theory, are questions as yet undecided. Both Korn and Callendar have promised in their papers to follow them by further ones.

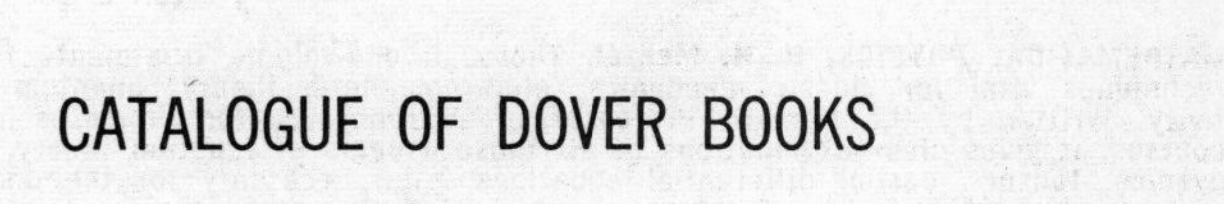

CATALOGUE OF DOVER BOOKS

PHYSICS

General physics

FOUNDATIONS OF PHYSICS, R. B. Lindsay & H. Margenau. Excellent bridge between semi-popular works & technical treatises. A discussion of methods of physical description, construction of theory; valuable for physicist with elementary calculus who is interested in ideas that give meaning to data, tools of modern physics. Contents include symbolism, mathematical equations; space & time foundations of mechanics; probability; physics & continua; electron theory; special & general relativity; quantum mechanics; causality. "Thorough and yet not overdetailed. Unreservedly recommended," NATURE (London). Unabridged, corrected edition. List of recommended readings. 35 illustrations. xi + 537pp. 5⅜ x 8.
S377 Paperbound **$2.75**

FUNDAMENTAL FORMULAS OF PHYSICS, ed. by D. H. Menzel. Highly useful, fully inexpensive reference and study text, ranging from simple to highly sophisticated operations. Mathematics integrated into text—each chapter stands as short textbook of field represented. Vol. 1: Statistics, Physical Constants, Special Theory of Relativity, Hydrodynamics, Aerodynamics, Boundary Value Problems in Math. Physics; Viscosity, Electromagnetic Theory, etc. Vol. 2: Sound, Acoustics, Geometrical Optics, Electron Optics, High-Energy Phenomena, Magnetism, Biophysics, much more. Index. Total of 800pp. 5⅜ x 8. Vol. 1 S595 Paperbound **$2.00**
Vol. 2 S596 Paperbound **$2.00**

MATHEMATICAL PHYSICS, D. H. Menzel. Thorough one-volume treatment of the mathematical techniques vital for classic mechanics, electromagnetic theory, quantum theory, and relativity. Written by the Harvard Professor of Astrophysics for junior, senior, and graduate courses, it gives clear explanations of all those aspects of function theory, vectors, matrices, dyadics, tensors, partial differential equations, etc., necessary for the understanding of the various physical theories. Electron theory, relativity, and other topics seldom presented appear here in considerable detail. Scores of definitions, conversion factors, dimensional constants, etc. "More detailed than normal for an advanced text . . . excellent set of sections on Dyadics, Matrices, and Tensors," JOURNAL OF THE FRANKLIN INSTITUTE. Index. 193 problems, with answers. x + 412pp. 5⅜ x 8. S56 Paperbound **$2.00**

THE SCIENTIFIC PAPERS OF J. WILLARD GIBBS. All the published papers of America's outstanding theoretical scientist (except for "Statistical Mechanics" and "Vector Analysis"). Vol I (thermodynamics) contains one of the most brilliant of all 19th-century scientific papers—the 300-page "On the Equilibrium of Heterogeneous Substances," which founded the science of physical chemistry, and clearly stated a number of highly important natural laws for the first time; 8 other papers complete the first volume. Vol II includes 2 papers on dynamics, 8 on vector analysis and multiple algebra, 5 on the electromagnetic theory of light, and 6 miscellaneous papers. Biographical sketch by H. A. Bumstead. Total of xxxvi + 718pp. 5⅝ x 8⅜.
S721 Vol I Paperbound **$2.00**
S722 Vol II Paperbound **$2.00**
The set **$4.00**

BASIC THEORIES OF PHYSICS, Peter Gabriel Bergmann. Two-volume set which presents a critical examination of important topics in the major subdivisions of classical and modern physics. The first volume is concerned with classical mechanics and electrodynamics: mechanics of mass points, analytical mechanics, matter in bulk, electrostatics and magnetostatics, electromagnetic interaction, the field waves, special relativity, and waves. The second volume (Heat and Quanta) contains discussions of the kinetic hypothesis, physics and statistics, stationary ensembles, laws of thermodynamics, early quantum theories, atomic spectra, probability waves, quantization in wave mechanics, approximation methods, and abstract quantum theory. A valuable supplement to any thorough course or text.
Heat and Quanta: Index. 8 figures. x + 300pp. 5⅜ x 8½. S968 Paperbound **$1.75**
Mechanics and Electrodynamics: Index. 14 figures. vii + 280pp. 5⅜ x 8½.
S969 Paperbound **$1.75**

THEORETICAL PHYSICS, A. S. Kompaneyets. One of the very few thorough studies of the subject in this price range. Provides advanced students with a comprehensive theoretical background. Especially strong on recent experimentation and developments in quantum theory. Contents: Mechanics (Generalized Coordinates, Lagrange's Equation, Collision of Particles, etc.), Electrodynamics (Vector Analysis, Maxwell's equations, Transmission of Signals, Theory of Relativity, etc.), Quantum Mechanics (the Inadequacy of Classical Mechanics, the Wave Equation, Motion in a Central Field, Quantum Theory of Radiation, Quantum Theories of Dispersion and Scattering, etc.), and Statistical Physics (Equilibrium Distribution of Molecules in an Ideal Gas, Boltzmann statistics, Bose and Fermi Distribution, Thermodynamic Quantities, etc.). Revised to 1961. Translated by George Yankovsky, authorized by Kompaneyets. 137 exercises. 56 figures. 529pp. 5⅜ x 8½. S972 Paperbound **$2.50**

ANALYTICAL AND CANONICAL FORMALISM IN PHYSICS, André Mercier. A survey, in one volume, of the variational principles (the key principles—in mathematical form—from which the basic laws of any one branch of physics can be derived) of the several branches of physical theory, together with an examination of the relationships among them. Contents: the Lagrangian Formalism, Lagrangian Densities, Canonical Formalism, Canonical Form of Electrodynamics, Hamiltonian Densities, Transformations, and Canonical Form with Vanishing Jacobian Determinant. Numerous examples and exercises. For advanced students, teachers, etc. 6 figures. Index. viii + 222pp. 5⅜ x 8½. S1077 Paperbound **$1.75**

Acoustics, optics, electricity and magnetism, electromagnetics, magneto-hydrodynamics

THE THEORY OF SOUND, Lord Rayleigh. Most vibrating systems likely to be encountered in practice can be tackled successfully by the methods set forth by the great Nobel laureate, Lord Rayleigh. Complete coverage of experimental, mathematical aspects of sound theory. Partial contents: Harmonic motions, vibrating systems in general, lateral vibrations of bars, curved plates or shells, applications of Laplace's functions to acoustical problems, fluid friction, plane vortex-sheet, vibrations of solid bodies, etc. This is the first inexpensive edition of this great reference and study work. Bibliography. Historical introduction by R. B. Lindsay. Total of 1040pp. 97 figures. 5⅜ x 8.
S292, S293, Two volume set, paperbound, **$4.70**

THE DYNAMICAL THEORY OF SOUND, H. Lamb. Comprehensive mathematical treatment of the physical aspects of sound, covering the theory of vibrations, the general theory of sound, and the equations of motion of strings, bars, membranes, pipes, and resonators. Includes chapters on plane, spherical, and simple harmonic waves, and the Helmholtz Theory of Audition. Complete and self-contained development for student and specialist; all fundamental differential equations solved completely. Specific mathematical details for such important phenomena as harmonics, normal modes, forced vibrations of strings, theory of reed pipes, etc. Index. Bibliography. 86 diagrams. viii + 307pp. 5⅜ x 8. S655 Paperbound **$1.50**

WAVE PROPAGATION IN PERIODIC STRUCTURES, L. Brillouin. A general method and application to different problems: pure physics, such as scattering of X-rays of crystals, thermal vibration in crystal lattices, electronic motion in metals; and also problems of electrical engineering. Partial contents: elastic waves in 1-dimensional lattices of point masses. Propagation of waves along 1-dimensional lattices. Energy flow. 2 dimensional, 3 dimensional lattices. Mathieu's equation. Matrices and propagation of waves along an electric line. Continuous electric lines. 131 illustrations. Bibliography. Index. xii + 253pp. 5⅜ x 8.
S34 Paperbound **$1.85**

THEORY OF VIBRATIONS, N. W. McLachlan. Based on an exceptionally successful graduate course given at Brown University, this discusses linear systems having 1 degree of freedom, forced vibrations of simple linear systems, vibration of flexible strings, transverse vibrations of bars and tubes, transverse vibration of circular plate, sound waves of finite amplitude, etc. Index. 99 diagrams. 160pp. 5⅜ x 8. S190 Paperbound **$1.35**

LIGHT: PRINCIPLES AND EXPERIMENTS, George S. Monk. Covers theory, experimentation, and research. Intended for students with some background in general physics and elementary calculus. Three main divisions: 1) Eight chapters on geometrical optics—fundamental concepts (the ray and its optical length, Fermat's principle, etc.), laws of image formation, apertures in optical systems, photometry, optical instruments etc.; 2) 9 chapters on physical optics—interference, diffraction, polarization, spectra, the Rayleigh refractometer, the wave theory of light, etc.; 3) 23 instructive experiments based directly on the theoretical text. "Probably the best intermediate textbook on light in the English language. Certainly, it is the best book which includes both geometrical and physical optics," J. Rud Nielson, PHYSICS FORUM. Revised edition. 102 problems and answers. 12 appendices. 6 tables. Index. 270 illustrations. xi +489pp. 5⅜ x 8½. S341 Paperbound **$2.45**

PHOTOMETRY, John W. T. Walsh. The best treatment of both "bench" and "illumination" photometry in English by one of Britain's foremost experts in the field (President of the International Commission on Illumination). Limited to those matters, theoretical and practical, which affect the measurement of light flux, candlepower, illumination, etc., and excludes treatment of the use to which such measurements may be put after they have been made. Chapters on Radiation, The Eye and Vision, Photo-Electric Cells, The Principles of Photometry, The Measurement of Luminous Intensity, Colorimetry, Spectrophotometry, Stellar Photometry, The Photometric Laboratory, etc. Third revised (1958) edition. 281 illustrations. 10 appendices. xxiv + 544pp. 5½ x 9¼. S319 Clothbound **$10.00**

EXPERIMENTAL SPECTROSCOPY, R. A. Sawyer. Clear discussion of prism and grating spectrographs and the techniques of their use in research, with emphasis on those principles and techniques that are fundamental to practically all uses of spectroscopic equipment. Beginning with a brief history of spectroscopy, the author covers such topics as light sources, spectroscopic apparatus, prism spectroscopes and graphs, diffraction grating, the photographic process, determination of wave length, spectral intensity, infrared spectroscopy, spectrochemical analysis, etc. This revised edition contains new material on the production of replica gratings, solar spectroscopy from rockets, new standard of wave length, etc. Index. Bibliography. 111 illustrations. x + 358pp. 5⅜ x 8½. S1045 Paperbound **$2.00**

FUNDAMENTALS OF ELECTRICITY AND MAGNETISM, L. B. Loeb. For students of physics, chemistry, or engineering who want an introduction to electricity and magnetism on a higher level and in more detail than general elementary physics texts provide. Only elementary differential and integral calculus is assumed. Physical laws developed logically, from magnetism to electric currents, Ohm's law, electrolysis, and on to static electricity, induction, etc. Covers an unusual amount of material; one third of book on modern material: solution of wave equation, photoelectric and thermionic effects, etc. Complete statement of the various electrical systems of units and interrelations. 2 Indexes. 75 pages of problems with answers stated. Over 300 figures and diagrams. xix +669pp. 5⅜ x 8. S745 Paperbound **$2.75**

MATHEMATICAL ANALYSIS OF ELECTRICAL AND OPTICAL WAVE-MOTION, Harry Bateman. Written by one of this century's most distinguished mathematical physicists, this is a practical introduction to those developments of Maxwell's electromagnetic theory which are directly connected with the solution of the partial differential equation of wave motion. Methods of solving wave-equation, polar-cylindrical coordinates, diffraction, transformation of coordinates, homogeneous solutions, electromagnetic fields with moving singularities, etc. Index. 168pp. 5⅜ x 8. S14 Paperbound **$1.75**

PRINCIPLES OF PHYSICAL OPTICS, Ernst Mach. This classical examination of the propagation of light, color, polarization, etc. offers an historical and philosophical treatment that has never been surpassed for breadth and easy readability. Contents: Rectilinear propagation of light. Reflection, refraction. Early knowledge of vision. Dioptrics. Composition of light. Theory of color and dispersion. Periodicity. Theory of interference. Polarization. Mathematical representation of properties of light. Propagation of waves, etc. 279 illustrations, 10 portraits. Appendix. Indexes. 324pp. 5⅜ x 8. S178 Paperbound **$1.75**

THE THEORY OF OPTICS, Paul Drude. One of finest fundamental texts in physical optics, classic offers thorough coverage, complete mathematical treatment of basic ideas. Includes fullest treatment of application of thermodynamics to optics; sine law in formation of images, transparent crystals, magnetically active substances, velocity of light, apertures, effects depending upon them, polarization, optical instruments, etc. Introduction by A. A. Michelson. Index. 110 illus. 567pp. 5⅜ x 8. S532 Paperbound **$2.45**

ELECTRICAL THEORY ON THE GIORGI SYSTEM, P. Cornelius. A new clarification of the fundamental concepts of electricity and magnetism, advocating the convenient m.k.s. system of units that is steadily gaining followers in the sciences. Illustrating the use and effectiveness of his terminology with numerous applications to concrete technical problems, the author here expounds the famous Giorgi system of electrical physics. His lucid presentation and well-reasoned, cogent argument for the universal adoption of this system form one of the finest pieces of scientific exposition in recent years. 28 figures. Index. Conversion tables for translating earlier data into modern units. Translated from 3rd Dutch edition by L. J. Jolley. x + 187pp. 5½ x 8¾. S909 Clothbound **$6.00**

ELECTRIC WAVES: BEING RESEARCHES ON THE PROPAGATION OF ELECTRIC ACTION WITH FINITE VELOCITY THROUGH SPACE, Heinrich Hertz. This classic work brings together the original papers in which Hertz—Helmholtz's protegé and one of the most brilliant figures in 19th-century research—probed the existence of electromagnetic waves and showed experimentally that their velocity equalled that of light, research that helped lay the groundwork for the development of radio, television, telephone, telegraph, and other modern technological marvels. Unabridged republication of original edition. Authorized translation by D. E. Jones. Preface by Lord Kelvin. Index of names. 40 illustrations. xvii + 278pp. 5⅜ x 8½. S57 Paperbound **$1.75**

PIEZOELECTRICITY: AN INTRODUCTION TO THE THEORY AND APPLICATIONS OF ELECTROMECHANICAL PHENOMENA IN CRYSTALS, Walter G. Cady. This is the most complete and systematic coverage of this important field in print—now regarded as something of scientific classic. This republication, revised and corrected by Prof. Cady—one of the foremost contributors in this area—contains a sketch of recent progress and new material on Ferroelectrics. Time Standards, etc. The first 7 chapters deal with fundamental theory of crystal electricity. 5 important chapters cover basic concepts of piezoelectricity, including comparisons of various competing theories in the field. Also discussed: piezoelectric resonators (theory, methods of manufacture, influences of air-gaps, etc.); the piezo oscillator; the properties, history, and observations relating to Rochelle salt; ferroelectric crystals; miscellaneous applications of piezoelectricity; pyroelectricity; etc. "A great work," W. A. Wooster, NATURE. Revised (1963) and corrected edition. New preface by Prof. Cady. 2 Appendices. Indices. Illustrations. 62 tables. Bibliography. Problems. Total of 1 + 822pp. 5⅜ x 8½.
S1094 Vol. I Paperbound **$2.50**
S1095 Vol. II Paperbound **$2.50**
Two volume set Paperbound **$5.00**

MAGNETISM AND VERY LOW TEMPERATURES, H. B. G. Casimir. A basic work in the literature of low temperature physics. Presents a concise survey of fundamental theoretical principles, and also points out promising lines of investigation. Contents: Classical Theory and Experimental Methods, Quantum Theory of Paramagnetism, Experiments on Adiabatic Demagnetization. Theoretical Discussion of Paramagnetism at Very Low Temperatures, Some Experimental Results, Relaxation Phenomena. Index. 89-item bibliography. ix + 95pp. 5⅜ x 8. S943 Paperbound **$1.25**

SELECTED PAPERS ON NEW TECHNIQUES FOR ENERGY CONVERSION: THERMOELECTRIC METHODS; THERMIONIC; PHOTOVOLTAIC AND ELECTRICAL EFFECTS; FUSION, Edited by Sumner N. Levine. Brings together in one volume the most important papers (1954-1961) in modern energy technology. Included among the 37 papers are general and qualitative descriptions of the field as a whole, indicating promising lines of research. Also: 15 papers on thermoelectric methods, 7 on thermionic, 5 on photovoltaic, 4 on electrochemical effect, and 2 on controlled fusion research. Among the contributors are: Joffe, Maria Telkes, Herold, Herring, Douglas, Jaumot, Post, Austin, Wilson, Pfann, Rappaport, Morehouse, Domenicali, Moss, Bowers, Harman, Von Doenhoef. Preface and introduction by the editor. Bibliographies. xxviii + 451pp. 6⅛ x 9¼. S37 Paperbound **$3.00**

SUPERFLUIDS: MACROSCOPIC THEORY OF SUPERCONDUCTIVITY, Vol. I, Fritz London. The major work by one of the founders and great theoreticians of modern quantum physics. Consolidates the researches that led to the present understanding of the nature of superconductivity. Prof. London here reveals that quantum mechanics is operative on the macroscopic plane as well as the submolecular level. Contents: Properties of Superconductors and Their Thermodynamical Correlation; Electrodynamics of the Pure Superconducting State; Relation between Current and Field; Measurements of the Penetration Depth; Non-Viscous Flow vs. Superconductivity; Micro-waves in Superconductors; Reality of the Domain Structure; and many other related topics. A new epilogue by M. J. Buckingham discusses developments in the field up to 1960. Corrected and expanded edition. An appreciation of the author's life and work by L. W. Nordheim. Biography by Edith London. Bibliography of his publications. 45 figures. 2 Indices. xviii + 173pp. 5⅝ x 8⅜. S44 Paperbound **$1.45**

SELECTED PAPERS ON PHYSICAL PROCESSES IN IONIZED PLASMAS, Edited by Donald H. Menzel, Director, Harvard College Observatory. 30 important papers relating to the study of highly ionized gases or plasmas selected by a foremost contributor in the field, with the assistance of Dr. L. H. Aller. The essays include 18 on the physical processes in gaseous nebulae, covering problems of radiation and radiative transfer, the Balmer decrement, electron temperatives, spectrophotometry, etc. 10 papers deal with the interpretation of nebular spectra, by Bohm, Van Vleck, Aller, Minkowski, etc. There is also a discussion of the intensities of "forbidden" spectral lines by George Shortley and a paper concerning the theory of hydrogenic spectra by Menzel and Pekeris. Other contributors: Goldberg, Hebb, Baker, Bowen, Ufford, Liller, etc. viii + 374pp. 6⅛ x 9¼. S60 Paperbound **$2.95**

THE ELECTROMAGNETIC FIELD, Max Mason & Warren Weaver. Used constantly by graduate engineers. Vector methods exclusively: detailed treatment of electrostatics, expansion methods, with tables converting any quantity into absolute electromagnetic, absolute electrostatic, practical units. Discrete charges, ponderable bodies, Maxwell field equations, etc. Introduction. Indexes. 416pp. 5⅜ x 8. S185 Paperbound **$2.00**

THEORY OF ELECTRONS AND ITS APPLICATION TO THE PHENOMENA OF LIGHT AND RADIANT HEAT, H. Lorentz. Lectures delivered at Columbia University by Nobel laureate Lorentz. Unabridged, they form a historical coverage of the theory of free electrons, motion, absorption of heat, Zeeman effect, propagation of light in molecular bodies, inverse Zeeman effect, optical phenomena in moving bodies, etc. 109 pages of notes explain the more advanced sections. Index. 9 figures. 352pp. 5⅜ x 8. S173 Paperbound **$1.85**

FUNDAMENTAL ELECTROMAGNETIC THEORY, Ronold P. King, Professor Applied Physics, Harvard University. Original and valuable introduction to electromagnetic theory and to circuit theory from the standpoint of electromagnetic theory. Contents: Mathematical Description of Matter—stationary and nonstationary states; Mathematical Description of Space and of Simple Media—Field Equations, Integral Forms of Field Equations, Electromagnetic Force, etc.; Transformation of Field and Force Equations; Electromagnetic Waves in Unbounded Regions; Skin Effect and Internal Impedance—in a solid cylindrical conductor, etc.; and Electrical Circuits—Analytical Foundations, Near-zone and quasi-near zone circuits, Balanced two-wire and four-wire transmission lines. Revised and enlarged version. New preface by the author. 5 appendices (Differential operators: Vector Formulas and Identities, etc.). Problems. Indexes. Bibliography. xvi + 580pp. 5⅜ x 8½. S1023 Paperbound **$2.75**

Hydrodynamics

A TREATISE ON HYDRODYNAMICS, A. B. Basset. Favorite text on hydrodynamics for 2 generations of physicists, hydrodynamical engineers, oceanographers, ship designers, etc. Clear enough for the beginning student, and thorough source for graduate students and engineers on the work of d'Alembert, Euler, Laplace, Lagrange, Poisson, Green, Clebsch, Stokes, Cauchy, Helmholtz, J. J. Thomson, Love, Hicks, Greenhill, Besant, Lamb, etc. Great amount of documentation on entire theory of classical hydrodynamics. Vol I: theory of motion of frictionless liquids, vortex, and cyclic irrotational motion, etc. 132 exercises. Bibliography. 3 Appendixes. xii + 264pp. Vol II: motion in viscous liquids, harmonic analysis, theory of tides, etc. 112 exercises, Bibliography. 4 Appendixes. xv + 328pp. Two volume set. 5⅜ x 8.
S724 Vol I Paperbound **$1.75**
S725 Vol II Paperbound **$1.75**
The set **$3.50**

HYDRODYNAMICS, Horace Lamb. Internationally famous complete coverage of standard reference work on dynamics of liquids & gases. Fundamental theorems, equations, methods, solutions, background, for classical hydrodynamics. Chapters include Equations of Motion, Integration of Equations in Special Gases, Irrotational Motion, Motion of Liquid in 2 Dimensions, Motion of Solids through Liquid-Dynamical Theory, Vortex Motion, Tidal Waves, Surface Waves, Waves of Expansion, Viscosity, Rotating Masses of liquids. Excellently planned, arranged; clear, lucid presentation. 6th enlarged, revised edition. Index. Over 900 footnotes, mostly bibliographical. 119 figures. xv + 738pp. 6⅛ x 9¼. S256 Paperbound **$3.25**

HYDRODYNAMICS, H. Dryden, F. Murnaghan, Harry Bateman. Published by the National Research Council in 1932 this enormous volume offers a complete coverage of classical hydrodynamics. Encyclopedic in quality. Partial contents: physics of fluids, motion, turbulent flow, compressible fluids, motion in 1, 2, 3 dimensions; viscous fluids rotating, laminar motion, resistance of motion through viscous fluid, eddy viscosity, hydraulic flow in channels of various shapes, discharge of gases, flow past obstacles, etc. Bibliography of over 2,900 items. Indexes. 23 figures. 634pp. 5⅜ x 8. S303 Paperbound **$2.75**

Mechanics, dynamics, thermodynamics, elasticity

MECHANICS, J. P. Den Hartog. Already a classic among introductory texts, the M.I.T. professor's lively and discursive presentation is equally valuable as a beginner's text, an engineering student's refresher, or a practicing engineer's reference. Emphasis in this highly readable text is on illuminating fundamental principles and showing how they are embodied in a great number of real engineering and design problems: trusses, loaded cables, beams, jacks, hoists, etc. Provides advanced material on relative motion and gyroscopes not usual in introductory texts. "Very thoroughly recommended to all those anxious to improve their real understanding of the principles of mechanics." MECHANICAL WORLD. Index. List of equations. 334 problems, all with answers. Over 550 diagrams and drawings. ix + 462pp. 5⅜ x 8. S754 Paperbound **$2.00**

THEORETICAL MECHANICS: AN INTRODUCTION TO MATHEMATICAL PHYSICS, J. S. Ames, F. D. Murnaghan. A mathematically rigorous development of theoretical mechanics for the advanced student, with constant practical applications. Used in hundreds of advanced courses. An unusually thorough coverage of gyroscopic and baryscopic material, detailed analyses of the Coriolis acceleration, applications of Lagrange's equations, motion of the double pendulum, Hamilton-Jacobi partial differential equations, group velocity and dispersion, etc. Special relativity is also included. 159 problems. 44 figures. ix + 462pp. 5⅜ x 8. S461 Paperbound **$2.00**

THEORETICAL MECHANICS: STATICS AND THE DYNAMICS OF A PARTICLE, W. D. MacMillan. Used for over 3 decades as a self-contained and extremely comprehensive advanced undergraduate text in mathematical physics, physics, astronomy, and deeper foundations of engineering. Early sections require only a knowledge of geometry; later, a working knowledge of calculus. Hundreds of basic problems, including projectiles to the moon, escape velocity, harmonic motion, ballistics, falling bodies, transmission of power, stress and strain, elasticity, astronomical problems. 340 practice problems plus many fully worked out examples make it possible to test and extend principles developed in the text. 200 figures. xvii + 430pp. 5⅜ x 8. S467 Paperbound **$2.00**

THEORETICAL MECHANICS: THE THEORY OF THE POTENTIAL, W. D. MacMillan. A comprehensive, well balanced presentation of potential theory, serving both as an introduction and a reference work with regard to specific problems, for physicists and mathematicians. No prior knowledge of integral relations is assumed, and all mathematical material is developed as it becomes necessary. Includes: Attraction of Finite Bodies; Newtonian Potential Function; Vector Fields, Green and Gauss Theorems; Attractions of Surfaces and Lines; Surface Distribution of Matter; Two-Layer Surfaces; Spherical Harmonics; Ellipsoidal Harmonics; etc. "The great number of particular cases . . . should make the book valuable to geophysicists and others actively engaged in practical applications of the potential theory," Review of Scientific Instruments. Index. Bibliography. xiii + 469pp. 5⅜ x 8. S486 Paperbound **$2.25**

THEORETICAL MECHANICS: DYNAMICS OF RIGID BODIES, W. D. MacMillan. Theory of dynamics of a rigid body is developed, using both the geometrical and analytical methods of instruction. Begins with exposition of algebra of vectors, it goes through momentum principles, motion in space, use of differential equations and infinite series to solve more sophisticated dynamics problems. Partial contents: moments of inertia, systems of free particles, motion parallel to a fixed plane, rolling motion, method of periodic solutions, much more. 82 figs. 199 problems. Bibliography. Indexes. xii + 476pp. 5⅜ x 8. S641 Paperbound **$2.00**

MATHEMATICAL FOUNDATIONS OF STATISTICAL MECHANICS, A. I. Khinchin. Offering a precise and rigorous formulation of problems, this book supplies a thorough and up-to-date exposition. It provides analytical tools needed to replace cumbersome concepts, and furnishes for the first time a logical step-by-step introduction to the subject. Partial contents: geometry & kinematics of the phase space, ergodic problem, reduction to theory of probability, application of central limit problem, ideal monatomic gas, foundation of thermo-dynamics, dispersion and distribution of sum functions. Key to notations. Index. viii + 179pp. 5⅜ x 8. S147 Paperbound **$1.50**

ELEMENTARY PRINCIPLES IN STATISTICAL MECHANICS, J. W. Gibbs. Last work of the great Yale mathematical physicist, still one of the most fundamental treatments available for advanced students and workers in the field. Covers the basic principle of conservation of probability of phase, theory of errors in the calculated phases of a system, the contributions of Clausius, Maxwell, Boltzmann, and Gibbs himself, and much more. Includes valuable comparison of statistical mechanics with thermodynamics: Carnot's cycle, mechanical definitions of entropy, etc. xvi + 208pp. 5⅜ x 8. S707 Paperbound **$1.45**

PRINCIPLES OF MECHANICS AND DYNAMICS, Sir William Thomson (Lord Kelvin) and Peter Guthrie Tait. The principles and theories of fundamental branches of classical physics explained by two of the greatest physicists of all time. A broad survey of mechanics, with material on hydrodynamics, elasticity, potential theory, and what is now standard mechanics. Thorough and detailed coverage, with many examples, derivations, and topics not included in more recent studies. Only a knowledge of calculus is needed to work through this book. Vol. I (Preliminary): Kinematics; Dynamical Laws and Principles; Experience (observation, experimentation, formation of hypotheses, scientific method); Measures and Instruments; Continuous Calculating Machines. Vol. II (Abstract Dynamics): Statics of a Particle—Attraction; Statics of Solids and Fluids. Formerly Titled "Treatise on Natural Philosophy." Unabridged reprint of revised edition. Index. 168 diagrams. Total of xlii + 1035pp. 5⅜ x 8½.
Vol. I: S966 Paperbound **$2.35**
Vol. II: S967 Paperbound **$2.35**
Two volume Set Paperbound **$4.70**

INVESTIGATIONS ON THE THEORY OF THE BROWNIAN MOVEMENT, Albert Einstein. Reprints from rare European journals. 5 basic papers, including the Elementary Theory of the Brownian Movement, written at the request of Lorentz to provide a simple explanation. Translated by A. D. Cowper. Annotated, edited by R. Fürth. 33pp. of notes elucidate, give history of previous investigations. Author, subject indexes. 62 footnotes. 124pp. 5⅜ x 8.
S304 Paperbound **$1.25**

MECHANICS VIA THE CALCULUS, P. W. Norris, W. S. Legge. Covers almost everything, from linear motion to vector analysis: equations determining motion, linear methods, compounding of simple harmonic motions, Newton's laws of motion, Hooke's law, the simple pendulum, motion of a particle in 1 plane, centers of gravity, virtual work, friction, kinetic energy of rotating bodies, equilibrium of strings, hydrostatics, sheering stresses, elasticity, etc. 550 problems. 3rd revised edition. xii + 367pp. 6 x 9. S207 Clothbound **$4.95**

THE DYNAMICS OF PARTICLES AND OF RIGID, ELASTIC, AND FLUID BODIES; BEING LECTURES ON MATHEMATICAL PHYSICS, A. G. Webster. The reissuing of this classic fills the need for a comprehensive work on dynamics. A wide range of topics is covered in unusually great depth, applying ordinary and partial differential equations. Part I considers laws of motion and methods applicable to systems of all sorts; oscillation, resonance, cyclic systems, etc. Part 2 is a detailed study of the dynamics of rigid bodies. Part 3 introduces the theory of potential; stress and strain, Newtonian potential functions, gyrostatics, wave and vortex motion, etc. Further contents: Kinematics of a point; Lagrange's equations; Hamilton's principle; Systems of vectors; Statics and dynamics of deformable bodies; much more, not easily found together in one volume. Unabridged reprinting of 2nd edition. 20 pages of notes on differential equations and the higher analysis. 203 illustrations. Selected bibliography. Index. xi + 588pp. 5⅜ x 8. S522 Paperbound **$2.45**

A TREATISE ON DYNAMICS OF A PARTICLE, E. J. Routh. Elementary text on dynamics for beginning mathematics or physics student. Unusually detailed treatment from elementary definitions to motion in 3 dimensions, emphasizing concrete aspects. Much unique material important in recent applications. Covers impulsive forces, rectilinear and constrained motion in 2 dimensions, harmonic and parabolic motion, degrees of freedom, closed orbits, the conical pendulum, the principle of least action, Jacobi's method, and much more. Index. 559 problems, many fully worked out, incorporated into text. xiii + 418pp. 5⅜ x 8.
S696 Paperbound **$2.25**

DYNAMICS OF A SYSTEM OF RIGID BODIES (Elementary Section), E. J. Routh. Revised 7th edition of this standard reference. This volume covers the dynamical principles of the subject, and its more elementary applications: finding moments of inertia by integration, foci of inertia, d'Alembert's principle, impulsive forces, motion in 2 and 3 dimensions, Lagrange's equations, relative indicatrix, Euler's theorem, large tautochronous motions, etc. Index. 55 figures. Scores of problems. xv + 443pp. 5⅜ x 8. S664 Paperbound **$2.50**

DYNAMICS OF A SYSTEM OF RIGID BODIES (Advanced Section), E. J. Routh. Revised 6th edition of a classic reference aid. Much of its material remains unique. Partial contents: moving axes, relative motion, oscillations about equilibrium, motion. Motion of a body under no forces, any forces. Nature of motion given by linear equations and conditions of stability. Free, forced vibrations, constants of integration, calculus of finite differences, variations, precession and nutation, motion of the moon, motion of string, chain, membranes. 64 figures. 498pp. 5⅜ x 8. S229 Paperbound **$2.45**

DYNAMICAL THEORY OF GASES, James Jeans. Divided into mathematical and physical chapters for the convenience of those not expert in mathematics, this volume discusses the mathematical theory of gas in a steady state, thermodynamics, Boltzmann and Maxwell, kinetic theory, quantum theory, exponentials, etc. 4th enlarged edition, with new material on quantum theory, quantum dynamics, etc. Indexes. 28 figures. 444pp. 6⅛ x 9¼.
S136 Paperbound **$2.65**

THE THEORY OF HEAT RADIATION, Max Planck. A pioneering work in thermodynamics, providing basis for most later work, Nobel laureate Planck writes on Deductions from Electrodynamics and Thermodynamics, Entropy and Probability, Irreversible Radiation Processes, etc. Starts with simple experimental laws of optics, advances to problems of spectral distribution of energy and irreversibility. Bibliography. 7 illustrations, xiv + 224pp. 5⅜ x 8.
S546 Paperbound **$1.50**

FOUNDATIONS OF POTENTIAL THEORY, O. D. Kellogg. Based on courses given at Harvard this is suitable for both advanced and beginning mathematicians. Proofs are rigorous, and much material not generally avaliable elsewhere is included. Partial contents: forces of gravity, fields of force, divergence theorem, properties of Newtonian potentials at points of free space, potentials as solutions of Laplace's equations, harmonic functions, electrostatics, electric images, logarithmic potential, etc. One of Grundlehren Series. ix + 384pp. 5⅜ x 8.
S144 Paperbound **$1.98**

THERMODYNAMICS, Enrico Fermi. Unabridged reproduction of 1937 edition. Elementary in treatment; remarkable for clarity, organization. Requires no knowledge of advanced math beyond calculus, only familiarity with fundamentals of thermometry, calorimetry. Partial Contents: Thermodynamic systems; First & Second laws of thermodynamics; Entropy; Thermodynamic potentials: phase rule, reversible electric cell; Gaseous reactions: van't Hoff reaction box, principle of LeChatelier; Thermodynamics of dilute solutions: osmotic & vapor pressures, boiling & freezing points; Entropy constant. Index. 25 problems. 24 illustrations. x + 160pp. 5⅜ x 8.
S361 Paperbound **$1.75**

THE THERMODYNAMICS OF ELECTRICAL PHENOMENA IN METALS and A CONDENSED COLLECTION OF THERMODYNAMIC FORMULAS, P. W. Bridgman. Major work by the Nobel Prizewinner: stimulating conceptual introduction to aspects of the electron theory of metals, giving an intuitive understanding of fundamental relationships concealed by the formal systems of Onsager and others. Elementary mathematical formulations show clearly the fundamental thermodynamical relationships of the electric field, and a complete phenomenological theory of metals is created. This is the work in which Bridgman announced his famous "thermomotive force" and his distinction between "driving" and "working" electromotive force. We have added in this Dover edition the author's long unavailable tables of thermodynamic formulas, extremely valuable for the speed of reference they allow. Two works bound as one. Index. 33 figures. Bibliography. xviii + 256pp. 5⅜ x 8. S723 Paperbound **$1.65**

TREATISE ON THERMODYNAMICS, Max Planck. Based on Planck's original papers this offers a uniform point of view for the entire field and has been used as an introduction for students who have studied elementary chemistry, physics, and calculus. Rejecting the earlier approaches of Helmholtz and Maxwell, the author makes no assumptions regarding the nature of heat, but begins with a few empirical facts, and from these deduces new physical and chemical laws. 3rd English edition of this standard text by a Nobel laureate. xvi + 297pp. 5⅜ x 8.
S219 Paperbound **$1.75**

THE MATHEMATICAL THEORY OF ELASTICITY, A. E. H. Love. A wealth of practical illustration combined with thorough discussion of fundamentals—theory, application, special problems and solutions. Partial Contents: Analysis of Strain & Stress, Elasticity of Solid Bodies, Elasticity of Crystals, Vibration of Spheres, Cylinders, Propagation of Waves in Elastic Solid Media, Torsion, Theory of Continuous Beams, Plates. Rigorous treatment of Volterra's theory of dislocations, 2-dimensional elastic systems, other topics of modern interest. "For years the standard treatise on elasticity," AMERICAN MATHEMATICAL MONTHLY. 4th revised edition. Index. 76 figures. xviii + 643pp. 6⅛ x 9¼.
S174 Paperbound **$3.00**

STRESS WAVES IN SOLIDS, H. Kolsky, Professor of Applied Physics, Brown University. The most readable survey of the theoretical core of current knowledge about the propagation of waves in solids, fully correlated with experimental research. Contents: Part I—Elastic Waves: propagation in an extended plastic medium, propagation in bounded elastic media, experimental investigations with elastic materials. Part II—Stress Waves in Imperfectly Elastic Media: internal friction, experimental investigations of dynamic elastic properties, plastic waves and shock waves, fractures produced by stress waves. List of symbols. Appendix. Supplemented bibliography. 3 full-page plates. 46 figures. x + 213pp. 5⅜ x 8½.
S1098 Paperbound **$1.55**

Relativity, quantum theory, atomic and nuclear physics

SPACE TIME MATTER, Hermann Weyl. "The standard treatise on the general theory of relativity" (Nature), written by a world-renowned scientist, provides a deep clear discussion of the logical coherence of the general theory, with introduction to all the mathematical tools needed: Maxwell, analytical geometry, non-Euclidean geometry, tensor calculus, etc. Basis is classical space-time, before absorption of relativity. Partial contents: Euclidean space, mathematical form, metrical continuum, relativity of time and space, general theory. 15 diagrams. Bibliography. New preface for this edition. xviii + 330pp. 5⅜ x 8.
S267 Paperbound **$2.00**

ATOMIC SPECTRA AND ATOMIC STRUCTURE, G. Herzberg. Excellent general survey for chemists, physicists specializing in other fields. Partial contents: simplest line spectra and elements of atomic theory, building-up principle and periodic system of elements, hyperfine structure of spectral lines, some experiments and applications. Bibilography. 80 figures. Index. xii + 257pp. 5⅜ x 8.
S115 Paperbound **$2.00**

THE PRINCIPLE OF RELATIVITY, A. Einstein, H. Lorentz, H. Minkowski, H. Weyl. These are the 11 basic papers that founded the general and special theories of relativity, all translated into English. Two papers by Lorentz on the Michelson experiment, electromagnetic phenomena. Minkowski's SPACE & TIME, and Weyl's GRAVITATION & ELECTRICITY. 7 epoch-making papers by Einstein: ELECTROMAGNETICS OF MOVING BODIES, INFLUENCE OF GRAVITATION IN PROPAGATION OF LIGHT, COSMOLOGICAL CONSIDERATIONS, GENERAL THEORY, and 3 others. 7 diagrams. Special notes by A. Sommerfeld. 224pp. 5⅜ x 8.
S81 Paperbound **$1.75**

EINSTEIN'S THEORY OF RELATIVITY, Max Born. Revised edition prepared with the collaboration of Gunther Leibfried and Walter Biem. Steering a middle course between superficial popularizations and complex analyses, a Nobel laureate explains Einstein's theories clearly and with special insight. Easily followed by the layman with a knowledge of high school mathematics, the book has been thoroughly revised and extended to modernize those sections of the well-known original edition which are now out of date. After a comprehensive review of classical physics, Born's discussion of special and general theories of relativity covers such topics as simultaneity, kinematics, Einstein's mechanics and dynamics, relativity of arbitrary motions, the geometry of curved surfaces, the space-time continuum, and many others. Index. Illustrations, vii + 376pp. 5⅜ x 8. S769 Paperbound **$2.00**

ATOMS, MOLECULES AND QUANTA, Arthur E. Ruark and Harold C. Urey. Revised (1963) and corrected edition of a work that has been a favorite with physics students and teachers for more than 30 years. No other work offers the same combination of atomic structure and molecular physics and of experiment and theory. The first 14 chapters deal with the origins and major experimental data of quantum theory and with the development of conceptions of atomic and molecular structure prior to the new mechanics. These sections provide a thorough introduction to atomic and molecular theory, and are presented lucidly and as simply as possible. The six subsequent chapters are devoted to the laws and basic ideas of quantum mechanics: Wave Mechanics, Hydrogenic Atoms in Wave Mechanics, Matrix Mechanics, General Theory of Quantum Dynamics, etc. For advanced college and graduate students in physics. Revised, corrected republication of original edition, with supplementary notes by the authors. New preface by the authors. 9 appendices. General reference list. Indices. 228 figures. 71 tables. Bibliographical material in notes, etc. Total of xxiii + 810pp. 5⅜ x 8⅜.
S1106 Vol. I Paperbound **$2.50**
S1107 Vol. II Paperbound **$2.50**
Two volume set Paperbound **$5.00**

WAVE MECHANICS AND ITS APPLICATIONS, N. F. Mott and I. N. Sneddon. A comprehensive introduction to the theory of quantum mechanics; not a rigorous mathematical exposition it progresses, instead, in accordance with the physical problems considered. Many topics difficult to find at the elementary level are discussed in this book. Includes such matters as: the wave nature of matter, the wave equation of Schrödinger, the concept of stationary states, properties of the wave functions, effect of a magnetic field on the energy levels of atoms, electronic spin, two-body problem, theory of solids, cohesive forces in ionic crystals, collision problems, interaction of radiation with matter, relativistic quantum mechanics, etc. All are treated both physically and mathematically. 68 illustrations. 11 tables. Indexes. xii + 393pp. 5⅜ x 8½. S1070 Paperbound **$2.25**

BASIC METHODS IN TRANSFER PROBLEMS, V. Kourganoff, Professor of Astrophysics, U. of Paris. A coherent digest of all the known methods which can be used for approximate or exact solutions of transfer problems. All methods demonstrated on one particular problem —Milne's problem for a plane parallel medium. Three main sections: fundamental concepts (the radiation field and its interaction with matter, the absorption and emission coefficients, etc.); different methods by which transfer problems can be attacked; and a more general problem—the non-grey case of Milne's problem. Much new material, drawing upon declassified atomic energy reports and data from the USSR. Entirely understandable to the student with a reasonable knowledge of analysis. Unabridged, revised reprinting. New preface by the author. Index. Bibliography. 2 appendices. xv + 281pp. 5⅜ x 8½.
S1074 Paperbound **$2.00**

PRINCIPLES OF QUANTUM MECHANICS, W. V. Houston. Enables student with working knowledge of elementary mathematical physics to develop facility in use of quantum mechanics, understand published work in field. Formulates quantum mechanics in terms of Schroedinger's wave mechanics. Studies evidence for quantum theory, for inadequacy of classical mechanics, 2 postulates of quantum mechanics; numerous important, fruitful applications of quantum mechanics in spectroscopy, collision problems, electrons in solids; other topics. "One of the most rewarding features . . . is the interlacing of problems with text," Amer. J. of Physics. Corrected edition. 21 illus. Index. 296pp. 5⅜ x 8. S524 Paperbound **$1.85**

PHYSICAL PRINCIPLES OF THE QUANTUM THEORY, Werner Heisenberg. A Nobel laureate discusses quantum theory; Heisenberg's own work, Compton, Schroedinger, Wilson, Einstein, many others. Written for physicists, chemists who are not specialists in quantum theory, only elementary formulae are considered in the text; there is a mathematical appendix for specialists. Profound without sacrifice of clarity. Translated by C. Eckart, F. Hoyt. 18 figures. 192pp. 5⅜ x 8. S113 Paperbound **$1.25**

PHYSICS, HISTORIES AND CLASSICS

A HISTORY OF PHYSICS: IN ITS ELEMENTARY BRANCHES (THROUGH 1925), INCLUDING THE EVOLUTION OF PHYSICAL LABORATORIES, Florian Cajori. Revised and enlarged edition. The only first-rate brief history of physics. Still the best entry for a student or teacher into the antecedents of modern theories of physics. A clear, non-mathematical, handy reference work which traces in critical fashion the developments of ideas, theories, techniques, and apparatus from the Greeks to the 1920's. Within each period he analyzes the basic topics of mechanics, light, electricity and magnetism, sound, atomic theory and structure of matter, radioactivity, etc. A chapter on modern research: Curie, Kelvin, Planck's quantum theory, thermodynamics, Fitzgerald and Lorentz, special and general relativity, J. J. Thomson's model of an atom, Bohr's discoveries and later results, wave mechanics, and many other matters. Much bibliographic detail in footnotes. Index. 16 figures. xv + 424pp. 5⅜ x 8. T970 Paperbound **$2.00**

A HISTORY OF THE MATHEMATICAL THEORIES OF ATTRACTION AND THE FIGURE OF THE EARTH: FROM THE TIME OF NEWTON TO THAT OF LAPLACE, I. Todhunter. A technical and detailed review of the theories concerning the shape of the earth and its gravitational pull, from the earliest investigations in the seventeenth century up to the middle of the nineteenth. Some of the greatest mathematicians and scientists in history applied themselves to these questions: Newton ("Principia Mathematica"), Huygens, Maupertuis, Simpson, d'Alembert, etc. Others discussed are Poisson, Gauss, Plana, Lagrange, Boit, and many more. Particular emphasis is placed on the theories of Laplace and Legendre, several chapters being devoted to Laplace's "Mécanique Céleste" and his memoirs, and several others to the memoirs of Legendre. Important to historians of science and mathematics and to the specialist who desires background information in the field. 2 volumes bound as 1. Index. xxxvi + 984pp. 5⅜ x 8.
S148 Clothbound **$7.50**

OPTICKS, Sir Isaac Newton. In its discussions of light, reflection, color, refraction, theories of wave and corpuscular theories of light, this work is packed with scores of insights and discoveries. In its precise and practical discussion of construction of optical apparatus, contemporary understandings of phenomena it is truly fascinating to modern physicists, astronomers, mathematicians. Foreword by Albert Einstein. Preface by I. B. Cohen of Harvard University. 7 pages of portraits, facsimile pages, letters, etc. cxvi + 414pp. 5⅜ x 8.
S205 Paperbound **$2.25**

TREATISE ON LIGHT, Christiaan Huygens. The famous original formulation of the wave theory of light, this readable book is one of the two decisive and definitive works in the field of light (Newton's "Optics" is the other). A scientific giant whose researches ranged over mathematics, astronomy, and physics, Huygens, in this historic work, covers such topics as rays propagated in straight lines, reflection and refraction, the spreading and velocity of light, the nature of opaque bodies, the non-spherical nature of light in the atmosphere, properties of Iceland Crystal, and other related matters. Unabridged republication of original (1912) English edition. Translated and introduced by Silvanus P. Thompson. 52 illustrations. xii + 129pp. 5⅜ x 8. S179 Paperbound **$1.35**

FARADAY'S EXPERIMENTAL RESEARCHES IN ELECTRICITY. Faraday's historic series of papers containing the fruits of years of original experimentation in electrical theory and electrochemistry. Covers his findings in a variety of areas: Induction of electric currents, Evolution of electricity from magnetism, New electrical state or condition of matter, Explication of Arago's magnetic phenomena, New law of electric conduction, Electro-chemical decomposition, Electricity of the Voltaic Pile, Static Induction, Nature of the electric force or forces, Nature of electric current, The character and direction of the electric force of the Gymnotus, Magneto-electric spark, The magnetization of light and the illumination of magnetic lines of force, The possible relation of gravity to electricity, Sub-terraneous electro-telegraph wires, Some points of magnetic philosophy, The diamagnetic conditions of flame and gases, and many other matters. Complete and unabridged republication. 3 vols. bound as 2. Originally reprinted from the Philosophical Transactions of 1831-8. Indices. Illustrations. Total of 1463pp. 5⅜ x 8. S783-4, Clothbound **$17.50** (tentative)

REFLECTIONS ON THE MOTIVE POWER OF FIRE, Sadi Carnot, and other papers on the 2nd law of thermodynamics by E. Clapeyron and R. Clausius. Carnot's "Reflections" laid the groundwork of modern thermodynamics. Its non-technical, mostly verbal statements examine the relations between heat and the work done by heat in engines, establishing conditions for the economical working of these engines. The papers by Clapeyron and Clausius here reprinted added further refinements to Carnot's work, and led to its final acceptance by physicists. Selections from posthumous manuscripts of Carnot are also included. All papers in English. New introduction by E. Mendoza. 12 illustrations. xxii + 152pp. 5⅜ x 8.
S661 Paperbound **$1.50**

DIALOGUES CONCERNING TWO NEW SCIENCES, Galileo Galilei. This classic of experimental science, mechanics, engineering, is as enjoyable as it is important. A great historical document giving insights into one of the world's most original thinkers, it is based on 30 years' experimentation. It offers a lively exposition of dynamics, elasticity, sound, ballistics, strength of materials, the scientific method. "Superior to everything else of mine," Galileo. Trans. by H. Crew, A. Salvio. 126 diagrams. Index. xxi + 288pp. 5⅜ x 8.
S99 Paperbound **$1.75**

TREATISE ON ELECTRICITY AND MAGNETISM, James Clerk Maxwell. For more than 80 years a seemingly inexhaustible source of leads for physicists, mathematicians, engineers. Total of 1082pp. on such topics as Measurement of Quantities, Electrostatics, Elementary Mathematical Theory of Electricity, Electrical Work and Energy in a System of Conductors, General Theorems, Theory of Electrical Images, Electrolysis, Conduction, Polarization, Dielectrics, Resistance, etc. "The greatest mathematical physicist since Newton," Sir James Jeans. 3rd edition. 107 figures, 21 plates. 1082pp. 5⅜ x 8. S636-7, 2 volume set, paperbound **$4.00**

A HISTORY OF THE THEORY OF ELASTICITY AND THE STRENGTH OF MATERIALS, I. Todhunter and K. Pearson. For over 60 years a basic reference, unsurpassed in scope or authority. Both a history of the mathematical theory of elasticity from Galileo, Hooke, and Mariotte to Saint Venant, Kirchhoff, Clebsch, and Lord Kelvin and a detailed presentation of every important mathematical contribution during this period. Presents proofs of thousands of theorems and laws, summarizes every relevant treatise, many unavailable elsewhere. Practically a book apiece is devoted to modern founders: Saint Venant, Lamé, Boussinesq, Rankine, Lord Kelvin, F. Neumann, Kirchhoff, Clebsch. Hundreds of pages of technical and physical treatises on specific applications of elasticity to particular materials. Indispensable for the mathematician, physicist, or engineer working with elasticity. Unabridged, corrected reprint of original 3-volume 1886-1893 edition. Three volume set. Two indexes. Appendix to Vol. I. Total of 2344pp. 5⅜ x 8⅜. S914–916 The set, Clothbound **$15.00**

DE MAGNETE, William Gilbert. This classic work on magnetism founded a new science. Gilbert was the first to use the word "electricity", to recognize mass as distinct from weight, to discover the effect of heat on magnetic bodies; invent an electroscope, differentiate between static electricity and magnetism, conceive of the earth as a magnet. Written by the first great experimental scientist, this lively work is valuable not only as an historical landmark, but as the delightfully easy to follow record of a perpetually searching, ingenious mind. Translated by P. F. Mottelay. 25-page biographical memoir. 90 figures. lix +368pp. 5⅜ x 8. S470 Paperbound **$2.00**

ASTRONOMY

THE INTERNAL CONSTITUTION OF THE STARS, Sir A. S. Eddington. Influence of this has been enormous; first detailed exposition of theory of radiative equilibrium for stellar interiors, of all available evidence for existence of diffuse matter in interstellar space. Studies quantum theory, polytropic gas spheres, mass-luminosity relations, variable stars, etc. Discussions of equations paralleled with informal exposition of intimate relationship of astrophysics with great discoveries in atomic physics, radiation. Introduction. Appendix. Index. 421pp. 5⅜ x 8. S563 Paperbound **$2.25**

PLANETARY THEORY, E. W. Brown and C. A. Shook. Provides a clear presentation of basic methods for calculating planetary orbits for today's astronomer. Begins with a careful exposition of specialized mathematical topics essential for handling perturbation theory and then goes on to indicate how most of the previous methods reduce ultimately to two general calculation methods: obtaining expressions either for the coordinates of planetary positions or for the elements which determine the perturbed paths. An example of each is given and worked in detail. Corrected edition. Preface. Appendix. Index. xii + 302pp. 5⅜ x 8½. S1133 Paperbound **$2.25**

CANON OF ECLIPSES (CANON DER FINSTERNISSE), Prof. Theodor Ritter von Oppolzer. Since its original publication in 1887, this has been the standard reference and the most extensive single volume of data on the calculation of solar and lunar eclipses, past and future. A comprehensive introduction gives a full explanation of the use of the tables for the calculations of the exact dates of eclipses, etc. Data furnished for the calculation of 8,000 solar and 5,200 lunar eclipses, going back as far as 1200 B.C. and giving predictions up to the year 2161. Information is also given for partial and ring eclipses. All calculations based on Universal (Greenwich) Time. An unsurpassed reference work for astronomers, scientists engaged in space research and developments, historians, etc. Unabridged republication, with corrections. Preface to this edition by Donald Menzel and Owen Gingerich of the Harvard College Observatory. Translated by Owen Gingerich. 160 charts. lxx + 538pp. 8⅜ x 11¼. S114 Clothbound **$10.00**

THEORY OF THE MOTION OF THE HEAVENLY BODIES MOVING ABOUT THE SUN IN CONIC SECTIONS, Karl Friedrich Gauss. A landmark of theoretical astronomy by the great German scientist. Still authoritative and invaluable to the practicing astronomer. Part I develops the relations between the quantities on which the motion about the sun of the heavenly bodies depends—relations pertaining simply to position in the orbit, simply to position in space, between several places in orbit, and between several places in space. The calculation methods of Part II based on the groundwork of Part I include: determination of an orbit from 3 complete observations, from 4 observations (of which only two are complete), determination of an orbit satisfying as nearly as possible any number of observations whatever, and determination of orbits, taking into account the perturbations. Translation of "Theoria Motus" and with an appendix by C. H. Davis. Unabridged republication. Appendices and tables. 13 figures. xviii + 376pp. 6½ x 9¼. S1056 Paperbound **$2.95**

History and classics

STAR NAMES AND THEIR MEANINGS, Richard Hinckley Allen. An unusual book documenting the various attributions of names to the individual stars over the centuries. Here is a treasure-house of information on a topic not normally delved into even by professional astronomers; provides a fascinating background to the stars in folk-lore, literary references, ancient writings, star catalogs and maps over the centuries. Constellation-by-constellation analysis covers hundreds of stars and other asterisms, including the Pleiades, Hyades, Andromedan Nebula, etc. Introduction. Indices. List of authors and authorities. xx + 563pp. 5⅜ x 8½. T1079 Paperbound **$2.35**

A HISTORY OF ASTRONOMY FROM THALES TO KEPLER, J. L. E. Dreyer. (Formerly A HISTORY OF PLANETARY SYSTEMS FROM THALES TO KEPLER.) This is the only work in English to give the complete history of man's cosmological views from prehistoric times to Kepler and Newton. Partial contents: Near Eastern astronomical systems, Early Greeks, Homocentric Spheres of Eudoxus, Epicycles, Ptolemaic system, medieval cosmology, Copernicus, Kepler, etc. Revised, foreword by W. H. Stahl. New bibliography. xvii + 430pp. 5⅜ x 8. S79 Paperbound **$1.98**

A SHORT HISTORY OF ASTRONOMY, A. Berry. Popular standard work for over 50 years, this thorough and accurate volume covers the science from primitive times to the end of the 19th century. After the Greeks and the Middle Ages, individual chapters analyze Copernicus, Brahe, Galileo, Kepler, and Newton, and the mixed reception of their discoveries. Post-Newtonian achievements are then discussed in unusual detail: Halley, Bradley, Lagrange, Laplace, Herschel, Bessel, etc. 2 Indexes. 104 illustrations, 9 portraits. xxxi + 440pp. 5⅜ x 8. T210 Paperbound **$2.00**

THREE COPERNICAN TREATISES, translated with notes by Edward Rosen. 3 papers available nowhere else in English: "The Commentariolus" and "Letter against Werner" of Copernicus; the "Narratio prima" of Rheticus. The "Commentariolus" is Copernicus's most lucid exposition of his system. The "Letter against Werner" throws light on development of Copernicus's thought. The "Narratio prima" is earliest printed presentation of the new astronomy. "Educational and enjoyable," Astrophysical Journal. Corrected edition. Biographical introduction. 877-item bibliography of virtually every book, article, on Copernicus published 1939-1958. Index. 19 illustrations. 218pp. 5⅜ x 8. S585 Paperbound **$1.75**

Prices subject to change without notice.

Dover publishes books on art, music, philosophy, literature, languages, history, social sciences, psychology, handcrafts, orientalia, puzzles and entertainments, chess, pets and gardens, books explaining science, intermediate and higher mathematics, mathematical physics, engineering, biological sciences, earth sciences, classics of science, etc. Write to:

Dept. catrr.
Dover Publications, Inc.
180 Varick Street, N.Y. 14, N.Y.

A HISTORY OF [illegible]

A SHORT HISTORY OF [illegible]

[illegible]

[illegible]

Dept. [illegible]

[illegible]